MW00843993

Fiber Amplifiers
and
Fiber Lasers

Fiber Amplifiers
and
Fiber Lasers

Niloy K Dutta
University of Connecticut, USA

 **World Scientific**

NEW JERSEY · LONDON · SINGAPORE · BEIJING · SHANGHAI · HONG KONG · TAIPEI · CHENNAI

Published by

World Scientific Publishing Co. Pte. Ltd.

5 Toh Tuck Link, Singapore 596224

USA office: 27 Warren Street, Suite 401-402, Hackensack, NJ 07601

UK office: 57 Shelton Street, Covent Garden, London WC2H 9HE

British Library Cataloguing-in-Publication Data
A catalogue record for this book is available from the British Library.

FIBER AMPLIFIERS AND FIBER LASERS

ISBN 978-981-4630-38-2

Typeset by Stallion Press
Email: enquiries@stallionpress.com

Printed in Singapore by B & Jo Enterprise Pte Ltd

Preface

The laser emission in various rare earth (Nd, Pr, Er, Ho, Tm, Yb)-doped glasses have been studied since the 1960's. However, the potential for rare earth-doped fiber amplifiers and fiber lasers were not recognized until the late 1980's and it began with a demonstration of very low threshold fiber amplifier. This pioneering demonstration conveyed an important message: that using well established low loss fiber fabrication technology and semiconductor laser fabrication technology a new class of rare doped lasers and amplifiers could be produced for new applications. This message was particularly well received immediately by optical communication technologists and they went on to develop Er-doped fiber amplifiers for various fiber communication applications.

It was also recognized that an amplifier chain could be used for long ($\sim$1000–7000 km) undersea optical communication links and that such a system could be easily upgraded to higher data rates simply by replacing the transmitters and repeaters on the shore — a much easier task than laying a new cable. The first undersea fiber optic link using an amplifier chain went into operation in the mid-1990s.

The market demand for higher capacity transmission was helped by the fact that computers continued to become more powerful and needed to be interconnected. This is one of the key reasons why the explosive growth of optical fiber technology parallels that of computer processing and other key information technologies. The need for higher capacity is continuing to encourage research in wavelength division multiplexed (WDM) based transmission, which needs high power fiber amplifier and tunable lasers. An important research area would continue to be the development of Er, Er–Yb co-doped fiber amplifiers and Raman amplifiers for this application.

Optical networking and space communications (satellite to satellite) represents the next advancement in optical communications technology. Optical fiber amplifier is a key device for all-optical networks. The advances in research and many technological innovations have led to superior designs of fiber amplifiers. Today most optical communication systems use optical fiber amplifiers for signal amplification. High power short wavelength amplifiers using Nd or Yb are important for space communication application due to low beam divergence.

Fiber-based Raman lasers and amplifiers represent an important area for lasers and amplifiers for wavelength regions where a rare earth dopant may not be efficient. Using the cascaded Raman process and multiple Stokes shifts, very efficient fiber Raman lasers and amplifiers have been demonstrated.

High power fiber lasers producing kWs of power using double clad fiber geometries is expected to become increasingly important in future industrial applications. The development of short pulse fiber laser is expected to become important in many applications such as tomography and sensors.

The book is aimed at researchers already engaged in or wishing to enter the field of rare earth-doped lasers and amplifiers. It is also useful for graduate students, scientists and engineers interested in fiber optics communication. An attempt has been made to make the book self-contained and each chapter has a set of references which can be consulted for further study.

N. K. Dutta

Contents

Preface   v

1. Introduction   1

   1.1. Historical Developments   1

   1.2. Materials   2

   1.3. Operating Principles   4

   1.4. Applications   6

   1.5. Book Overview   8

   1.6. Future Challenges   10

   References   12

2. Basic Concepts   15

   2.1. Introduction   15

   2.2. Three-Level and Four-Level Laser   17

      2.2.1. Three-Level Laser   18

      2.2.2. Four-Level Laser   22

   2.3. Optical Waveguide   25

   2.4. Rate Equations for Fiber Amplifier   29

   2.5. Pump Laser   33

   2.6. Optical Transitions and Gain   35

      2.6.1. Er-doped Glass Fiber   35

      2.6.2. Nd-doped Glass Fiber   39

   2.7. Single Mode Fiber Amplifier   44

   2.8. High Power Cladding Pumped Devices   45

   References   48

3. Absorption and Emission in Rare Earths   51

    3.1. Introduction 51
    3.2. Atomic Transitions in Rare Earth Atoms 52
    3.3. Er-Doped Glass 56
    3.4. Yb-Doped Glass 57
    3.5. Nd-Doped Glass 61
    3.6. Tm-Doped Glass 65
    3.7. Model of Emission Cross Section 69
        3.7.1. Er-Doped Amplifier 69
        3.7.2. Yb-Doped Amplifier 76
    References 83

4. Amplifier Fiber Fabrication   87

    4.1. Introduction 87
    4.2. Transmission Optical Fiber Fabrication 88
        4.2.1. MCVD Process 88
        4.2.2. PCVD Process 89
        4.2.3. OVD Process 90
        4.2.4. VAD Process 90
        4.2.5. Doping and Fiber Drawing 91
    4.3. Rare Earth Doping 94
    4.4. Alternate Glass Host Fabrication 95
    4.5. Photonic Crystal Fiber Fabrication 99
    References 102

5. Amplifier Design — Model and Results   105

    5.1. Introduction 105
    5.2. Er-Doped Fiber Characterization 106
    5.3. Single Mode Amplifier Model 111
    5.4. Photonic Crystal Fiber Amplifier 119
    References 122

6. Amplifier Dynamic Characteristics   125

    6.1.   Introduction 125
    6.2.   Gain Dynamics 125
    6.3.   Multichannel Amplification 129
    6.4.   Amplifier Noise 134
        6.4.1.   Noise Analysis for Optical Transmission . . . 137
        6.4.2.   Er-Doped Amplifier Noise 144
        6.4.3.   Noise Measurements 147
    6.5.   Preamplifier Results 149
    6.6.   Pulse Propagation 151
        6.6.1.   Pulse Propagation in Regular Fibers 152
        6.6.2.   Pulse Propagation in EDFA 156
    References 161

7. High Power Amplifiers   165

    7.1.   Introduction 165
    7.2.   Waveguide Designs and Pumping 167
        7.2.1.   End Pumping 168
        7.2.2.   Side Pumping 171
    7.3.   DCF Laser and Amplifier Results 174
    7.4.   Er–Yb Co-doped Cladding Pumped Amplifier 177
    7.5.   DCF Model 187
    References 191

8. Pump Laser   195

    8.1.   Introduction 195
    8.2.   Materials, Epitaxial Growth and Operating
        Principle 196
        8.2.1.   Metal Organic Chemical Vapor Deposition . 198
        8.2.2.   Operating Principle and Designs 200
    8.3.   980 nm Laser 209
        8.3.1.   Single Mode 980 nm Laser 209
        8.3.2.   Multimode 970 nm Laser 214

8.4.   1480 nm Laser 216
    8.4.1.   Leakage Current 218
    8.4.2.   Laser Design and Performance 219
8.5.   808 nm Laser 222
    8.5.1.   Single Mode 808 nm Laser 223
    8.5.2.   Multimode 808 nm Laser 225
References 228

9.   Transmission System Application   233

9.1.   Introduction 233
9.2.   Long Distance Transmission 234
    9.2.1.   Bit-Rate Flexible Link 234
    9.2.2.   WDM Transmission Experiment 237
    9.2.3.   Loop Transmission Experiment 238
    9.2.4.   Distributed EDFA 240
9.3.   Coherent Transmission 241
9.4.   Subscriber Transmission 245
9.5.   Soliton Transmission 252
References 254

10.   Nonlinear Effects   259

10.1.   Introduction 259
10.2.   FWM 260
10.3.   Stimulated Raman Scattering 266
10.4.   Stimulated Brillouin Scattering 271
10.5.   Supercontinuum Generation 274
    10.5.1.   Theoretical Model 276
    10.5.2.   Results and Discussion 278
References 283

11.   Planar Waveguide Amplifiers and Lasers   287

11.1.   Introduction 287
11.2.   Er-Doped Planar Waveguide 289
    11.2.1.   Optical Gain and Gain Saturation 293
11.3.   Nd-Doped Planar Waveguide 294
11.4.   Er–Yb Co-Doped Planar Waveguide 299

11.5. Yb-Doped Planar Waveguide 302
11.6. High-Power Waveguide Lasers 304
11.7. Supercontinuum Generation 308
    11.7.1. Results and Discussions 314
References 316

12. Fiber Laser   321

12.1. Introduction 321
12.2. Fiber Laser Designs 321
    12.2.1. Er-Doped Fiber Laser 322
    12.2.2. Nd-Doped Fiber Laser 324
    12.2.3. Yb-Doped Fiber Laser 326
12.3. Multiwavelength Laser 328
12.4. Tunable Fiber Lasers 335
12.5. High Power Fiber Lasers 339
    12.5.1. Yb-Doped Fiber Laser 340
    12.5.2. Nd-Doped Fiber Laser 343
    12.5.3. Er–Yb Co-Doped Fiber Laser 347
References 352

13. Fiber Raman Lasers and Amplifiers   357

13.1. Introduction 357
13.2. Fiber Bragg Gratings 360
13.3. Raman Laser 363
13.4. Cascaded Raman Laser 369
13.5. Raman Amplifier 370
References 376

14. Mode Locked Pulse Generation   379

14.1. Introduction 379
14.2. Harmonic Mode Locking 380
14.3. Rational Harmonic Mode Locking 385
    14.3.1. Time Domain Analysis 389
14.4. Stability of Mode Locked Operation 397
    14.4.1. Stable Mode Locked Operation Using PLL . 399
    14.4.2. Dual Wavelength Mode Locking 403

14.5. Pulse Compression 408

    14.5.1. Pulse Compression Using NOLM 408

14.6. Passive Mode Locking Schemes 411

14.7. Other Mode Locked Laser Systems 418

    14.7.1. Yb-Doped Mode Locked Laser 418

    14.7.2. Passive Mode Locking Theory 422

References 425

Index 429

Chapter 1

Introduction

1.1. Historical Developments

Laser is an acronym for Light Amplification by Stimulated Emission of Radiation. The laser operating in the microwave region (maser) was invented in 1955.[1] Extension of this to the visible wavelength range was proposed in 1958.[2] As opposed to other sources of light the laser emission is highly directional, nearly monochromatic, has high brightness, and a high degree of coherence. Laser emission requires an optical gain medium in an optical cavity; the latter provides optical feedback.[2-5] The first laser operation in doped solid state material — chromium-doped Al_2O_3 ($Cr:Al_2O_3$) was demonstrated by Maiman in 1960.[3] The laser material was mostly Al_2O_3-doped with ~0.1 wt.% of Cr_2O_3. The material was pumped with a high intensity pulsed flashlamp and emitted at 693.4 nm.

Since then laser emissions in various rare earth (Nd, Pr, Er, Ho, Tm, Yb)-doped glasses have been observed in the 1960's.[6-9] Although typical doping levels for obtaining gain is low (~0.1 to 0.3 wt.% or 100 to 500 ppm), higher doping levels have been used, which are feasible, for high power laser operation. The doped fiber laser was demonstrated in 1964 by Koester and Snitzer.[8] They reported a flashlamp pumped Nd-doped fiber amplifier with a high gain. The diode laser pumped Nd-doped fiber laser was reported in 1970 by Stone and Burrus.[10] However, the potential for rare earth-doped fiber amplifiers and fiber lasers was not recognized until the late 1980's and it began with a demonstration of very low threshold fiber amplifier by Payne and his co-workers in 1985.[11-13]

They reported a Nd-doped fiber laser emitting at 1088 nm pumped by a AlGaAs diode laser with an absorbed pump power for threshold of only 0.6 mW. At that time few tens of mW of pump power was widely available from semiconductor lasers made using GaAs/AlGaAs and InP/InGaAsP material systems. So, this pioneering demonstration conveyed an important message: that using well established low loss fiber fabrication technology and semiconductor laser fabrication technology, a new class of rare doped lasers and amplifiers could be produced for new applications. This message was particularly well received immediately by optical communication technologists and they went on to develop the Erbium (Er)-doped fiber amplifiers for various fiber communication applications. It was also recognized that an amplifier chain could be used for long (~1000 to 7000 km) undersea optical communication links and that such a system could be easily upgraded to higher data rates simply by replacing the transmitters and repeaters on the shore — a much easier task than laying a new cable. The first undersea fiber optic link using an amplifier chain went into operation in the mid 1990s. Er-doped optical amplifiers have been described in several books.[14–17]

Since then, rare earth-doped fiber lasers have been developed for many applications. Diode laser pumped fiber lasers have been produced that generate kWs of power, amplifiers with small signal gains of >50 dB and laser sources with fs pulse widths. Although many rare earth dopants have been studied, Er, Yb, Nd, Tm-doped glasses continue to be the work horse for many applications.

1.2. Materials

Rare earth ions doped in crystalline or glassy materials have been studied extensively for optical applications. Glasses provide a broad emission and absorption spectrum, as a result glass hosts are used in many applications. Typical glass hosts are oxide and fluoride glasses. The ground state of rare earth ions are characterized by an open 4f shell. The free ion energy level structure of rare earth ions are quite complex.[18] The spin-orbit interaction creates a fine structure and the levels are labeled not only by their J values but also the L and S values.

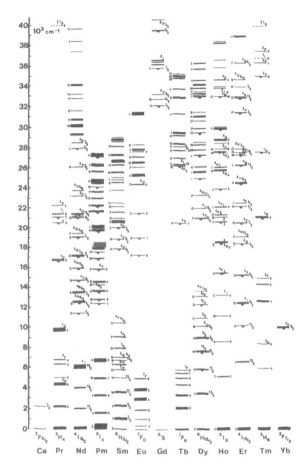

Fig. 1.1 Dieke diagram of trivalent rare earth ions.[18, 19] The width of each level represents crystal field splitting.[20]

The atomic forces split the $4f^N$ orbital to $^{2S+1}L_J$ levels, then the weaker crystal field splits each free ion level into a large number of stark levels. The crystal field splitting is $\sim$100 to 500 cm^{-1} (see Sec. 3.2).[18]

The energy level diagram for several trivalent ions, due to Dieke, is shown in Fig. 1.1 which is often called the Dieke diagram.[18] Rare earth ions in glass comprise an important class of laser materials. The ordinary glass (SiO$_2$) has the advantage that it can be drawn into low loss optical fibers providing long interaction lengths. The spectroscopy of rare earth ions in glasses has been well studied. In addition to crystal field splitting, other factors such as symmetry, co-ordination, site location, determine the optical properties. They have been studied using site selection spectroscopy.[18]

1.3. Operating Principles

The schematic of a typical Er-doped fiber amplifier is shown in Fig. 1.2. It consists of a pump laser diode and typically a ~10 m long Er-doped fiber. The light from the diode laser and the input light near 1550 nm are both coupled into the fiber using a coupler. The pump light excites the rare earth ions to high energy levels which decay fast to an intermediate energy level (higher level of lasing transition) from which it decays to a lower lasing energy level with the emission of a photon. In the presence of another photon of the same

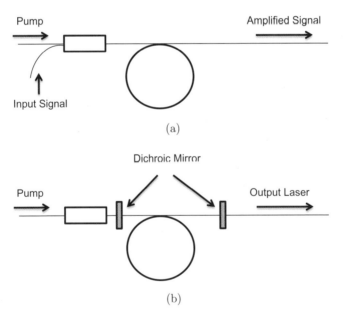

Fig. 1.2 (a) Schematic of a rare earth-doped fiber amplifier. The circle represents the rare earth-doped fiber. (b) Schematic of a fiber laser. The mirrors could be fiber Bragg gratings. The figure shows coiled fiber (circle). A wavelength division multiplexed (WDM) coupler couples both pump and input signal into the doped fiber in (a).

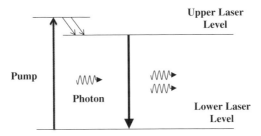

Fig. 1.3 Schematic illustration of gain (or amplification). An electron makes a transition to generate a photon. This photon is emitted in the same direction as the incident photon. The process is known as stimulated emission.

wavelength stimulated emission is observed as shown in Fig. 1.3 For fiber laser operation, dichroic mirrors (mirrors with high reflectivity for lasing light and high transmission for pump light) are added at the input and output. The typical reflectivity for the laser light at the pump input end is >90% and at the output end it is ~50%. A ring fiber laser geometry is often used for the generation of short pulses (Chapter 14).

The stimulated emission in a fiber amplifier arises from electron transition in the rare earth ion in the doped core region, and the light generated is confined and guided by a circular waveguide consisting of the core and cladding regions. The core region has a slightly higher index (~0.3%) than the cladding region, and the two regions form a waveguide. Index raising dopants for SiO_2 glass are germanium, phosphorus, and aluminum and index lowering dopants are boron and flourine. A typical fiber has a Ge-doped SiO_2 core and SiO_2 cladding. The optical mode propagation in a fiber waveguide using the ray approach is shown in Fig. 1.4. The rays incident at an angle θ, with $\sin \theta > (n_2/n_1)$, undergoes total internal reflection at the interface of the cladding and active region. Thus rays with these sets of angle of incidence continue to propagate through the amplifier and gets amplified. Other rays escape from the gain region.

An alternative view is an optical mode with a certain intensity profile determined by the thickness of the gain region and the indices can propagate through the amplifier without any diffraction loss. The intensity profile of a propagating mode is also sketched in Fig. 1.4

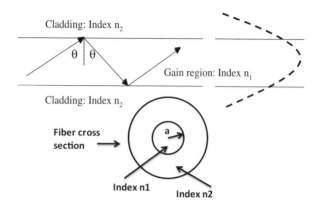

Fig. 1.4 Waveguiding in a fiber waveguide. The gain region of index n_1 has cladding region of index n_2 around it. The index $n_1 > n_2$. The figure shows the total internal reflection of a ray incident at an angle θ (with $\sin \theta > (n_2/n_1)$) propagating in the gain region. An alternate view is that a confined optical mode with intensity profile (shown as dashes in the figure) propagates in the waveguide.

(see Chapter 2 for details). A fraction of the incident optical signal can, in general, be coupled to the propagating mode. The remaining fraction is lost.

1.4. Applications

Optical fiber amplifier as the name implies could be used as an amplifier in a fiber optic communication system or other types of optical amplifier applications. The Er-doped optical amplifier (EDFA) is most commonly used in optical communication systems because it amplifies signals near 1550 nm which is the region of low loss transmission in optical fibers. Many studies on applications of EDFA in optical fiber systems have been reported.[14–17] The EDFA is well suited for application in single channel fiber systems for data rates exceeding 100 Gb/s and for multichannel WDM transmission systems.

The EDFA is also used as a preamplifier for increasing the receiver sensitivity, as a signal amplifier in long distance transmission systems and as a replacement for repeaters in long distance undersea fiber optic transmission systems. Schematics of submarine optical fiber

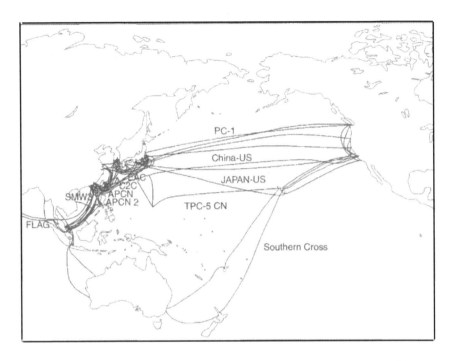

Fig. 1.5 Optical amplifier submarine fiber network in the Pacific Ocean.[21]

network in the Pacific and Atlantic oceans are shown in Figs. 1.5 and 1.6 respectively.

Nd-doped optical amplifiers and lasers have been demonstrated for space communication applications and for high power operation.[22–24] Yb-doped amplifiers are important for high power applications because high Yb doping without any loss process (such as up conversion) is feasible for Yb-doped glasses. High powers (kW level) have been demonstrated for Yb-doped fiber lasers using a large area fiber.[25] These lasers emit near 1000 nm. Er–Yb co-doping has been used to make higher power amplifiers and lasers emitting near 1550 nm. In these cases, the exited Yb ions transfers its energy to Er, allowing for lower Er concentration and hence reduced concentration quenching which would otherwise happen in high doped Er fibers. Double clad fiber designs and innovative pump coupling methods have been developed for these high power lasers and amplifiers.

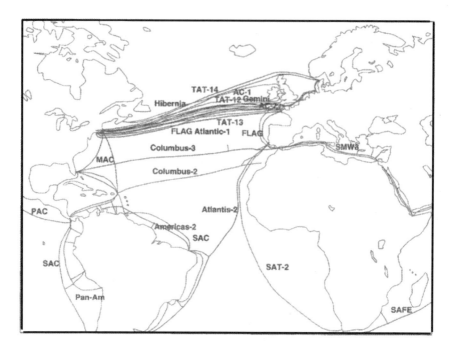

Fig. 1.6 Optical amplifier submarine fiber network in the Atlantic Ocean.[21]

1.5. Book Overview

Rare earth-doped fiber amplifiers and fiber lasers are important for a wide range of applications including fiber optic communications, free space communications, optical networks, high power laser systems, and, sensors. The book describes the advances in research, technology and commercial trends in the area of rare earth-doped fiber amplifiers and fiber lasers.

The fundamental operating principles of rare earth-doped optical amplifiers and lasers are described in Chapter 2. The optical gain spectrum, saturation of gain at high powers and the mechanism for gain is discussed. Rate equation model for three-level and four-level lasers which are good representatives of rare earth-doped lasers are discussed. The minimum pump power needed for amplification is given. The propagation of optical mode through the fiber waveguide and mode confinement is discussed. A typical semiconductor pump laser is discussed. A few rare earth-doped amplifiers such as Er and Yb for specific performance is described.

Chapter 3 describes absorption and emission in rare earth-doped glasses. Energy levels and transitions in rare earth ions are discussed. Absorption and emission spectrum and the relationship between them is described. Examples of specific rare earth-doped ions are considered. A model for emission cross section in rare earth-doped ions is described.

The fabrications of rare earth-doped fibers are described in Chapter 4. Single mode fiber pre-form fabrication methods are described. The drawing of fibers from these performs is described. Incorporation of rare earth dopants by various methods and microstructure fiber fabrication is described.

The amplifier performance optimization and design processes are described in Chapter 5. These include optical characterization (absorption and emission) of amplifier fiber and materials characterization of fiber pre-forms. A steady state rate equation model for single mode amplifier which takes into account pump depletion and gain saturation is described. Design and characterization of microstructure fiber is described.

The rate equations for pulse propagation in an optical amplifier are developed in Chapter 6. Transient gain effects are discussed. Effect of multiple channel amplification on gain and output modulation is discussed. Various factors for optical noise in amplifiers such as spontaneous-spontaneous beat noise, signal-spontaneous beat noise are described. Pulse propagation and soliton propagation are discussed.

The design and performance of several high power optical amplifier and laser designs are described in Chapter 7. Double clad fiber amplifier, high power pump coupling methods and the Cladding pumped amplifier model are described.

The pump laser design and fabrication are described in Chapter 8 along with the epitaxial growth of laser materials. Various laser designs and fabrication methods are described. Index guided amplifier structures and their fabrication is described. Strained layer gain region important for polarization independent gain is described along with specific pump lasers.

Application of optical amplifier (Er-doped fiber amplifier) in optical transmission systems is described. These include long distance transmission, undersea transmission, coherent transmission and analog transmission.

Nonlinear processes in single mode fibers and fiber amplifiers are discussed in Chapter 10. These include four wave mixing, stimulated Raman effect and stimulated Brillouin effect. Supercontinuum generation which includes many of the nonlinear processes is discussed.

The fiber amplifier is generally long (few m in length). In order to make compact amplifiers, doped planar waveguide devices ($\sim$10 cm long) has been investigated. The fabrication and performance of silica based doped planar waveguide amplifiers and lasers are discussed in Chapter 11. The discussion includes high power amplifiers and supercontinuum generation.

The fabrication of fiber lasers and their performances are described in Chapter 12. The description includes high power fiber lasers using double clad fiber design, tunable fiber lasers and fiber lasers that emit in multiple wavelengths.

Raman lasers based on the stimulated Raman effect in silica fibers are important for newer emission wavelengths from fiber lasers. The fabrication of fiber Bragg gratings which are generally used to provide feedback in Raman laser is described. Cascaded Raman laser designs are described.

Short pulse generation using fiber lasers are described in Chapter 14. Both active and passive mode locking schemes are described. Harmonic and rational harmonic mode locked pulse generation is described along with the use of saturable absorbers for generating sub-ps pulses is described.

1.6. Future Challenges

Tremendous advances in rare earth-doped fiber amplifier and fiber laser technology have occurred over the last two decades. The advances in research and many technological innovations have led to improved designs of fiber amplifiers. Most lightwave systems use EDFA for signal amplification. These include terrestrial lightwave transmission, undersea lightwave transmission and subscriber networks.

The need for higher capacity is continuing to encourage research in WDM based and optical time division multiplexing (OTDM) based transmission, which needs optical amplification and high power tunable lasers. An important research area would continue to be the optimized development of fiber amplifiers for use as preamplifiers at high data rate and for multichannel transmission using new data transmission (pulse code modulation, phase shifting, and duo-binary) formats.

Improving Nd or Yb-doped amplifier performance for space communication application is important. These materials emit at a shorter wavelength and thus the diffraction limited spot size is smaller for these amplifiers. Along the same line of thought, the development of shorter wavelength optical amplifiers is important.

Although significant developments have occurred in high power optical fiber lasers, the need for higher power for commercial (metal cutting and shaping) applications will continue to drive the research on higher power fiber lasers using Nd or Yb based systems and possibly others.

For compact fiber amplifiers and lasers, the planar waveguide geometry is an important candidate. Progress in waveguide design, packaging which includes heat removal and, optimum pump coupling can make these devices competitive with fiber based amplifiers with considerable reduction in size.

Short pulse generation is important for a range of applications. For communication systems, stable short pulse generation using active mode locking would continue to be investigated. Femto-second pulse generation would continue to be investigated for optical coherence tomography and other sensor applications. Newer set of wavelengths may be required for some of these applications. Thus materials research and the cascaded Raman gain are important research areas.

Finally, much of the advances in the rare earth-doped fiber amplifier and fiber laser development would not have been possible without the advances in doping and materials fabrication technology. The challenges of much of the current amplifier and laser research are intimately linked with the challenges in materials design and fabrication which include not only the investigation of new material systems but also improvements in existing technologies, to make them more reproducible and predictable.

References

1. J.P. Gordon, H.J. Zeiger and C.H. Townes, *Phys. Rev.* **18** (1955) 1274.
2. A.L. Schawlow and C.H. Townes, *Phys. Rev.* **112** (1958) 1940.
3. T.H. Maiman, *Nature.* **187** (1960) 493.
4. A. Javan, W.R. Bennett, Jr and D.R. Herriot, *Phys. Rev. Lett.* **6** (1961) 106.
5. N.G. Basov, O.N. Krokhin and Yu. M. Popov, *Sov. Phys. JETP.* **13** (1961) 1320.
6. J.E. Geusic, H.M. Marcos and L.G. Van Uitert, *Appl Phys. Lett.* **4** (1964) 182.
7. E. Snitzer, *J. Appl. Phys.* **32** (1961) 36.
8. C.J. Koster and E. Snitzer, *Appl. Opt,* **3** (1964) 1182.
9. E. Snitzer and R. Woodcock, *Appl Phys. Lett.* **6** (1965) 45.
10. J. Stone and C.A. Burrus, *Appl. Phys. Lett.* **23** (1973) 388.
11. S.B. Poole. D.N. Payne and M.E. Freeman, *Electron Lett.* **21** (1985) 737.
12. R.J. Mears, L. Reekie, S.B. Poole and D.N. Payne, *Electron. Lett.* **22** (1986) 870.
13. R.J. Mears, L. Reekie, I.M. Jauncie and D.N. Payne, *Electron. Lett.* **23** (1987) 1026.
14. E. Desurvire, *Erbium doped fiber amplifiers.* John Wiley and Sons. 1994.
15. P.C. Becker, N.A. Olsson and J.R. Simpson, *Erbium doped fiber amplifiers.* Academic Press. 1997.
16. M.J. Digonnet (Ed.), *Rare earth doped fiber lasers and amplifiers.* Marcel Dekker, Inc. 1993.
17. S. Shimoda and H. Ishio (Eds), Optical amplifiers and their applications. John Wiley and Sons. 1994.
18. B. Henderson and R. Bertram, *Crystal field engineering of soild-state laser materials.* Cambridge: Cambridge Univ. Press. 2000.
19. G. H. Dieke, *Spectra and energy levels of rare earth ions in crystals.* New York: John Wiley. 1968.
20. B. Henderson and G.F. Imbusch, *Optical spectroscopy of inorganic solids.* Oxford University. Press. 1989.
21. S. Yamamoto and T. Miyazaki, Chapter 5 Submarine Networks. In *WDM Technologies — Optical Networks*, A.K. Dutta, N.K. Dutta and M. Fujiwara (Eds) USA: Elsevier. 2004.
22. E. Rochat, K. Haroud and R.Dïdliker, *IEEE JQE.* **35** (1999) 1419.

23. E. Rochat, R. Dändliker, K. Haroud, R.H. Czichy, U. Roth, D. Costantini and R. Holzner, *IEEE J Selected Area of Quantum Electronics.* **7** (2001) 64.
24. I. Zawischa, K. Plamann, C. Fallnich, H. Welling, H. Zellmer and A. Tünnermann, *Opt. Lett.* **24** (1999) 469.
25. Y. Fan, F. Lu, S-L. Hu, K-C. Lu, H-J. Wang, X-Y. Dong and G-Y. Zhang. *IEEE Photonic Tech. Lett.* **15** (2003) 652.

Chapter 2

Basic Concepts

2.1. Introduction

Significant advances in research in the development and application of optical fiber amplifiers and fiber lasers have occurred over the last two decades. The fiber optic revolution in telecommunication which provided several orders of magnitude improvement in transmission capacity at low cost would not have been possible without the development of reliable semiconductor lasers and fiber amplifiers. The optical fiber amplifier is an important device for both terrestrial and submarine optical communication systems and next generation all-optical networks.

Fiber amplifier, as the name implies, is a device that amplifies an input optical signal. The amplification factor or gain can be higher than 1000 (>30 dB) in some devices. There are two principal types of optical amplifiers. They are, the semiconductor optical amplifier and the fiber optical amplifier. In a semiconductor optical amplifier, amplification of light takes place when it propagates through a semiconductor medium. In a fiber amplifier the light propagates through a glass (typically SiO_2 based) fiber which is doped with another material (Nd, Yb, Er etc). The dopant atoms are excited to a higher energy state by the absorption of a pump light (typically from another laser) and when they make a transition to a lower energy state, photons (light) at an appropriate energy are emitted. Thus the fiber amplifier used in commercial systems need reliable pump lasers for operation.

The gain media (core region of the fiber) with the dopants are located within a small region (typically 3 to $10\,\mu$m in diameter) of

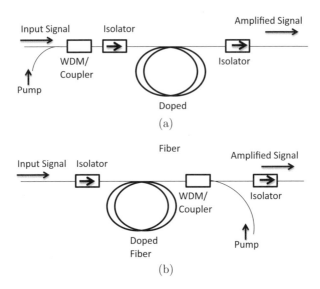

Fig. 2.1 Schematic of an optical fiber amplifier. The isolators are needed for reducing the effect of amplified spontaneous emission noise. (a) Forward pumping or co-propagating pump, (b) Backward pumping or counter propagating pump. Bidirectional pumping is also used.

the optical fiber. This region is surrounded by a cladding region about $100\,\mu$m in diameter. The two regions form a waveguide through which the light travels and undergoes amplification. Optical fiber amplifiers (OFAs) are typically $\sim$10 to 30 m in length. The operating principles, design, fabrication and performance characteristics of optical amplifiers are described in this chapter. The schematic of a fiber amplifier is shown in Fig. 2.1.

Fiber laser is a device very similar to a fiber amplifier.[1–12] Fiber amplifiers amplify light through stimulated emission which is responsible for gain and fiber lasers utilize the same fiber gain medium in addition to having optical feedback. The gain and feedback together are responsible for laser action. Hence their operating principles, fabrication and design are also similar. The gain in the fiber laser is produced by optically pumping the gain medium using a pump laser of suitable wavelength. The pump laser is typically a semiconductor laser which produces light by current injection. For details on lasers please see Refs. 13–18 and Chapter 8.

Table 2.1 Stimulated emission wavelength for various rare earths. Silica based fiber host is more desirable due to the ease of fabrication.

Rare Earth-Dopant (Host)	Principal Gain Wavelength Region (nm)
Nd (Silica)	1060, 940
Yb (Silica)	1100
Er (Silica)	1550
Pr (Flouride)	1300
Pr (Silica)	1050
Tm (Silica)	1650, 2000
Tm (Flouride)	2300
Ho (Silica)	2040
Ho (Flouride)	2900

2.2. Three-level and Four-level Laser

Rare earth ions have been studied extensively for optical and magnetic applications. These ions are generally doped in crystalline or glassy materials. Glasses provide broad emission and absorption spectrum, as a result glass hosts are used in many applications. Typical glass hosts are oxide and fluoride glasses. Fiber amplifiers used in optical transmission generally use silica (SiO_2) as the host material. Table 2.1 shows a simplified table of the stimulated emission wavelength for various dopants.

For rare earth-doped amplifiers population inversion is important i.e., there needs to be more ions in the high energy excited state compared to that in the ground state. The energy stored in the excited state ions are released in the form of stimulated emission when an incident signal is present and this signal undergoes amplification. The energy levels in rare doped ions are generally classified as three or four-level laser systems (Fig. 2.2). Erbium (Er) is often considered a three-level system, whereas Nd and Pr are considered four-level systems. In reality, the lower laser energy level of Er in glass consists of a group of levels broadened by the crystal field in glass i.e., it is not an ideal three-level system.

For three-level systems, the low energy level of the stimulated emission transition is the ground state of the ion and for four-level systems the ground state of the ion is at a lower energy level than

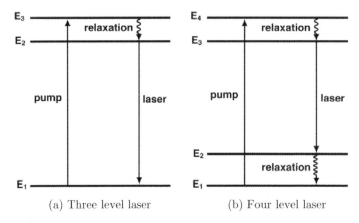

(a) Three level laser (b) Four level laser

Fig. 2.2 Schematic of the energy levels in (a) Three-level lasers, (b) Four-level lasers.[19, 20]

the low energy level of the amplifying transition. For a four-level amplifier, the low energy level is naturally depopulated by transition to the ground state; hence it is easier to achieve population inversion in such systems.

For a three-level laser at least half of the ions have to be excited, otherwise the system will have optical loss and not optical gain. This results in an optimum length for Er amplifiers (three-level system) pumped at one end for a given pump power. If the length is too large, the ions at the far end may not achieve population inversion and that region will contribute to optical loss of the transmitted signal. The four-level system remains transparent.

Schematic of energy level diagram of three-level and four-level lasers are shown in Fig. 2.2. An example of a three-level laser is the Cr-doped Al_2O_3 (ruby) laser operating on the $^2E \rightarrow {}^4A_2$ transition at $0.69\,\mu$m. An example of a four-level laser is the Nd-doped YAG (Yttrium–aluminum–Garnet) laser operating on the $^4F_{3/2} \rightarrow {}^4I_{11/2}$ transition at $1.064\,\mu$m.

2.2.1. *Three-level Laser*

For a three-level laser, (Fig. 2.2), the ground state (1) has energy (E_1), the upper laser level (2), has energy E_2, and there is a higher energy level (3), of energy E_3. The pump excites the atom from ground state to excited state (3), the atom makes a fast transition from 3 to 2, and the laser transition is from 2 to 1, i.e., the ground state of the atom or ion is the lower energy level of the laser transition. The rate equation for a three-level laser is described in the following.[20]

The population density at levels 1, 2, 3 are labeled N_1, N_2, N_3 respectively. The pump rate is denoted by P, so that PN_1 is the number of atoms excited per cm^{-3}. The total number of atoms per unit volume is:

$$N = N_1 + N_2 + N_3$$

The rate equations due to pump are: (assuming fast decay from level 3 to 2):

$$\left(\frac{dN_1}{dt}\right)_{pump} = -PN_1 = \left(\frac{dN_3}{dt}\right)_{pump} = \left(\frac{dN_2}{dt}\right)_{pump}, \qquad (2.1)$$

Thus the rate equations for N_1, N_2 are:

$$\frac{dN_1}{dt} = -PN_1 + \Gamma N_2 + \sigma(v)\phi_v(N_2 - N_1),$$

$$\frac{dN_2}{dt} = PN_1 - \Gamma N_2 - \sigma(v)\phi_v(N_2 - N_1), \qquad (2.2)$$

where ϕ_ν is the optical photon density at frequency ν, $\sigma(\nu)$ is the stimulated emission cross section at frequency ν, and Γ is the spontaneous decay rate from level 2 to level 1. Γ includes both spontaneous radiation rate and nonradiative rates. Γ is the inverse of the lifetime of level 2. If the decay rate from level 3 to level 2 is fast, $N_3 \sim 0$, thus the total atom density (N) is given by:

$$N_1 + N_2 = N, \qquad (2.3)$$

If the intensity is small (i.e., $\phi_\nu = 0$), then in steady state:

$$\bar{N}_1 = \frac{\Gamma}{P + \Gamma}N \quad \bar{N}_2 = \frac{P}{P + \Gamma}N, \qquad (2.4)$$

where $\bar{N}_1$ and $\bar{N}_2$ are steady state values of N_1 and N_2 respectively. It follows:

$$\bar{N}_2 - \bar{N}_1 = \frac{P - \Gamma}{P + \Gamma}N. \qquad (2.5)$$

Thus the minimum pump rate needed for population inversion ($\bar{N}_2 > \bar{N}_1$) is $P > \Gamma$, i.e., $P_{\min} = \Gamma$.

Since N is the number of pump atoms per unit vol. and $h\upsilon_{31}$ is the energy needed per pump photon, it follows, that the minimum pump power for population inversion is:

$$P_{\min} = \frac{1}{2}\Gamma h \upsilon_{31} N. \tag{2.6}$$

Thus pump power larger than the minimum value given by the Eq. (2.6) is needed for producing population inversion or gain. Equation (2.5) shows that more than half of the atoms are in the excited state for producing gain. This phenomenon is known as population inversion.

For a ruby (Cr:Al$_2$O$_3$) laser, $\Gamma \sim 500\,\mathrm{s}^{-1}$. The density of atoms $N \sim 1.6 \times 10^{19}\,\mathrm{cm}^{-3}$, and assuming pump photon energy $h\nu \sim 2\,\mathrm{eV}$, the minimum pump power per unit volume is:

$$P \sim (1/2)\Gamma N h\nu \sim 1\,\mathrm{kWcm}^{-3}. \tag{2.7}$$

For a 5 cm long ruby rod of radius (with a stimulated emission area radius of 2 mm), the required pump threshold power is $\sim$600 W.

Another three-level laser system is Nd-doped glass operating at 920 nm. For this system, $\Gamma \sim 100\,\mathrm{s}^{-1}$, $h\nu \sim 1\,\mathrm{eV}$, $N \sim 10^{19}\,\mathrm{cm}^{-3}$. Using this formula, the threshold pump power is $\sim$80 Wcm^{-3}.

So far, the rate equations has been solved in the absence of stimulated emission, (i.e., $\phi_\nu = 0$). For a non zero ϕ_ν in steady state from Eq. (2.2):

$$\bar{N}_2 = \frac{PN}{P + \Gamma + 2\sigma(\upsilon)\phi_\upsilon},$$

$$\bar{N}_2 - \bar{N}_1 = \frac{(P - \Gamma)N}{P + \Gamma + 2\sigma(\upsilon)\phi_\upsilon}, \tag{2.8}$$

and the gain, $g(\nu)$ is given by ($\sigma(\nu)$ is the stimulated emission cross section at frequency ν):

$$g(\upsilon) = \frac{\sigma(\upsilon)\,(P - \Gamma)\,N}{P + \Gamma + 2\sigma(\upsilon)\phi_\upsilon}. \tag{2.9}$$

Thus the gain is smaller in the presence of stimulated emission, i.e., the gain saturates. The gain saturation is rewritten as:

$$g(v) = \frac{g_0(v)}{1 + \phi_v/\phi_{vs}}.$$ (2.10)

The quantity $g_0(\nu)$ is the unsaturated gain and $\phi_{\nu s}$ is the saturation intensity. They are given by:

$$g_0(v) = \frac{\sigma(v)(P - \Gamma)N}{P + \Gamma},$$

$$\phi_{vs} = \frac{P + \Gamma}{2\sigma(v)}.$$ (2.11)

The saturation power is $I_{\nu s} = h\nu\phi_{\nu s}$. For a laser, gain = loss, i.e., $g = \alpha$ where α is the loss per unit length. It follows from Eq. (2.10), removing the subscript ν:

$$\phi = \left(\frac{g_0}{\alpha} - 1\right)\phi_s.$$ (2.12)

Since the intensity is proportional to the photon density, the laser intensity I is given by:

$$I = \left(\frac{g_0}{\alpha} - 1\right)I_s.$$ (2.13)

where I_s is the saturation intensity. I_s is given by:

$$I_s = h\upsilon v_g \left(\frac{P + \Gamma}{2\sigma}\right).$$ (2.14)

where v_g is the group velocity. If the number of pump photons is N_p, the pump rate is given by:

$$P = N_p v_g \sigma_a,$$ (2.15)

where σ_a is the pump absorption cross section and v_g is the group velocity. If $h\nu_p$ is the pump photon energy, the pump power I_p is given by:

$$I_p = h\upsilon_p N_p v_g,$$ (2.16)

From Eqs. (2.13)–(2.16):

$$I_{\text{laser}} = \left(\frac{g_0}{\alpha} - 1\right)\frac{h\upsilon v_g}{2\sigma}\left[\left(\frac{\sigma_a}{h\upsilon_p}\right)I_p + \Gamma\right].$$ (2.17)

Thus the laser power is linearly proportional to the pump power for pump power greater than threshold power $(P > P_{\text{min}})$, i.e., when $g_0 > \alpha$. For the specific case of Er-doped amplifier, the upper and lower energy levels are broadened by Stark splitting (Sec. 2.4: Fig. 2.5). The pump laser wavelengths are at 980 nm and 1480 nm respectively. For 980 nm pump, the laser can be represented by a three-level system and for the 1480 nm pump the laser is similar to a two-level laser. The population distribution in the band (stark split levels) is determined by the usual Boltzmann distribution. Nearly complete inversion of the Er levels can be achieved using 980 nm pumping whereas for 1480 nm pumping the inversion is generally lower. The conversion efficiency is higher for 1480 nm pump due to closer matching with the emission wavelength (1520 to 1570 nm). The noise figure with 980 nm pump is generally lower than that for 1480 nm pump due to more complete inversion. This is discussed further in Chapter 6.

2.2.2. *Four-level Laser*

An example of a four-level laser is the Nd:YAG laser operating at 1064 nm on the $^4F_{3/2} \rightarrow {}^4I_{11/2}$ transition. In these lasers, the lower laser level is emptied very rapidly to the ground state (Fig. 2.2). The quantities N_1, N_2, N_3, N_4 are the populations of the four levels shown in Fig. 2.2. While deriving the rate equations, it is assumed, as before, that the transition from level 4 where pump absorption takes place to level 3 (high energy laser level) is very fast, i.e.:

$$\left(\frac{dN_4}{dt}\right)_{\text{pump}} = \left(\frac{dN_3}{dt}\right)_{\text{pump}}. \tag{2.18}$$

The rate equations are:

$$\frac{dN_1}{dt} = -PN_1 + \Gamma_{21}N_2,$$

$$\frac{dN_2}{dt} = -\Gamma_{21}N_2 + \Gamma_{32}N_3 + \sigma(v)(N_3 - N_2)\phi_v,$$

$$\frac{dN_3}{dt} = PN_1 - \Gamma_{32}N_3 - \sigma(v)(N_3 - N_2)\phi_v, \tag{2.19}$$

where P is the pump rate to level N_4, but all level 4 atoms relax to level 3 very rapidly. The quantities Γ_{32} and Γ_{21} are decay rates from level 3 to level 2 and level 2 to level 1 (ground state) respectively. Hence P is also pumping rate for level 3. The last term is stimulated emission. The total number of atoms per unit volume in all levels is N, a constant.

$$N = N_1 + N_2 + N_3, \tag{2.20}$$

The steady state population inversion in the absence of stimulated emission (i.e., $\phi_\nu = 0$) is:

$$\bar{N}_3 - \bar{N}_2 = \frac{P\left(\Gamma_{21} - \Gamma_{32}\right) N}{\Gamma_{21}\Gamma_{32} + \Gamma_{21}P + \Gamma_{32}P}. \tag{2.21}$$

Thus the condition for population inversion is $\Gamma_{21} > \Gamma_{32}$ for a nonzero P i.e., any amount of pump would cause population inversion. This shows there is no threshold (i.e., no minimum pump power requirement) for population inversion for four-level case compared to such a requirement for a three-level case. This condition, $\Gamma_{21} > \Gamma_{32}$, implies that the lower laser level decays faster than the upper laser level. When, $\Gamma_{21} \gg \Gamma_{32}$, P, Eq. (2.21) becomes:

$$\Delta N = \bar{N}_3 - \bar{N}_2 \approx \bar{N}_3 \approx \frac{P}{P + \Gamma_{32}} N, \tag{2.22}$$

The power per unit vol. (P_w) needed (using photons of energy $h\nu_{41}$) for a population inversion per unit volume ΔN is given by:

$$P_w = h\nu_{41}\Delta N\Gamma_{32}. \tag{2.23}$$

The gain of the laser is given by:

$$g(v) = \sigma(v)\Delta N. \tag{2.24}$$

The threshold for a four-level laser depends on the condition gain = loss for a laser. This is estimated as follows. For a 5 cm long Nd rod with 96% and 100% reflectivity at the ends with a round trip scattering loss of 3% ($0.03 = e^{-2\alpha l}$, $\alpha = 0.003\,\mathrm{cm}^{-1}$ for $l = 5\,\mathrm{cm}$), the gain at threshold (g_t) is calculated using the formula which assumes gain = loss at threshold:

$$g_t = \frac{1}{2l} \ln\left(\frac{1}{r_1 r_2}\right) + \alpha. \tag{2.25}$$

The calculated threshold gain from Eq. (2.25) is $g_t = 7 \times 10^{-3}\,\mathrm{cm}^{-1}$. For the 1060 nm transition in Nd, $\Gamma_{32} = 1800\,\mathrm{s}^{-1}$, and $\sigma \sim 9 \times 10^{-19}\,\mathrm{cm}^2$. Using these equations, the threshold population inversion for this gain is $\Delta N = 8 \times 10^{15}\,\mathrm{cm}^{-3}$, and the threshold power per unit volume for a pump photon energy of 1.5 eV is $\sim 3.4\,\mathrm{Wcm}^{-3}$. This is about a factor of 100 less than that for a three-level laser. For a 5 cm long rod of radius 2 mm (radius of stimulated emission area), the threshold power is $\sim 3\,\mathrm{W}$.

The optical gain a fiber amplifier depends on the pump power and the energy level of the dopants. As stated earlier, the dopants are generally modeled as a three-level or four-level laser. An efficient design for the conversion of pump photons to signal photons (amplification) uses a configuration where both the pump and signal beams are confined in the core of the optical fiber. For this design, the launched power needed to provide gain (threshold pump power — P_{th}) is a reasonable figure of merit. For high efficiency low P_{th} is desirable. From Eqs. (2.23) and (2.24), this quantity is proportional to (for a fixed gain g — gain at threshold is determined by loss):

$$P_{th} \sim h\nu_p g A_{\mathrm{eff}}/(\sigma(\nu)\varepsilon\tau), \qquad (2.26)$$

where A_{eff} is the effective area of the core ($\sim 100\,\mu\mathrm{m}^2$), $h\nu_p$ is the pump photon energy (1.5 eV), σ is the stimulated emission cross section ($9 \times 10^{-19}\,\mathrm{cm}^2$), ε is the fraction of absorbed pump power (~ 0.2), $\tau(= 1/\Gamma_{32})$ is the fluorescence lifetime of the excited energy level ($\Gamma_{32} = 1800\,\mathrm{s}^{-1}$). For a gain ($g$) of $1\,\mathrm{cm}^{-1}$, the calculated pump power needed using the values and Eq. (2.26) is $\sim 3\,\mathrm{mW}$. In a fiber amplifier, the result gets modified due to the broadening of energy levels, pump depletion and gain saturation. This is discussed in a later section and in Chapters 5 and 6. The efficiency of the device can be increased by decreasing the core area, by increasing the stimulated emission cross section, and by increasing the pump absorption cross section.

The cross section $\sigma(\nu)$ has a lineshape. For homogeneous broadening, the lineshape function is a Lorentzian:

$$\sigma(v) = \frac{\sigma(v_0)}{1 + (v - v_0)^2/\Delta v^2}, \qquad (2.27)$$

where $\Delta\nu$ is the spectral width. Since $\sigma(\nu)$ varies with frequency, the gain also varies with frequency and power as given by Eqs. (2.22)–(2.27). For a rare earth-doped amplifier, the gain spectrum is more complicated due to the presence of multiple energy levels and homogeneous and inhomgeneous broadening.

2.3. Optical Waveguide

An optical fiber consists of a central core surrounded by a cladding region. The core region has a slightly higher index ($\sim$0.3%) than the cladding region, and the two regions form a dielectric waveguide which guides the light in the core region. Conceptually, stimulated emission in a fiber amplifier arises from the atomic transitions in the doped core region, and the light generated is confined and guided by a circular waveguide consisting of the core and cladding regions (Fig. 2.3), which shows schematically the cross section and refractive index profile of a step index fiber. A graded index fiber has a graded index region between core and cladding and a step index fiber has an index step ($\Delta n = n_1 - n_2$) from core to cladding region. A fraction of the optical mode is confined in the core region.

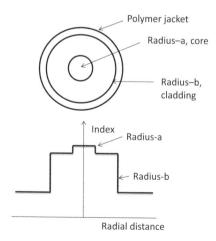

Fig. 2.3 The circular waveguide of a fiber amplifier. n_2 is the refractive index of the cladding region and n_1 that of the core region. $n_1 > n_2$. A jacket (polymer) is also shown.

The parameters that characterize the fiber are the core radius and refractive index difference Δ given by:

$$\Delta = (n_1 - n_2)/n_1. \tag{2.28}$$

The core radius (a) is typically in the 3 to $5\,\mu$m range for a standard single mode fiber. The cladding layer radius (b) is $\sim 50\,\mu$m. The cladding radius (as long as it is large enough to confine the mode i.e., $>20\,\mu$m) is not an important parameter for the waveguide in a typical single mode transmission fiber or a typical single mode fiber amplifier. Index raising dopants for silica are germanium, phosphorus, and aluminum and index lowering dopants are boron and fluorine. A typical fiber has a Ge-doped SiO_2 core. The quantity Δ is $\sim 3 \times 10^{-3}$. Another parameter, V, is important for charactering waveguide properties, it is given by[21]:

$$V = k_0 a (n_1^2 - n_2^2)^{1/2}, \tag{2.29}$$

The quantity $k_0 = 2\pi/\lambda$. The step index fiber (where there is a single index step as shown in Fig. 2.3 as opposed to a graded index fiber) supports a single fiber mode for $V < 2.405$. The optical wave propagation equation in the fiber is derived from Maxwell's equation. The Fourier transform of the electric field is defined as:

$$\vec{E}(\vec{r}, t) = \frac{1}{2\pi} \int_{-\infty}^{\infty} \vec{E}(\vec{r}, \omega) \exp(-i\omega t) d\omega. \tag{2.30}$$

In cylindrical coordinates, (ρ, ϕ, z — which is representative of wave propagation in fibers) the propagation equation for $\mathbf{E}(r, \omega)$ is:

$$\frac{\partial^2 \vec{E}}{\partial \rho^2} + \frac{1}{\rho}\frac{\partial \vec{E}}{\partial \rho} + \frac{1}{\rho^2}\frac{\partial^2 \vec{E}}{\partial \phi^2} + \frac{\partial^2 \vec{E}}{\partial z^2} + n^2 k_0^2 \vec{E} = 0, \tag{2.31}$$

where $k_0 = \omega/c = 2\pi/\lambda$. The components of $\mathbf{E}$ and $\mathbf{H}$ (electric and magnetic fields) are related by Maxwell's equations, only two components out of six are independent. It is convenient to choose E_z and H_z as independent variables. The wave propagation for E_z is solved by assuming (based on symmetry):

$$E_z = E_0 F(\rho) \exp(im\phi) \exp(i\beta z), \tag{2.32}$$

where E_0 is a constant, β is the propagation constant and m is an integer. By substituting Eq. (2.31) in Eq. (2.32), the following equation for $F(\rho)$ is obtained:

$$\frac{d^2 F}{d\rho^2} + \frac{1}{\rho}\frac{dF}{d\rho} + \left(k^2 - \frac{m^2}{\rho^2}\right) F = 0, \qquad (2.33)$$

with

$$k^2 = n^2 k_0^2 - \beta^2.$$

The refractive index (n) for a step index fiber of core radius a (where ρ is the radial coordinate) is given by:

$$n = n_1 \quad \text{for } \rho < a,$$
$$= n_2 \quad \text{for } \rho > a, \qquad (2.34)$$

The Eq. (2.33) is a well known equation whose solutions are Bessel functions:

$$F(\rho) = A_1 J_m(\kappa\rho) \quad \text{for } \rho < a,$$
$$= A_2 K_m(\gamma\rho) \quad \text{for } \rho > a, \qquad (2.35)$$

with $\kappa = n_1^2 k_0^2 - \beta^2$, $\gamma = \beta^2 - n_2^2 k_0^2$. J_m and K_m are Besssel functions of mth order. The function $K_m (\gamma\rho)$ decays exponentially for large ρ. The quantities A_1, A_2 and β are constants. The ratio between A_1 and A_2, and β are determined by the boundary condition that the electric field and its first derivative is continuous at $\rho = a$. For light polarized along the propagation axis (z axis) in the fundamental mode $(m = 0)$:

$$F(\rho) = J_0(\kappa\rho) \quad \text{for } \rho < a,$$
$$F(\rho) = (a/\rho)^{1/2} J_0(\kappa a) \exp[-\gamma(\rho - a)] \quad \text{for } \rho > a, \qquad (2.36)$$

Since the exact solutions are somewhat complex, it is often convenient to use a Gaussian approximation:

$$F(\rho) = \exp[-\rho^2/\omega^2], \qquad (2.37)$$

where $\rho^2 = x^2 + y^2$, ρ is the radial coordinate. The mode width parameter ω in the Gaussian approximation is obtained by fitting to the exact solution. Figure 2.4 shows the mode width parameter

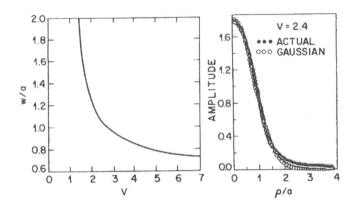

Fig. 2.4 Variation of the mode width parameter ω with the fiber parameter V. Also, shown is the actual field distribution (calculated using Bessel functions) and a Gaussian fit for V = 2.4.[22]

as a function of V. The same figure also shows that the Gaussian approximation is quite good.

The fit is good for V around 2. The spot size (ω) in the Gaussian approximation can be determined from fits similar to that in Fig. 2.4. For a good fit, a good approximation for ω (accurate to within 1%) for $1.2 < V < 2.4$ is given by (a is the radius of core):

$$\omega/a = 0.65 + 1.619\,V^{-3/2} + 2.879\,V^{-6}, \qquad (2.38)$$

The mode index (n_m) is approximately given by:

$$n_m = n_2 + (1 + b\Delta) \quad \text{where } \Delta = (n_1 - n_2)/n_1, \qquad (2.39)$$

The quantity b is a function of V and is given by:

$$b(V) = (1.1428 - 0.9960/V)^2, \qquad (2.40)$$

The optical gain of a signal in the fundamental mode traveling through the amplifier is given by:

$$g_m = \Gamma_g, \qquad (2.41)$$

The mode gain (g_m) is proportional to the mode confinement factor Γ. Since the optical amplifier is circularly symmetric, it generally exhibits a polarization independent gain (for stress induced polarization dependence or birefringent fibers, see Sec. 12.4). If P_s is the saturation power of the gain medium, the observed saturation power is given by:

$$P_s(\text{observed}) = P_s/\Gamma, \qquad (2.42)$$

Thus amplifiers with small mode confinement factor (small Γ), for example, microstructure fiber (Secs. 4.5–5.4) gain medium, exhibit high saturation power.

2.4. Rate Equations for Fiber Amplifier

For a rare earth-doped amplifier, the energy levels are broadened. A specific example of an Er-doped amplifier is considered here. The relevant energy levels of Er in a glass matrix are shown in Fig. 2.5. The analysis described is similar to that in Ref. 23. A similar analysis is applicable to other rare earth fiber amplifier systems.

The broadened energy levels of Er result in a broad emission and absorption spectrum. For Er-doped glass, the absorption and emission cross section as a function of wavelength is shown in Fig. 2.6. The absorption cross section is obtained using absorption measurements using a white light source. The emission cross sections are calculated using Fuchtbauer–Landenberg relationship using measured fluorescence spectrum and fluorescence lifetimes (see Chapter 5). Note the

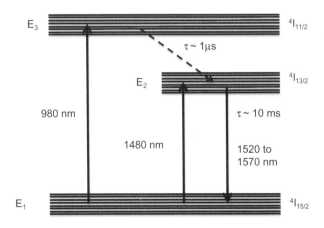

Fig. 2.5 Energy levels of Er. The pump transitions (980 nm) and amplifier transitions (1550 nm) are also shown. The ion levels are broadened by the crystal field.

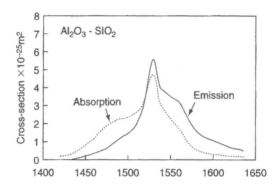

Fig. 2.6 Emission and absorption spectrum of Er in a silica host.

emission and absorption cross section at a given wavelength are different unlike the case of an isolated atom considered in Sec. 2.3.

The transition from level E_3 to E_2 is fast. Thus for the purposes of this analysis, the pump absorption creates Er ions in the excited state labeled E_2. The Er ions are in either level E_2 or E_1. Let N_2 and N_1 be the population of levels E_2 and E_1 respectively. The rate equation for the population of level E_2 is given by:

$$\frac{dN_2}{dt} = -\frac{N_2}{\tau} + \frac{\sigma_{pa}I_p}{h\nu_p}N_1 - (\sigma_{se}N_2 - \sigma_{sa}N_1)\frac{I_s}{h\nu_s}, \qquad (2.43)$$

where I_p, I_s are the intensities of the pump and signal respectively, σ_{pa} is the pump absorption cross section, σ_{sa} is the signal absorption cross section, σ_{se} is the signal emission cross section, $h\nu_p$ is the pump photon energy, $h\nu_s$ is the signal photon energy and τ is the spontaneous lifetime of level E_2. The three terms on the right hand side of Eq. (2.43) are spontaneous emission, pump absorption and absorption and stimulated emission of signal respectively. Since $N_3 \sim 0$ due to fast relaxation, $N = N_1 + N_2$ where N is the total number of atoms. As light travels through the fiber, the quantities I_p and I_s depends on the position (z) in the fiber. The equations for I_p and I_s are given by:

$$\frac{dI_p}{dz} = -\Gamma_p\sigma_{pa}N_1 I_p,$$

$$\frac{dI_s}{dz} = \Gamma_s(\sigma_{se}N_2 - \sigma_{sa}N_1)I_s. \qquad (2.44)$$

Both the pump and the signal propagate in the fiber as modes of the fiber, i.e., there is a radial dependence of the intensity as discussed in Section 2.3. The pump and signal photon densities N_p and N_s are related to I_p and I_s by:

$$N_p = \left(\frac{I_p}{h\nu_p}\right)\frac{\Gamma_p}{A_p},$$

$$N_s = \left(\frac{I_s}{h\nu_s}\right)\frac{\Gamma_s}{A_s}, \tag{2.45}$$

where Γ_p and Γ_s are pump and signal confinement factors respectively and A_p and A_s are pump and signal mode areas respectively. Thus the gain is given by:

$$g = \Gamma_s(\sigma_{se}N_2 - \sigma_{sa}N_1), \tag{2.46}$$

In steady state, Eqs. (2.43)–(2.45) can be solved to yield the following expression for gain g:

$$g = \frac{g_0}{1 + I_s/I_{\text{sat}}}, \tag{2.47}$$

with

$$g_0 = \frac{\Gamma_s\sigma_{se}N(I_p - I_{pth})}{I_p + I_{pth}(\sigma_{se}/\sigma_{sa})}, \tag{2.48}$$

$$I_{pth} = \frac{h\nu_p A_p}{\Gamma_p\tau\sigma_{pa}}\left(\frac{\sigma_{sa}}{\sigma_{se}}\right), \tag{2.49}$$

and

$$I_{\text{sat}} = \frac{h\nu_s A_s}{\Gamma_p\tau(\sigma_{se} + \sigma_{sa})}\left(1 + \frac{I_p}{I_{pth}}\frac{\sigma_{sa}}{\sigma_{se}}\right). \tag{2.50}$$

For the case of a plane wave with $\sigma_{sa} = \sigma_{se} = \sigma$, the equations reduce to Eqs. (2.9)–(2.11) as follows: The equivalences (using $\Gamma_p = \Gamma_s = 1$ and $A_s = A_p$) are: $P = \sigma_p I_p$, $\Gamma = 1/\tau$, so that $P_{\text{th}} = \Gamma$ and $\phi_{\text{sat}} = (P+\Gamma)/2\sigma$ from Eq. (2.47)–(2.50). Thus the equation for gain derived in this section reduces to those in Section 2.2.

For a typical Er-doped fiber the Er concentration is 100–500 parts per million which corresponds to a concentration of $5.7 \times 10^{24}\,\text{m}^{-3}$ to $2.9 \times 10^{25}\,\text{m}^{-3}$. A typical Er-doped amplifier has a numerical aperture of ~0.2 and a cut off wavelength of $\sim900\,\mathrm{nm}$ (i.e., the fiber supports higher order modes for wavelength $<900\,\mathrm{nm}$). The fiber needs to be single mode for $980\,\mathrm{nm}$ pump. This results in a core diameter of $\sim3.5\,\mu\mathrm{m}$. From Fig. 2.9, the stimulated emission (σ_{se}) and absorption cross sections (σ_{sa}) at $1550\,\mathrm{nm}$ are $4 \times 10^{-25}\,\mathrm{m}^2$ and $3 \times 10^{-25}\,\mathrm{m}^2$ respectively. Using $h\nu_p = 1.26\,\mathrm{eV}$, $A_p = 10\,\mu\mathrm{m}^2$, $\Gamma_p = 0.8$, $\sigma_{pa} = 2 \times 10^{-25}\,\mathrm{m}^2$ and $\tau = 10\,\mathrm{ms}$, the calculated I_{pth} from Eq. (2.47) is $\sim1\,\mathrm{mW}$ i.e., the signal will experience gain for pump power greater than $1\,\mathrm{mW}$. Using $A_s = 12\,\mu\mathrm{m}^2$, and the parameter values, the calculated I_{sat} from Eq. (2.47) is $I_{sat} = 0.27\,(1+0.88\,I_p\,(\mathrm{mW}))$, i.e., for a pump power of $10\,\mathrm{mW}$, the saturation power is $\sim2.7\,\mathrm{mW}$.

For a pump propagating through an amplifier which is typically 10 to $40\,\mathrm{m}$ in length, pump depletion takes place and the signal grows following Eq. (2.44). These equations need to be solved numerically. The parameter of importance is gain at the exit of the amplifier. The gain is the ratio of the output signal power to the input signal power often expressed in *dB* i.e., gain in $dB = 10\,\log\,(\mathrm{P_{out}/P_{in}})$. The calculated gain as function of fiber length for different pump powers is shown in Fig 2.7.

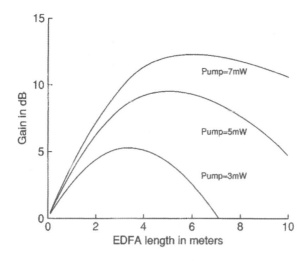

Fig. 2.7 Signal gain plotted as a function of length of Er-doped fiber amplifier.[23]

2.5. Pump Laser

In early research on rare earth-doped lasers,[5,6] the pump light for exciting the rare earth ions were obtained using high intensity flashlamps or pulsed lasers (such as the N_2 laser). For the flashlamp pumped system, the lamp light is absorbed by the active region creating ions in different excited states which then relax back to the desired excited state needed for laser action at a particular wavelength. For a UV laser pump, the ions were excited to a high energy level which then cascaded down to the desired excited state needed for laser action. Thus both of these processes were inefficient, i.e., a small fraction of pump light was converted to amplified signal or laser action.

With the advances in semiconductor laser technology, most current rare earth-doped lasers use a semiconductor laser as a pump.[24] The semiconductor laser wavelength can be chosen to optimize absorption of pump laser light and the subsequent relaxation to the excited state of the ion needed for amplification/laser action. This allows higher efficiency (larger fraction of pump light is converted to rare earth laser light), less heating of the rare earth active material, and hence also CW operation.

The typical pump laser wavelengths for efficient operation for Nd-doped, and Yb-doped amplifiers are 808 nm and 940 nm respectively.[3] For Er-doped amplifiers the typical pump laser wavelengths are 980 nm and 1480 nm. The choice of a particular pump wavelength is often dictated by the amplifier application requirements such as low noise or high efficiency.

The schematic of a 980 nm semiconductor laser used for Er-doped amplifiers is shown in Fig. 2.8. The active region (light emitting region) of the laser is composed of a semiconductor material ($In_{0.2}Ga_{0.8}As$) sandwiched between P-type and N-type AlGaAs layers which is further sandwiched between P-type and N-type GaAs layers. There are often multiple layers of active material ($In_{0.2}Ga_{0.8}As$), surrounded by GaAs layers. These $In_{0.2}Ga_{0.8}As$ layers are typically 8 to 10 nm thick and the GaAs layers are ~10 nm thick. The entire structure consisting of thin $In_{0.2}Ga_{0.8}As$ and GaAs layers

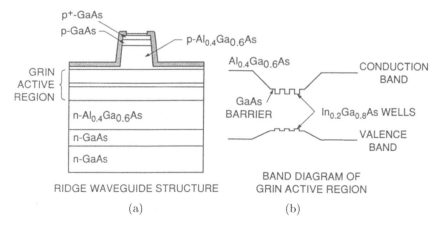

Fig. 2.8 Schematic of a ridge waveguide laser which emits near 980 nm. GRIN: graded index. For the GRIN region, the semiconductor bandgap is graded from the active region to the AlGaAs cladding region, and hence the index is graded. The GRIN design is effective in reducing the far field divergence and reducing threshold current.

is called a multiquantum well active region. The laser structure is grown on a N-GaAs substrate by an epitaxial growth process. The high band gap AlGaAs layers also have lower index than the layers in the active region. Thus they form a dielectric waveguide in the lateral direction where the lasing light is confined. For transverse confinement, generally a ridge waveguide design is used (shown in Fig. 2.8).

The ridge waveguide design consists of a mesa (ridge) on the wafer with SiO_2 deposited around it. SiO_2 has a lower index than semiconductor. Thus the region outside the ridge has a low index which leads to confinement of the light in the region of the ridge. This type of laser design is known as a ridge waveguide design. The wafer is processed into ridge waveguide lasers by thinning, cleaving and coating the facets. The cleaved facets of the semiconductor crystal form naturally reflecting parallel mirrors which are coated with dielectric to produce asymmetric laser cavity which allows more light emission from the low reflectivity coated facet. For laser action, the P–N junction is forward biased, and a current is injected into the laser.[13-15] For currents higher than a certain current (threshold current), laser emission taken place. The light vs. current characteristics

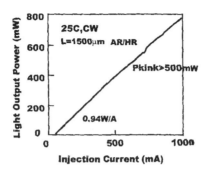

Fig. 2.9 Light vs. current characteristics of a laser emitting near 980 nm.[24]

of a typical 980 nm laser is shown in Fig. 2.9. The typical power used for fiber amplifiers is ~100 to 200 mW. Semiconductor lasers of different designs have also been used as pump lasers. The pump lasers and their designs for various rare earth-doped systems are described in Chapter 8.

2.6. Optical Transitions and Gain

Many rare earth-doped lasers and amplifiers have been fabricated.[1–3] The energy levels of several of these rare earth materials are shown in Fig. 2.10. Many of these transitions are similar to that of a four-level laser and they emit in the near infrared. Most of the rare earth dopants can be used as a dopant in several types of glasses, such as silica, fluorides, ZBLAN etc. The most studied dopants are Nd, Er, Yb, Ho and Tm. The specific cases of Er and Nd-doped glass fibers are described in detail in the next two sections.

2.6.1. *Er-doped Glass Fiber*

The energy levels of Er^{3+} ion in a glass (SiO_2) fiber is shown in Fig. 2.11. The energy level in the doped glass is primarily determined by the energy levels of the isolated Er ion. The local electric field introduces a small perturbation which results in a splitting of each of the energy levels of the ion into a number of closely spaced levels. These closely spaced levels are further broadened by the characteristic lifetimes and inhomogeneities of the glass host.

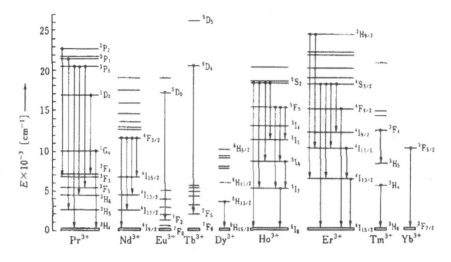

Fig. 2.10 Energy levels and main transitions in rare earth elements.[25]

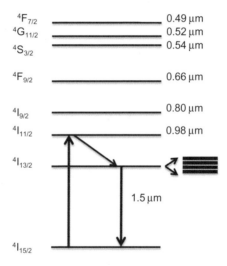

Fig. 2.11 Energy levels of Er ion.[15] Each of the ionic levels are broadened by the crystal field.

This results in the observation of a broad emission and absorption spectrum.

The absorption spectrum of a Er-doped silica fiber is shown in Fig. 2.12. The peaks in the absorption spectrum correspond to

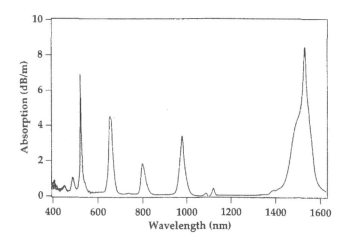

Fig. 2.12 Absorption spectrum of Er.[15]

absorption to a specific energy level in the Er ion. These wavelengths are 510, 640, 820, 980 and 1480 nm respectively. These specific wavelengths could also serve as pump wavelengths because the Er ion relaxes to a longer lived metastable state from these excited states. The fluorescence spectrum from the excited state $(^4I_{13/2})$ to the ground state $(^4I_{15/2})$ lies fortuitously near the low loss transmission window of the silica optical fibers. Although the energy levels are primarily determined by the ion, the host material plays a significant role in determining radiative and nonradiative lifetimes and absorption and emission cross sections.

All of these quantities are suitable for stimulated emission in Er-doped silica glass, and thus Er-doped amplifier is an important device for fiber optic communication systems. The lifetime of $^4I_{13/2}$ level is $\sim$10 ms. Erbium ions excited to high energy state cascade down to lower levels by losing energy nonradiatively. The typical pump lasers used for Er-doped amplifiers emit near 980 nm or 1480 nm. The 1480 nm pump laser excites the Er ion to the higher energy of the $^4I_{13/2}$ broadened energy level.

Equation (2.10) shows that the material gain depends on the optical signal power (P). Initially the gain increases with increasing optical pump power and beyond a certain point when the signal power gets high enough the gain decreases. This is the origin of gain saturation. Since g is reduced when P comparable to P_s (saturation power), the amplifier gain G also decreases when P becomes large. For simplicity, we consider the case when the frequency of the incident light $\nu = \nu_0$, in this case, using Eqs. (2.10) and (2.11) it follows:

$$\frac{dP}{dz} = \frac{g_0 P}{1 + P/P_s}. \tag{2.51}$$

The Eq. (2.51) has to be solved numerically for a fiber amplifier since g_0 depends on the pump power which decreases due to pump absorption as the pump propagates through the amplifier i.e., g_0 is function of z. Eq. (2.51) shows that the gain G decreases from G_0 when P_{out} becomes close to P_s. Figure 2.13 shows the measured gain as a function of output power for Er-doped amplifier pumped at one end for different input pump powers. The figure shows the gain at two signal wavelengths at a constant pump power. At low signal levels (~-50 dBm), the gain exceeds 30 dB. A model of the amplifier gain is discussed in later chapters.

The Er-doped amplifiers used in lightwave system applications, either as preamplifiers in front of a receiver or as in line amplifiers

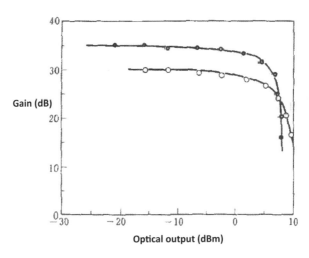

Fig. 2.13 Amplifier gain as a function of output power.[25] Pump power = 110 mW. Pump wavelength = 1.48 μm. The fiber is 200 m long and is doped with 13 ppm of Er. Signal wavelength = 1.535 μm for solid circles and 1.552 μm for open circles.

for single wavelength or multiple wavelength (WDM — wavelength division multiplexing) systems, must exhibit nearly equal optical gain for all polarizations and wavelengths of the input light. Generally fiber amplifiers have a very broad gain spectrum (~50 nm for Er-doped amplifier) due to both homogeneous and inhomogeneous broadening and high saturation power (~100 mW to 500 mW) which make them particularly suitable for multiple wavelength WDM system applications.

2.6.2. *Nd-doped Glass Fiber*

Prior to the interest in Er-doped amplifiers due to their application in fiber communication systems, Nd doped rare earth lasers were investigated for many years.[18,26–31] The energy levels of Nd $^{3+}$ ion in a glass (SiO_2) fiber is shown in Fig. 2.14. Nd doped glasses have been extensively studied for their applications in lasers and high peak power oscillator-amplifier systems. The energy level in the doped glass is primarily determined by the energy levels of the isolated Nd ion. The pump absorption is high near 0.81 μm for Nd-doped YAG. Although several possible laser transitions at 1.33, 1.06 and 0.92 μm are feasible, the most commonly used laser wavelength is at 1.06 μm. This wavelength also provides the highest output power.

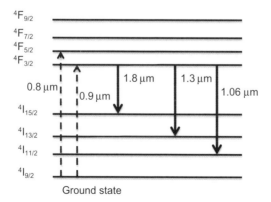

Fig. 2.14 Energy levels of Nd Pump absorption transitions are shown by dashed line. Solid lines show the emission transitions.

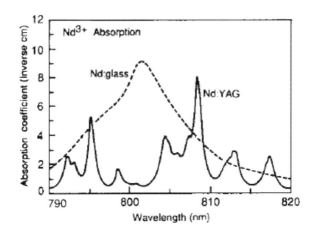

Fig. 2.15 Absorption spectrum of 1.1% doped Nd-YAG and 3% doped Nd glass around 800 nm is shown.[27]

The absorption spectrum of Nd-doped different glasses have been reported. The data from Ref. 27, is shown in Fig. 2.15.

Early version of Nd lasers often used flash lamp as a pump source, but with the development of high power semiconductor laser near $0.8\,\mu$m, the pump laser of choice is now a semiconductor laser. The absorption is highest near $0.81\,\mu$m. The typical dopant concentration for a Nd-doped fiber laser for 1060 nm emission is about $9 \times 10^{18}\,\text{cm}^{-3}$ (about 100 ppm).

One of the transitions in Nd is near 944 to 946 nm, this transition is of interest for characterization of water vapor concentration in the atmosphere. The energy levels of a Nd ion are broadened into a group of levels (often called a manifold) by the presence of a crystal field. A laser (or amplifier) operating at this wavelength behaves like a quasi-three level laser, i.e., although the laser operates between $^4F_{3/2}$ (upper laser level) and $^4I_{9/2}$ (lower laser level) manifolds, the lower states in the $4F_{3/2}$ manifold and the upper states in the $^4I_{9/2}$ manifold participate in laser action (Fig. 2.16).

An expression for gain taking into the pump loss and pump and signal intensity distribution in the unsaturated regime could be obtained analytically in this case. As example of a three-level laser the 946 nm transition in Nd is considered.

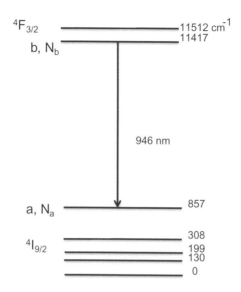

Fig. 2.16 Simplified energy level diagram for the 946 nm transition in Nd.[31]

The relative populations of the levels in the upper and lower manifold are given by the Boltzmann distribution. In the following, a simple model for the threshold and output power of an Nd-doped fiber laser is discussed. Only the fundamental TEM_{00} laser mode with a Gaussian intensity distribution is considered. The pump beam is also Gaussian and is assumed to propagate once through the gain medium. The normalized pump and laser intensity profiles are given by:

$$r_p(r, z) = \frac{2a}{\pi w_p^2 [1 - \exp(-aL)]} \exp(-az) \exp\left(-\frac{2r^2}{w_p^2}\right)$$

$$s_0(r, z) = \frac{2}{\pi w_0^2 L} \exp\left(-\frac{2r^2}{w_0^2}\right), \tag{2.52}$$

where a is the pump absorption coefficient of the pump, L is the length of the fiber, w_0 and w_p are parameters for the size of the laser and pump beam. The quantities $r_p(r, z)$ and $s_0(r, z)$ are the pump and laser mode distribution respectively. The normalization is carried out as follows:

$$\iiint s_0(r, z) dV = \iiint r_p(r, z) dV = 1. \tag{2.53}$$

The threshold condition of a laser is that the round trip gain exceeds the round trip loss. The upper laser level population, $N_2(r, z)$, (where r is the radial distance from the center of the fiber and z is the distance along the fiber length from the pump input position) in steady-state is given by the rate equation:

$$\frac{dN_2(r, z)}{dt} = 0 = -\frac{N_2(r, z)}{\tau} + Rr_p(r, z), \qquad (2.54)$$

and:

$$N_b(r, z) = f_b N_2(r, z) = f_b R r_p(r, z)\tau,$$

where R is the total pump rate and τ is the lifetime of the upper laser manifold population and $N_b(r, z)$ is the total population density in the upper manifold. The quantities f_a and f_b are the population fractions in the lower laser level and upper laser level respectively that participate in laser action. $f_a = 0.0075$ and $f_b = 0.63$ at 300 K.[31] The quantity $f_a = 0$ for a four-level laser. Thus this quasi-level laser is very similar to a four-level laser for which the threshold condition is easily achieved compared to that for a three-level laser.

In the small signal approximation, the gain g is given by:

$$g = \iiint \sigma_a L s_0(r, z)[f_b N_2(r, z)\sigma_e/\sigma_a - f_a N_0]dV, \qquad (2.55)$$

where L is the length of the fiber, σ_a, σ_e are stimulated absorption and emission cross section at signal wavelength respectively, $s_0(r, z)$ is the laser mode distribution function. Consider only the fundamental TEM$_{00}$ laser mode with a Gaussian intensity distribution. The pump beam is also Gaussian. Using Eq. (2.55) the incident pump power absorbed for gain g is given by (using $R = P/h\nu_p$):

$$P = \frac{\pi h \nu_p}{2 f_p \eta_p \tau} \left(w_0^2 + w_p^2\right) \left(\frac{g}{2\sigma_e} + f_a N_0 L \frac{\sigma_a}{\sigma_e}\right)\bigg/[1 - \exp(-aL)],$$

$$(2.56)$$

where η_p is the pump quantum efficiency, i.e., number of ions in the excited state created by each absorbed photon, $h\nu_p$ is the photon energy. N_0 is the total dopant concentration. The quantity η_p is ~1. The formulation shows that it is feasible to calculate gain analytically.

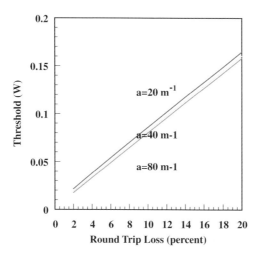

Fig. 2.17 The calculated threshold power for a Nd-doped fiber laser emitting at $^4F_{3/2} \to$ $^4I_{9/2}$ transition is plotted as a function of round trip cavity loss. The quantity a is the intensity absorption coefficient at the pump wavelength.

For a laser at this wavelength, the threshold power (absorbed pump power P_{th}) is slightly modified. It is given by:

$$P_{\text{th}} = \frac{\pi h \nu_p}{2 f_p \eta_p \tau} \left(w_0^2 + w_p^2 \right) \left(\frac{\delta}{2\sigma_e} + f_a N_0 L \frac{\sigma_a}{\sigma_e} \right) \Big/ [1 - \exp(-aL)],$$

$$(2.57)$$

where δ is the round trip loss. For a laser round trip gain equals round trip loss. The quantity a is the intensity absorption coefficient at the pump wavelength. The fiber core is Nd–Al co-doped, Nd concentration N_0 is 7×10^{19} cm^{-3}. According to the parameters from literature, the absorption cross section of the Nd–Al co-doped fiber is 9×10^{-21} cm^2.[29] Thus the intensity absorption coefficient, a is ~ 63 m^{-1}. $w_0 = w_p = 3.2\,\mu$m. The signal stimulated absorption cross- $\sigma_a = 4.22 \times 10^{-22}$ cm^2, stimulated emission cross-section $\sigma_e = 2.6 \times 10^{-22}$ cm^2, $\tau = 310\,\mu$s, and $\eta_p = 1$ The calculated threshold power using the equations and parameters for 0.2 m long fiber is shown in Fig. 2.17. The measured threshold power at room temperature for $\sim 1\%$ loss is ~ 10 mW.[31]

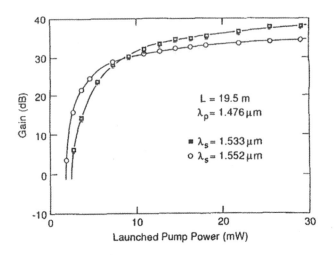

Fig. 2.18 Gain as a function of input pump power.[15]

2.7. Single Mode Fiber Amplifier

As mentioned previously, the fiber amplifier requires a pump laser to excite the ions to the high energy level. The pump power and the signal are combined, using a wavelength division multiplexer (WDM) based on a four-port fused coupler. Simple arrangements, shown in Fig. 2.1, were used in early experiments. In one configuration, the pump laser light and the signal co-propagates along the doped amplifier fiber (Fig. 2.1a). Other configurations include co- and counter propagating pumps, addition of filters and isolators to prevent laser action. An important characteristic of a device such as the optical amplifier is optical gain.

The small signal gain for two signal wavelengths as a function of pump power is shown in Fig. 2.18. The gain increases rapidly at pump powers near threshold and increases slowly at high pump powers where almost all the Er ions along the length of the fiber are inverted.

Amplifiers are often tailored to specific performance characteristics by using different pump configurations and amplifier lengths. In addition to signal amplification, the amplifier also amplifies the spontaneous emission from the excited ions. The amplified spontaneous emission (ASE) spectrum is shown in Fig. 2.19. Note that the ASE is quite high near 1530 nm. Partial inversion is needed for a flat

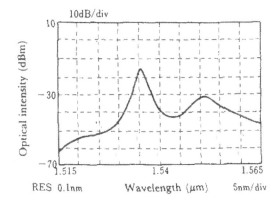

Fig. 2.19 Amplified spontaneous (ASE) spectrum of a Er-doped fiber amplifier.

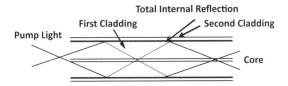

Fig. 2.20 Cladding pumped fiber amplifier design.[32] The pump light is launched into an inner (first) cladding which around the doped core. This inner cladding and core form a waveguide. An outer (second) cladding and the inner cladding form a waveguide for the pump.

gain spectrum which is important for multichannel amplification in WDM systems. Optical filters are used to limit the effect of ASE on amplifier performance.

When an amplifier is operated in the saturated regime with multiple input signals (for example, at different wavelengths) a cross talk (i.e., transfer of modulation from one signal to another) occurs. This crosstalk limits the use of amplifier in multi-channel transmission systems. These phenomenons are discussed in detail in later chapters.

2.8. High Power Cladding Pumped Devices

An approach to a high power fiber amplifier design is to use a single mode guide for the signal surrounded by a multimode pump guide (Fig. 2.20)[32] The core is doped with rare earth ions. Pump light is launched at one end into the undoped cladding, where it propagates with a fraction of the pump confined in the doped core as it travels along the fiber. The fraction confined in the doped core is absorbed by the ions leading to amplification of the signal.

Results on a large core area Yb-doped clad fiber laser are described. This double-clad fiber has been designed to produce high power levels (>1 kW). It was drawn from a preform that was fabricated by the MCDVD (modified chemical-vapor deposition) and solution-doping technique (see Chapter 4). The fiber had a 40 μm diameter Yb^{3+} doped aluminosilicate-based glass core with an NA of 0.05. The mode field area for the fundamental mode is estimated to be ∼0.9×10^3 μm^2. The D-shaped inner cladding had a 650/600 μm diameter for the longer/shorter axis. This diameter was chosen to enable efficient coupling of the large beams from high power diode pump sources. The fiber was coated with a low-refractive-index polymer outer cladding which provided a nominal inner-cladding NA of 0.48.

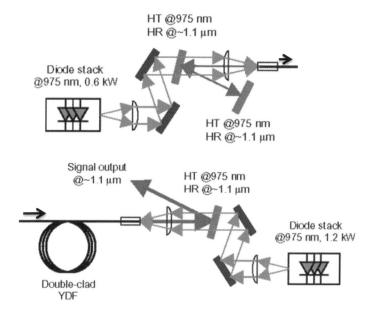

Fig. 2.21 YDCF experimental set up. Note two diode laser stacks for end pumping. HR: high reflectivity, HT: high transmission.[33] The components in the top figure are input to the components in the lower figure.

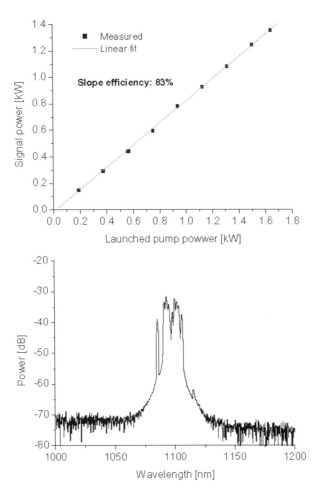

Fig. 2.22 (Top) Output power as a function of launched pump power from laser diodes (Bottom) output spectrum.[33]

The fiber length used in the laser experiments was 12 m. The experimental set up is shown in Fig. 2.21.[33] The fiber was pumped at both ends using diode laser stacks which emit near 975 nm. The absorption coefficient in the inner cladding is ~1.5 dB/m at the pump wavelength of 975 nm. This corresponds to an Yb^{3+} concentration of ~6000 ppm by weight.

The measured results on output power and output spectrum are shown in Fig. 2.22. One of the issues for high power lasers is fiber damage at the exit facet. No such damage was observed. The authors[33] believe their scheme is scalable to very high powers (>10 kW). Various other types of double clad fiber designs for different emission wavelengths and high power applications are discussed in Chapter 7. An advantage of the double clad amplifier design is that it allows coupling of high power pump into the amplifier efficiently from a high power diode laser.

References

1. See for example, E. Desurvire, *Erbium doped fiber amplifiers*, John Wiley and Sons. 1994.
2. P.C. Becker, N.A. Olsson and J.R. Simpson, Erbium doped fiber amplifiers, Academic Press. 1997.
3. M.J. Digonnet (Ed.), *Rare earth-doped fiber lasers and amplifiers*, Marcel Dekker, Inc. 1993.
4. S. Shimoda and H. Ishio (Ed.), *Optical amplifiers and their applications*, John Wiley and Sons. 1994.
5. E. Snitzer, *J. Appl. Phys.* **32** (1961) 36.
6. C.J. Koster and E. Snitzer, *Appl. Opt.* **3** (1964) 1182.
7. Z.J. Kiss and R.C. Duncan, Proc. IRE, 1531 (1962).
8. K. Kubodera and K. Otsuka, *J. Appl. Phys.* **50** (1979) 653.
9. M.J.F. Digonnet and C.J. Gaeta, *Appl. Opt.* **24**, (1985) 333.
10. M.J.F. Digonnet, *IEEE, J. Lightwave Tech.* **4**, (1986) 1631.
11. R.J. Mears, L. Reekie, S.B. Poole and D.N. *Payne Electron Lett.* **22** (1986) 159.
12. E. Desurvire, J.R. Simpson and P.C. Becker, *Optics Lett.* **12** (1987) 888.
13. L.A. Coldren and S.W. Corzine, *Diode Lasers and Photonic Integrated Circuits.* New York: John Wiley. 1995.
14. G.II.B. Thompson, *Physics of Semiconductor Laser Devices.* New York: John Wiley & Sons. 1980.
15. G.P. Agrawal and N.K. Dutta, *Semiconductor Lasers,* New York: Van Nostrand Reinhold. 1992.
16. N.K. Dutta, J. Lopata, D.L. Sivco and A.Y. Cho, *Appl. Phys. Lett.* **58** (1991) 1125.
17. T. Tanbun-Ek, R.A. Logan, N.A. Olsson, H. Temkin, A.M. Sergent and K.W. Wecht, *Appl. Phys. Lett.* **57** (1990) 224.
18. L.F. Johnson., J.E. Geusic and L.G. Van Uitert, *Appl. Phys. Lett* **8** (1966) 200.
19. B.M. Walsh, N.P. Barnes, B. Di Bartolo and J. Lumin. **75** (1997) 89.
20. P.W. Milloni and J.H. Eberly, *Lasers.* New York: John Wiley. 1988.
21. G.P. Agrawal, *Nonlinear fiber optics*, Chapter 1. Academic Press. 1989.
22. G.P. Agrawal, *Nonlinear fiber optics*, Chapter 2. Academic Press. 1989.

23. K. Thyagarajan, Erbium doped fiber amplifiers, Chapter 5. In *Guided wave optical components and devices*, B. P. Palm (Ed) Elsevier. 2006.

24. A.K. Dutta, N.K. Dutta and M. Fujiwara (Eds), WDM Technologies — Active optical components, Chapter 3. A. Kusukawa (Ed). Academic Press. 2002.

25. S. Shimoda and H. Ishio (Eds), *Optical amplifiers and their applications*, Chapter 5. K. Hagimoto (Ed). John Wiley and Sons. 1994.

26. S. Shimoda and H. Ishio (Eds). *Optical amplifiers and their applications*, Chapter 2. M. Saruwatari (Ed). John Wiley and Sons. 1994.

27. T.Y. Fan and R.L. Byer, *IEEE JQE.* **24** (1988) 895.

28. B. Henderson and R.H. Bertram, *Crystal field engineering of solid state laser materials* , Chapter 1. Cambridge: Cambridge University Press. 2000, pp. 13.

29. D.L. Sipes, *Appl. Phys. Lett.* **47** (1985) 74.

30. B. Zhou, T.J. Kane, G.J. Dixon and R.L. Byer, *Opt. Lett.* **10** (1985) 62.

31. T.Y. Fan and R.L. Byer, *IEEE, JQE.* QE-**23** (1987) 605.

32. A. Tunnermann and H. Zellmer, Chapter B4.2. In *Handbook of Laser Technology and Applications*, C. Webb and J. Jones (Eds). Institute of Physics. 2004.

33. Y. Jeong, J.K. Sahu, D.N. Payne and J. Nilsson, *Optics Express.* **12** (2004) 6088.

Chapter 3

Absorption and Emission
in Rare Earths

3.1. Introduction

Atomic transitions that result in photon emission in rare earth ions is
the primary mechanism responsible for optical amplification in rare
earth-doped amplifiers. Atomic transitions can, in general, be divided
into two categories: radiative (photon emission) and nonradiative.
The radiative transitions are responsible for stimulated optical emission or gain. Sufficient numbers of atoms must be excited in the doped
material for net optical gain. The optical processes associated with
radiative transition are: optical gain or optical absorption, spontaneous emission and stimulated emission. The optical processes in rare
earth-doped glasses have been previously described in Refs. 1–17. A
study of the energy levels and rates associated with these processes
for rare earth-doped materials are described in this chapter. The most
common rare earth dopants are Er, Yb, Nd and Tm. Historically; Nd-
doped materials have been studied for the longest time, due to their
application for very high power laser systems. Er-doped fiber amplifiers are important for optical transmission systems and have been
extensively studied since the 1990's. Yb-doped fiber amplifier and
Er–Yb-doped fiber amplifiers are important for high power optical
amplifier and laser systems. The primary emission wavelengths for
Er, Yb, Nd and Tm-doped laser systems are in the 1550, 1100, 1060,
and 2000 nm range respectively.

In addition to these wavelengths, laser and amplifier action at
other wavelengths from the rare earths have been observed. These
wavelengths are primarily determined by the energy levels of the rare

earth dopants, i.e., Er, Yb and Nd. Co-dopants i.e., addition of other doping materials (e.g., Mg, Al) in the host may somewhat alter these wavelengths.

Nonradiative transition, as the name implies, is characterized by the absence of an emitted photon in the transition process. These processes could be phonon assisted or may involve ion-pairs and can also occur at defect in the material. Up-conversion is a particular type of nonradiative process which reduces the number of excited atoms. A study of these nonradiative processes and other optical loss processes and their impact on amplifier performance is described.

3.2. Atomic Transitions in Rare Earth Atoms

Rare earth atoms are divided into two groups. They are lanthanides with atomic numbers from 57 to 71 and actinides with atomic numbers from 89 to 103. The majority of rare earth-doped fibers are doped with lanthanides (e.g., Er has atomic number Z = 68, Yb, Z= 70; and Nd, Z = 60). The atomic structure of lanthanides is important in understanding their behavior as dopants in a glass matrix.

The optical spectrum of rare earths was observed in the 1900's[17–20] and the first explanation of their spectrum was given by Mayer.[20] The simple picture of an atom is that of a nucleus surrounded by shells of electrons. Inner shells are filled and outer shells are unfilled. As the atomic number Z increases, the shells fill up according to the principles of quantum mechanics. In general, the successive shells have higher radii. However, at Z − 57, a change occurs. This change is due to an effective radial potential energy of electrons as explained by Mayer.[20]

The effective radial potential energy is derived using the Thomas–Fermi model of atoms. In this model an effective potential energy ($V(r)$) is used to predict the energy levels and wave functions of electrons by solving the quantum mechanical Schroedinger equation. This model allows a solution of the multi-electron problem in large atoms using a separable and tractable form. According to Mayer, the effective radial potential of electrons $V(r)$, which is the sum of the Coulomb potential energy and centrifugal potential energy, is given by:

$$V(r) = -\frac{e^2}{r}\left[1 + (Z-1)\varphi\left(\frac{r}{\mu}\right)\right] + \frac{h^2}{8\pi^2 m}\frac{l(l+1)}{r^2} \qquad (3.1)$$

where e is the charge of the electron, m is the mass of the electron, l is the angular momentum of the electron, h is the Planck's constant, μ is defined in Ref. 20 and $\phi(r/\mu)$ is the Thomas–Fermi function. Thus for large l values, the centrifugal force reduces the Coulomb potential. The following situation arises near $Z = 57$. The 5s and 5p shells ($5s^2 5p^6$) are full and f electrons (for f electrons $l = 3$) are progressively added (as Z increases) in the 4f shell. The 4f shell instead of being larger becomes smaller and bounded by the 5s and 5p shells. $V(r)$ is sketched in Fig. 3.1 for various Z values. For low Z values, $V(r)$ has one minimum at $r \sim 6$ A. At high Z values, a second minimum develops at small values of r ($r \sim 0.1$ to 0.2 A).

The 4f wavefunction $\psi(r)$ has a large value of $|\psi(r)|^2$ for small r, when the second minimum of $V(r)$ becomes sufficiently deep at high Z values. This effectively reduces the radius of the last added shell (4f) from that of the 5s and 5p.

According to Mayer's model, this should happen at $Z = 60$, experimentally this happens at the beginning of the lanthanides, $Z = 57$. As Z values increase in the lanthanide series, the average radius of the 4f shell decreases by about 10% from the beginning to the end of the lanthanide series. The average radius of the 4f shell is about 0.3 A. The 4f electrons are shielded from its environment in which the atoms are located by the 5s and 5p electrons. This leads to a series of narrow lines in the 4f electron spectrum of rare earth-doped glasses.

The radial distribution of the wavefunction, $|\Psi(r)|^2$ has been calculated numerically for the various orbitals of the Pr^{3+} ion. The calculation includes the interaction of multiple electrons and the nucleus. The results for 4f, 5s, 5p orbitals are shown in the top figure of Fig. 3.2. The figure shows the 4f orbitals have been effective shorter radius than 5s and 5p orbitals. Also shown in the bottom figure of Fig. 3.2 are the $|\Psi(r)|^2$ as a function of r for 4f, 5d, 5g orbitals. The 5d and 5g orbitals to which 4f electrons can get excited

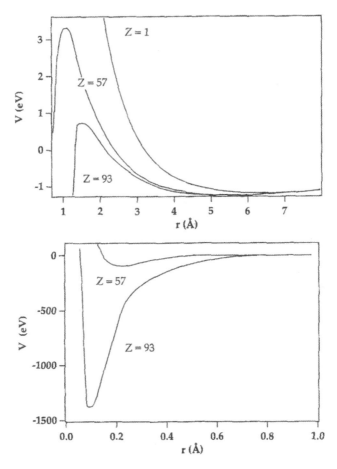

Fig. 3.1 Effective potential $V(r)$ for 4f electrons as a function of atomic number Z.[20] $V(r)$ for large r and small r are shown at the top and bottom respectively.[18]

are further removed from the nucleus and therefore are affected by the neighboring atoms of the host or neighboring ions.

The closest inert gas atom near the lanthanides is Xenon (Xe) which has 54 electrons (Z = 54). Its ground state configuration is $1s^2 2s^2 2p^6 3s^2 3p^6 3d^{10} 4s^2 4p^6 4d^{10} 5s^2 5p^6$. A neutral lanthanide element has more electrons than Xe and its ground state can be represented as $(Xe)4f^N 6s^2$ or $(Xe)4f^{N-1} 5d6s^2$ where N represents the number of electrons in the 4f state and (Xe) represents the xenon core.[18] The trivalent rare earth ions on which most active rare earth devices

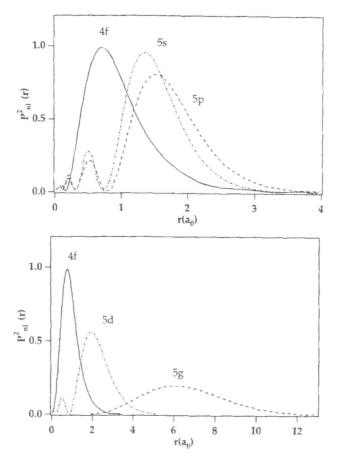

Fig. 3.2 Radial distribution of 4f, 5s, 5p, 5d and 5g orbitals calculated using the Hartree–Fock approximation. The 4f, 5s, 5p orbitals of the ground state ($4f^2 5s^2 5p^6$) are shown separately at the top. The ground state configuration shows that 4f orbital is within the 5s and 5p orbitals. The orbitals of the ground state ($4f^2 5s^2 5p^6$) and excited states ($4f5d5s^2 5p^6$), ($4f5g5s^2 5p^6$) are shown at the bottom. They are labeled 4f, 5d and 5g respectively. The figure shows that excited state 5d and 5g orbitals are larger than the 5s and 5p orbitals of the ground state.[18]

are based, have a Xenon core to which N 4f electrons ($4f^N$ configuration) are attached. The $4f^N$ configuration has a number of states. It is schematically shown in Fig. 3.3. Thus an electron can be excited within the 4f set of states before it gets excited to a higher energy 4d or 5g orbital. The $4f^N$ energy levels arise from

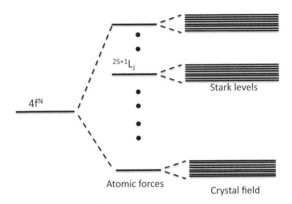

Fig. 3.3 Schematic of the energy level splitting of the $4f^N$ configuration due to atomic and crystal field interactions. The atomic forces are larger than the crystal field. The atomic forces splits the $4f^N$ orbital to $^{2S+1}L_J$ levels, then the weaker crystal field splits each free ion level into a large number of stark levels.

various interactions (coulomb interaction and spin-orbit interaction) between the electrons in the atom. A further splitting of the energy levels occurs when the atom is placed in a crystalline host. This is often referred to as the Stark splitting by the crystal field.

3.3. Er-Doped Glass

Er-doped glass amplifiers have been extensively studied for application in optical fiber communication systems.[2, 18, 21–27] The first Er-doped glass laser using the $^4I_{13/2}$ to $^4I_{15/2}$ transition was demonstrated in 1965. The laser operated near 1500 nm.

The absorption spectrum in Er-doped silica glass is shown in Fig. 3.4. The figure shows relatively narrow absorption bands. The energy levels of Er in Er-doped silicate glass are shown in Fig. 3.5. The energy levels are obtained using the absorption spectrum, and have been labeled using the atomic structure calculations. The numbers on the right at each excited state is the wavelength in nm of the ground state absorption transition which terminates at that level. The arrows represent the observed lasing transitions.

For optical communication application, the region of interest is 1550 nm. A common mechanism for exciting Er ions to the excited

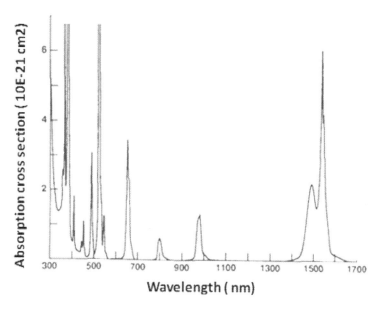

Wavelength (nm)

Fig. 3.4 Absorption cross section spectrum of Er-doped silicate glass. The peaks of the strong bands at 380 and 520 nm are 28 and 19 $\times$ 10^{-21} cm^2 respectively.[27]

state ($^4I_{13/2}$) is absorption of 980 nm or 1480 nm light from a pump laser. The emission cross sections near 1500 nm for Er ions doped in different hosts are shown in Fig. 3.6. The figure shows that the emission spectrum has different shapes and hence spectral widths for different hosts. This is due to different crystal field for different hosts. Note the emission spectra is broad for the ZBLAN host. Emission spectrum for silica host is narrow. This suggests the possibility of high gain in Er-doped silica fibers. The excited state ($^4I_{13/2}$) lifetime is about 10 ms for various hosts.

3.4. Yb-Doped Glass

Yb-doped glass amplifiers have been extensively studied by various authors for high power laser sources and amplifiers in the 1100 nm spectral region.[28-32] Yb ion in silica has two energy level manifolds.

They are the ground-state manifold ($^2F_{7/2}$) and the excited-state ($^2F_{5/2}$) manifold (Fig. 3.7). The numbers on the right at each excited state is the energy in cm^{-1} from the ground state. The solid lines

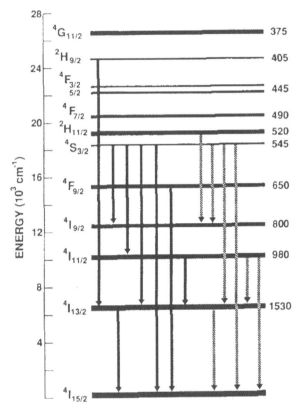

Fig. 3.5 Energy levels of Er^{3+} in silicate glass. The solid lines indicate observed lasing transitions. The numbers on the right are the absorption wavelength peaks for absorption from the ground state.[21]

are absorption transition which terminates at that level. The dashed arrows represent the observed fluorescence/lasing transitions. The transitions between the sublevels are not fully resolved for Yb ions in a glass at room temperature because of the strong homogeneous and inhomogeneous broadening. The Yb-doped silicate glass laser using the $^2F_{5/2}$ to $^4F_{7/2}$ transition was demonstrated in 1988. The laser operated near 1100 nm. The absorption and fluorescence spectrum in Yb-doped silica glass is shown in Fig. 3.8. The figure shows relatively narrow absorption band with a broad background. Also the emission spectrum is large over a narrow range of wavelengths. This indicates Yb-doped glass is a good candidate for laser action.

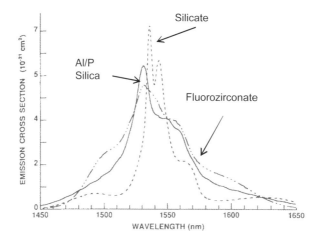

Fig. 3.6 Emission cross section spectrum of Er near 1500 nm for different glass hosts.[27] Fluorozirconate is also known as ZBLAN.

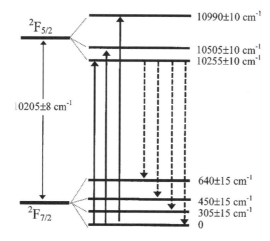

Fig. 3.7 Energy levels of Yb^{3+} in silicate glass. The solid lines indicate observed absorption transitions and the dashed lines are laser/fluorescence transitions.[33]

Absorption spectrum using white light excitation from a Yb-doped silica fiber have been measured.[34–36] From this data both absorption and emission cross sections were obtained. The results are shown in Fig. 3.9. Since the emission and absorption cross sections are related, it is useful to show the absorption cross section of Yb

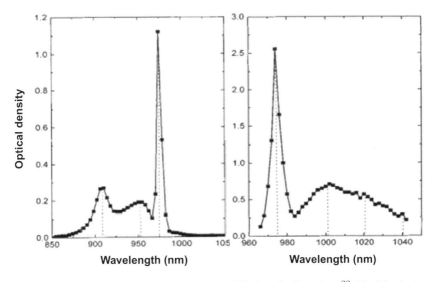

Fig. 3.8 Absorption and emission spectrum of Yb-doped silica glass.[33] The Yb doping density is 6.1×10^{20} cm^{-3}. Glass thickness = 3 mm. The figure on the right is absorption and figure on the left is emission (plotted is quantum efficiency in %/nm) with 940 nm excitation. T = 100 K.

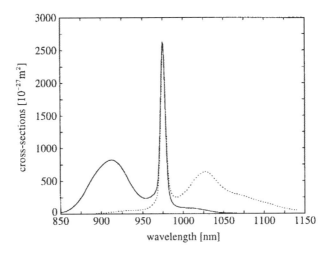

Fig. 3.9 Absorption (solid) and emission (dotted) cross section spectrum of Yb ions in silica glass.[34]

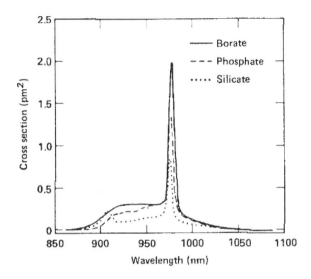

Fig. 3.10 Absorption cross section spectrum of Yb near 1500 nm for borate, phosphate and silicate glass hosts.[36]

for different glass hosts. This is shown in Fig. 3.10. The stimulated emission cross section for the $^2F_{5/2}$ to $^4F_{7/2}$ transition in Yb shows large variation with the composition of the glass host.[36]

3.5. Nd-Doped Glass

Nd-doped glass laser was reported in 1961,[37] since then several other work has been reported.[38–42] Nd has a strong absorption spectrum along the entire wavelength range from UV to near infrared. The absorption spectrum of Nd-doped in ZBLAN (Zr, Ba, La, Al, Na) flourozirconate glass is shown in Fig. 3.11. The sharp spectral lines are indicative of low influence of crystal field interaction as mentioned in Sec. 3.2.

The energy levels of Nd in Nd-doped flourozirconate glass is shown in Fig. 3.12. The energy levels are obtained using the absorption spectrum and has been labeled using the atomic structure calculations. The numbers on the right at each excited state is the wavelength in nm of the ground state absorption transition which terminates at

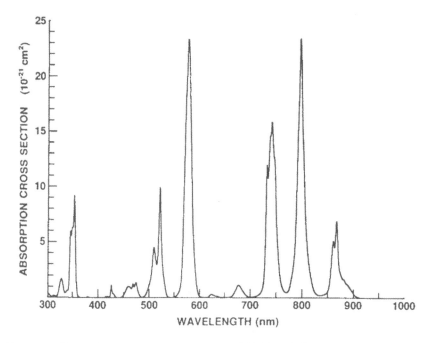

Fig. 3.11 Absorption cross section spectrum of Nd-doped flourozirconate glass. The peaks show strong absorption bands.[27]

that level. The arrows represent the observed lasing transitions from the $4F_{3/2}$ state.

The strong absorption near 800 nm from ground state $(^4I_{9/2})$ to $^2H_{9/2} + {}^4F_{5/2}$ metastable state is important for populating the upper laser level $(^4F_{3/2})$. This allows efficient lasing of Nd-doped glass lasers using a 800 nm semiconductor pump laser fabricated using the AlGaAs material system.

Nd-doped laser is most important for laser operation near 1060 nm but it also undergoes stimulated emission in other wavelength bands. The 1060 nm laser operation takes place on the $^4F_{3/2}$ to $^4I_{11/2}$ transition. The ground state is $^4I_{9/2}$. Fast relaxation from $^4I_{11/2}$ to $^4I_{9/2}$ makes laser based on the transition an efficient four-level laser. The emission cross sections for the $^4F_{3/2}$ to $^4I_{9/2}$ transition (near 900 nm) and for the $^4F_{3/2}$ to $^4I_{11/2}$ transition (near 1060 nm) for different glass with pump light at 800 nm are shown in Fig. 3.13.

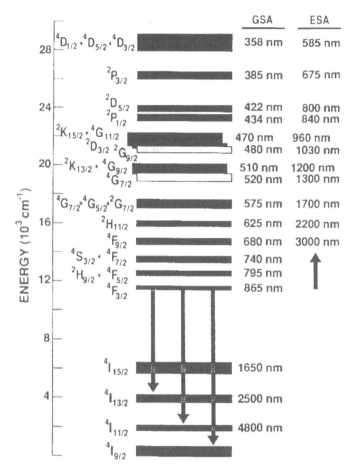

Fig. 3.12 Energy levels of Nd^{3+} in flourozirconate glass. The solid lines indicate observed lasing transitions. The numbers on the right are the absorption wavelength peaks for absorption from the ground state.[27,41]

The excited state ($^4F_{3/2}$) lifetime varies in the range of 300 to $1100\,\mu$s for different glass hosts. Nd-doped glass also undergoes laser action near $1300\,$nm based on $^4F_{3/2}$ to $^4I_{13/2}$ transition.[45,46] The emission cross section spectrum for different glass hosts near $1300\,$nm region is shown in Fig. 3.14. The excitation is at $800\,$nm. Comparing Figs. 3.13 and 3.14, it follows that the emission cross section and hence the gain is largest at $1060\,$nm.

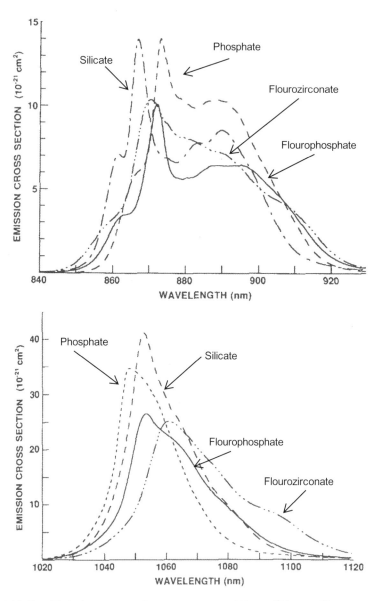

Fig. 3.13 Top: Emission cross section spectrum near 880 nm ($^4F_{3/2}$ to $^4I_{9/2}$ transition) Bottom: Emission cross section spectrum near 1060 nm ($^4F_{3/2}$ to $^4I_{11/2}$ transition), for different glass hosts when pumped by a 800 nm laser.[27, 43]

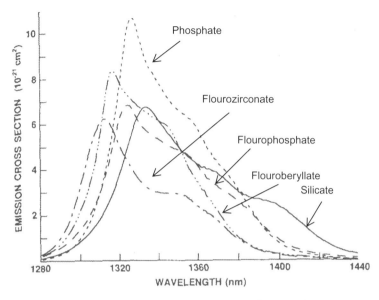

Fig. 3.14 Emission cross section spectrum near 1300 nm ($^4F_{3/2}$ to $^4I_{13/2}$ transition) for different glass hosts when excited by a 800 nm laser.[27, 46]

3.6. Tm-Doped Glass

Among the other principal rare earth dopants is Thulium (Tm). The main interest in Tm arises from emission bands in the 1400 to 2700 nm range particularly for energies where gaps exits between Er and Nd. Tm is generally doped in the usual glasses such as fluorides, tellurites, phosphates and silica. The emission strengths of different transitions depend on the glass host. The absorption spectrum of Tm has been measured. The data for a high fluorine content flourophosphate glass is shown in Fig. 3.15. Note the absorption cross section can be quite high. From this data the energy levels of Tm are shown in Fig. 3.16.

The $^3F_4$ to $^3H_6$ transition peaks near 1850 nm. It produces a broad emission band extending from 1700 to 2000 nm which can be used for tunable laser and high bandwidth optical amplifiers. The $^3H_4$ to $^3F_4$ emission band is in the range of 1300 to 1540 nm. The $^3H_4$ to $^3H_6$ transition in the 800 nm band operates as a laser. The $^3H_4$ to $^3H_5$ emission is in the 2100 to 2500 nm range and it is useful for lasers and

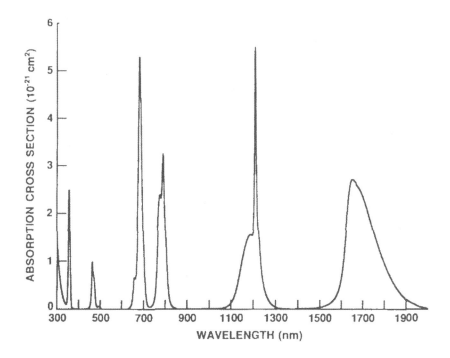

Fig. 3.15 Absorption cross section of a Tm-doped fluoride glass.

amplifiers in that range. Many of the Tm emission bands have been studied in ZBLAN glass. The emission spectrum for the $^3H_4$ to $^3H_5$ transition is shown in Fig. 3.17. Reliable semiconductor lasers can be fabricated in the entire wavelength range from $\sim$700 to 1600 nm. Thus it follows from Fig. 3.15, that semiconductor lasers are suitable as pump wavelengths for Tm-doped lasers and amplifiers. Tm-doped amplifiers also work on absorption of multiple pump photons for a shorter than pump wavelength emission and amplification.

The energy level diagram of Tm showing multiple transitions from excited levels is shown in Fig. 3.18. The pump laser is at 1060 nm. The mechanism for up-conversion is as follows. Tm ions in the ground state ($^3H_6$ energy level) is excited to the $^3H_5$ level by absorbing a pump photon at 1060 nm and these ions decay to the metastable $^3F_4$ level. The relaxation is through the emission of multiple phonons. The ions are re-excited from the $^3F_4$ energy level to the $^3F_2$ level by

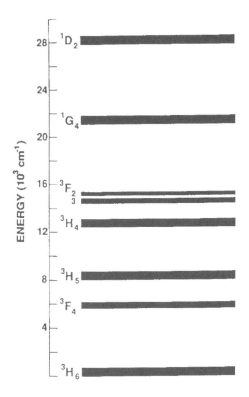

Fig. 3.16 Energy levels of Tm in a high fluorine content glass.

excited state absorption (ESA) of another pump photon and then decays to the $^3H_4$ level. The ESA increases the population of ions in $^3H_4$ level. In silica matrix the transition rate of ions from level $^3H_4$ to $^3G_4$ is small compared to the transition from level $^3H_4$ to $^3H_6$. Thus, a strong emission can be obtained at around 800 nm because of $^3H_4$ to level $^3H_6$ transition.

The absorption and emission cross section of Tm-doped silica fiber near 800 nm is shown in Fig. 3.19. The values are comparable to that for Er-doped silica glass. More than 20 dB of gain has been observed in a 40 m long fiber using 1060 nm pump. Tm-doped glass also exhibits gain in the 1450 to 1500 nm range when pumped with a 1040 to 1060 nm laser. For this situation a gain of 27 dB has been reported.[50]

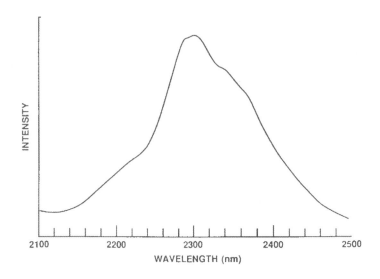

Fig. 3.17 Emission spectrum of Tm-doped ZBLAN in the $^3H_4$ to $^3H_5$ band.

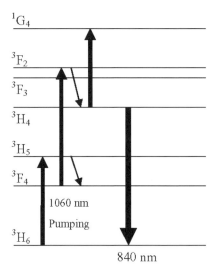

Fig. 3.18 Schematic of energy levels of Tm-doped in silica.[49]

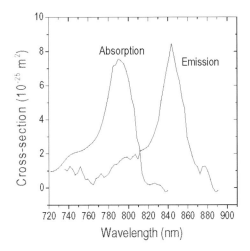

Fig. 3.19 Absorption and emission cross sections for Tm-doped silica fiber pumped by 1060 nm laser.[49]

3.7. Model of Emission Cross Section

A model of the emission cross section is described in this section. The model follows the work of Judd and Ofelt.[15, 16] Co-dopants such as Al, P, Na are investigated either for broadening the spectrum of the rare earth ions or shifting the energy level slightly. The co-dopants that directly participate in energy transfer process such as Er–Yb co-doped amplifiers are not discussed here. Er–Yb is used as dopant for high power double clad amplifiers. For details see Chapter 7.

3.7.1. *Er-Doped Amplifier*

There are two most important factors in selecting the right material: first, it must have high fluorescence emission intensity at the desired wavelength; secondly, the stimulated emission cross-section should be as large as possible in order to realize high gain. When the glass host is doped with rare earth ions, the degenerate energy levels of the ion are split by the influence of Coulomb field and the overlapping of electron shell with ligand shells.[11] The splitting of the energy levels by the Coulomb field as well as glass properties determines the emission wavelength. For a crystal, the peculiarities of stark splitting are related to the crystal structure and symmetry of the crystal and can be quantitatively calculated from first principles.[12] For low symmetry centers the phenomenological description of the stark splitting can be calculated using the same scheme as that for a symmetric crystal. For a large number of materials, a low symmetry of the optical center has been established.[13, 14] These materials include glass and a number of crystals that are also promising for optical applications. The method used for calculating the energy levels of an ion in a crystalline host can also be used for Er optical center in glass since it has short-range order.

When Er ions are placed in a glass host, it is subjected to a number of forces, which are absent in the free ions. These forces are of very complex nature. There are, for instance, electric and magnetic interactions with each individual ion in the vicinity, and resonant interactions with neighboring ions of the same kind if the doping concentration is high. A typical stark splitting for the $^4I_{13/2}$ and $^4I_{15/2}$ manifold is shown in Fig. 3.20. In the discussion, it is assumed that the center of the two $^4I_{13/2}$ and $^4I_{15/2}$ manifold does not change.

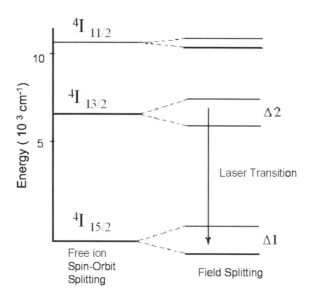

Fig. 3.20 Typical stark splitting of the $^4I_{13/2}$ and $^4I_{15/2}$ manifold.[51]

This is a valid assumption since the center (average shift in energy) is determined by the electrostatic force of ligand shells and spin-orbit interactions. They depend on the network anions and the same network anion, (oxygen) is used in all of the calculations. Different network modifier cause different stark splitting.

The stark splitting of the upper and lower manifold are Δ_1 and Δ_2, respectively. If the center of these manifolds have zero mean shift in energy, the relative populations N_a and N_b of the two stark levels involved (in laser action) in the upper and lower manifold could then be obtained using the Boltzmann approximation.

3.7.1.1. *Transition probability*

Large transition probability and hence large stimulated emission cross-section is needed to make a high gain amplifier. The ranges of the cross-sections and fluorescence lifetime have been observed to vary as a function of glass composition by more than a factor of 5. The stimulated emission cross-section depends strongly on the host material. If a Gaussian line shape is assumed, the peak stimulated emission cross-section between state aJ and bJ' having a probability A(aJ; bJ') is given by[15, 16]:

$$\sigma(aJ; bJ') = \frac{\lambda_p^4}{8\pi * c * n * \Delta\lambda_{\text{eff}}} \left[\frac{\ln 2}{\pi} \right]^{1/2} * A(aJ; bJ'), \qquad (3.2)$$

where λ_p is the wavelength of the peak emission, $\Delta\lambda_{\text{eff}}$ is the effective line width of the transition and n is the refractive index of the host. In terms of the line strength, S(aJ; bJ'), the spontaneous emission probability is:

$$A(aJ; bJ') = \frac{64\pi^4 e^2 \chi}{3h(2J + 1)\lambda_p^3} S(aJ; bJ'), \qquad (3.3)$$

The local field correction χ for an ion embedded in a medium of index n is usually approximated by $n(n^2 + 2)^2/9$ for electric dipole transition and n^3 for magnetic dipole transition.[15, 16] Optical transitions between states of ^4I_n configuration of rare earth ions in solids are predominantly electrical dipole like in character. Combining Eqs. (3.2) and (3.3), for electric dipole transition, the following is obtained:

$$\sigma(aJ;bJ') = \frac{4\pi^2 e^2}{3\hbar c(2J+1)} \left[\frac{\ln 2}{\pi}\right]^{1/2} \frac{(n^2+2)^2}{n} \frac{\lambda_p}{\Delta\lambda_{\text{eff}}} S(aJ;bJ'),$$

$$(3.4)$$

From Eq. (3.4), the factors affecting the emission cross-section are the line strength, line width of the transition, peak wavelength of the emission spectrum and the refractive index of the glass host. These four factors are now examined.

The line strength is the most host dependent quantity in determining the cross-section. The integrated absorption of an electric dipole, $\int k(\lambda)d\lambda$ can be related to the line strength through the relation:

$$\int_{\text{band}} k(\lambda)d\lambda = \rho \frac{8\pi^3 e^2 \overline{\lambda}}{3hc(2J+1)} \frac{1}{n} \left[\frac{(n^2+2)^2}{9}\right] S(aJ;bJ') \qquad (3.5)$$

where $k(\lambda)$ is the absorption coefficient at wavelength λ, ρ is the Er ion concentration. $\overline{\lambda}$ is the mean wavelength of the absorption band, J is the total angular momentum of the initial level, and $n = n(\overline{\lambda})$ is the bulk index at wavelength $\overline{\lambda}$. The value of Er concentration used in the calculation is $3 \times 10^{24}\,\text{m}^{-3}$. The factor $n(n^2+2)^2/9$ represents the local field correction for the ion in a dielectric medium under the tight binding approximation.

A model to calculate the radiative transition probability between electronic energy levels of trivalent rare-earth ions in solids has been developed by Judd and Ofelt.[15,16] In the Judd and Ofelt model (J–O model), the field induced electric dipole moments are expressed in terms of the odd-parity field expansion parameters describing the strength and symmetry of the ligand field at the rare earth sites. Using the approach of Judd and Ofelt, the associated line strength is described by:

$$S(aJ;bJ') = \sum_{t=2,4,6} \Omega_t |\langle [\alpha' S' L']J' ||U^{(t)}||[\alpha S L]J\rangle|^2, \qquad (3.6)$$

where the doubly reduced matrix elements of the tensor operator $U^{(t)}$ are evaluated for intermediate-coupled eigenstates $|[\alpha S L]J >$. The three coefficients Ω_2, Ω_4 and Ω_6 contain implicitly the odd-symmetry crystal field terms, radial integrals and perturbation terms. These coefficients, which are independent of quantum numbers with the ground ^4I_n configuration of the Er ion, may be regarded as phenomenological parameters characterizing the radiative transition probabilities. Description of the transition line strength in terms of the only three intensity parameters results from averaging dipole moments over the field split stark components. These three parameters can be determined by a least square fitting of the measured spectral absorption. The fluorescence branching ratios for transitions originating on a specific initial manifold $|(S'L')J'\rangle$ are defined by:

$$\beta[(S'L')J';(SL)J] = \frac{A[(S'L')J';(SL)J]}{\sum_J A[(S'L')J';(SL)J]}, \qquad (3.7)$$

where the sum is over all possible terminal manifolds $|(SL)J\rangle$. This sum represents the total transition probability for radiative decay from the initial manifold. The radiative lifetime is the reciprocal of transition probability:

$$\tau_{\text{rad}} = \left\{ \sum_J A[(S'L')J';(SL)J] \right\}^{-1}, \qquad (3.8)$$

Both the homogeneous and inhomogeneous line widths of the optical transition are host dependent. Inhomogeneous broadening is caused by the site-to-site variation and is unavoidable in glass material due to its disordered nature. In mixed-anion glasses (e.g., flurophosphates) and mixed-glass formers (e.g., phospho-tellurites), there can be even greater site-to-site variations. This results in large inhomogeneous broadening and dominates the linewidths measured at temperatures smaller than $300\,\text{K}$. At room temperature a broad, asymmetric band is usually observed. Therefore an effective linewidth of the fluorescence intensity is defined by:

$$\Delta\lambda_{\text{eff}} = \int \frac{I(\lambda)d\lambda}{I_{\text{max}}}, \qquad (3.9)$$

and it is used instead of the full width at half-maximum linewidth. This width is a measure of a combination of the extent of the stark splitting of the initial and final manifolds and the inhomogeneous broadening resulting from the site-to-site variations of the local field. Homogeneous broadening is caused by the broadening of the stark levels of the upper state and lower state of the optical transition. The emission peak wavelength of fluorescence intensity depends on the relative probability of the transition between the stark levels of the initial and final angular momentum (J) state. The center of a J state manifold is determined by the electrostatic and spin orbit interaction while the stark splitting is determined by the local field caused by the glass host as well as other co-dopants.

The calculation is carried out assuming there is only nearest neighbor interaction between the host glass material (silica) and the matrix modifier (co-dopant), i.e., the calculation assumes no interaction between the matrix modifier atoms. Also the effect of clustering of dopant ions (Er) and concentration quenching is not taken into account. For large concentrations of matrix modifiers, the interaction between these atoms can lead to site-to-site variations and hence inhomogeneous broadening particularly at low temperatures. Such site-to-site variations have not been considered in this model, hence it is valid for low concentration of matrix modifier atoms and near room temperature. The composition of several mixed glasses is shown in Table 3.1. The different spectral shapes and hence broadening observed in this model is primarily due to different Stark splitting of the upper and lower levels of the Er ion in the glass matrix in the presence of different matrix modifiers.

Table 3.1 Chemical composition of the mixed glasses.[51]

Glasses	Chemical Composition (mole %)
Ge Silica	10% GeO_2–90% SiO_2
Al/P Silica	5% Al_2O_3–5% P_2O_5–90% SiO_2
Ca/Ge/Al/P Silica	5% CaO–5% GeO_2–5% Al_2O_3–5% P_2O_5–80% SiO_2
P Silica	10% P_2O_5–90% SiO_2
Al Silica	10% Al_2O_3–90% SiO_2
Al/Ge silica	5% Al_2O_3–5%GeO_2–90% SiO_2
ZBLAN	53% ZrF_4–20% BaF_2–4% LaF_3–3% AlF_3–20% NaF

3.7.1.2. *Stimulated emission cross section in some Er-doped materials*

When generalized to account for the finite line width, the stimulated emission cross section can be obtained using the relation between the Einstein A and B coefficients, which leads to the following connection between the emission and absorption cross section:

$$g_a \cdot \int v^2 \sigma_{a,b}(v) dv = g_b \cdot \int v^2 \sigma_{b,a}(v) dv, \qquad (3.10)$$

where $g = 2J + 1$ are the degeneracy of the J multiplets involved.

Equation (3.10) is usually written in an approximate form, (sometimes referred as the Ladenburg–Fuchtbauer relationship) with v^2 replaced by the square of the average photon energy and taken outside of the integral. Therefore, if the relative spectrum for the reciprocal process (absorption) can be measured, Eq. (3.10) can be used to scale the emission cross section. For bulk samples, the absorption cross section is usually measured, since these are straightforward to obtain using commercial spectrophotometers if the ion concentration is known.

The calculated stimulated emission cross sections of the transition ($^4I_{13/2}$ and $^4I_{15/2}$) for several Er-doped glass are shown in Figs. 3.21 and 3.22. The spectrum for silica based fibers with different co-dopants are shown in Fig. 3.21. The results for non-silica based fibers are shown in Fig. 3.22. The stimulated emission cross sections of pure silica fibers are shown in Fig. 3.21 (top trace). There is a strong peak around 1530 nm and the cross section is 0.5 pm^2 (1 pm^2 = 10^{-24} m^2), which is similar to that for the other co-dopants.

From these graphs, it follows that although the shift in spectrum by co-dopants is small, a broadening of the spectrum is caused by co-dopants. The experimental results are shown in Fig. 3.6. A comparison of Figs. 3.6 and 3.21 shows that the spectrum are similar. These co-doped high Er concentration fibers are possible candidates for high gain short amplifiers. The results of the calculation of stimulated emission spectrum for several different co-dopants are summarized in Table 3.2. The co-dopants broaden the Er amplifier spectrum.

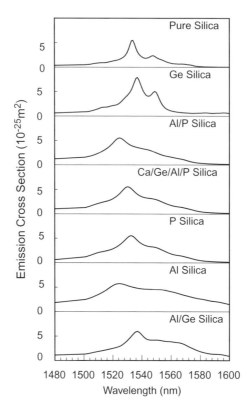

Fig. 3.21 The calculated results of stimulated emission cross section as a function of wavelength in co-doped silica glass. The various matrix modifiers (co-dopants) are indicated in the figure.[51]

Experimental results for various hosts are described earlier (Sec. 3.3). The maximum amount of dopant is limited by the onset of clustering of the Er ions. For Nd-doped glass, the clustering causes a fast decay component with a very short lifetime ($\sim 0.34\,\mu s$) in the fluorescence spectrum, which decreased the total radiative lifetime. Similar effect occurs for Er dopant. The non-radiative decay due to concentration quenching also decreases the pump absorption efficiency.

3.7.2. Yb-Doped Amplifier

Stimulated emission of Yb^{3+} involves transitions between stark levels of $^2F_{5/2}$ and $^2F_{7/2}$ electronic states. The principal wavelengths

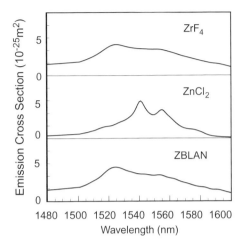

Fig. 3.22 The calculated results of stimulated emission cross section as a function of wavelength in several non-silica glass types. The various glass types are indicated in the figure.[51]

Table 3.2 The peak emission wavelength and peak cross section for the $^4I_{13/2} \rightarrow {}^4I_{15/2}$ transition of Er with different co-dopant in different glasses.[51]

	Peak Wavelength (nm)	Stark Splitting (cm^{-1}) $^4I_{15/2}$	Stark Splitting (cm^{-1}) $^4I_{13/2}$	Peak Cross Section $(10^{-25}\,m^2)$	Refractive Index
Al/P Silica	1530	389	512	5.5	1.57
Ca/Ge/Al/P Silica	1533	333	470	5.5	1.57
P Silica	1534	295	351	5.4	1.57
Pure Silica	1535	171	282	5.4	1.56
Ge Silica	1535	462	325	7.9	2.04
Al Silica	1528	476	462	5.7	1.64
Al/Ge Silica	1529	487	446	5.9	1.69
ZBLAN	1524	308	266	5.4	1.57
ZnCl$_2$	1537	320	277	5.9	1.69
ZrF$_4$	1523	448	427	4.9	1.44

for the various transitions in Yb-doped fiber glasses are shown in Fig. 3.23. The $^2F_{5/2}$ and $^2F_{7/2}$ electronic states are the only levels of the $4f^{12}$ ground state configuration. Levels of excited state configurations and charge transfer states are in the ultraviolet. Therefore, concentration quenching and multiphoton relaxation does not affect

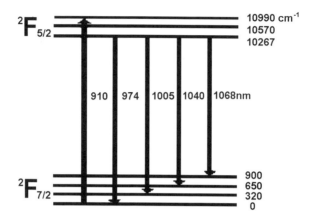

Fig. 3.23 Yb energy level diagram. Splitting and wavelengths are approximate values.[52]

the lasing or the excitation wavelengths for Yb-doped lasers. This allows high doping of Yb and is an attractive feature for optically pumped high-power laser.

For high power laser applications, silica glass is a very desirable host material because it can be fabricated in the form of a glass fiber which allows very long lengths of optical gain medium, and a robust laser design, if Bragg gratings written on the fiber are used as reflectors. For some applications which includes optical pumping of another gain medium or spectroscopic application, (such as weather monitoring), lasers with specific emission wavelengths are needed. Thus it is important to examine the change in emission wavelength of a Yb ion in a silica host for various co-dopants. The co-dopants discussed here are Al, B, Ga, Lu, Nb, P, Ta, and Ti. In the presence of these co-dopants the local field seen by a Yb ion gets modified which can result in a change in the peak emission wavelength and emission cross section. Silicate, borate and phosphate glasses have also been systematically studied with different glass modifying cations. Modifier ions include Cs, Rb, K, Na, Li, Ba, Sr, Ca, Al and Ge. The effects of different glass modifiers on Yb^{3+} spectroscopy has been studied for silicate, borate, and phosphate glasses.[52]

When Yb ions are placed in a glass host, subjected to a number very complex forces, which are absent in the free ions. There are, for instance, electric and magnetic interactions with each individual

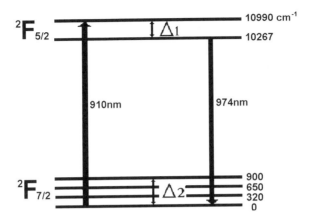

Fig. 3.24 Typical stark splitting of the $^2F_{5/2}$ and $^2F_{7/2}$ manifold, the wavenumbers listed in the graph are used as reference only.[52]

ion in its vicinity, and resonant interactions with neighboring Yb ions if the doping concentration is sufficiently high. A typical Stark splitting for the $^2F_{5/2}$ and $^2F_{7/2}$ manifold is shown in Fig. 3.24. In the discussion, it is assumed that the center (average shift in energy) of the two $^2F_{5/2}$ and $^2F_{7/2}$ manifold does not change. This is a valid assumption since the center is determined by the electrostatic force of ligand shells and spin-orbit interactions, which are dependent on the network anions and the same network anion, oxygen, is used in all of the calculations.

The Stark splitting of the upper and lower manifold are labeled as Δ_1 and Δ_2, respectively in Fig. 3.24. Different network modifier cations cause different Stark splitting. If the center of the manifold is set to zero (zero mean shift in energy), the relative populations N_a and N_b of the two Stark levels involved in the upper and lower manifold can then be obtained using a Boltzmann approximation.

Table 3.3 shows the Stark splitting of the $^2F_{5/2}$ level in silicate, borate and phosphate glasses and the potential difference (V) between glass network cations and modifiers. Figure 3.25 show the Stark splitting of the $^2F_{5/2}$ level of Yb in silicate glasses with different co-dopants.

The Stark splitting is plotted as a function of the potential difference between the modifier and the glass network cation. In the

Table 3.3 The Stark splitting of the $^2F_{5/2}$ level of Yb^{3+} in silicate, phosphate and borate glasses as a function of the potential difference between glass network cations and modifiers.[48]

Glass Modifiers	Silicate Glass		Phosphate Glass		Borate Glass	
	Potential Difference (V)	Stark splitting (cm^{-1})	Potential difference (V)	Stark splitting (cm^{-1})	Potential difference (V)	Stark splitting (cm^{-1})
Cs+	5.7	671.	8.1	85.	2.51	673.
Rb+	5.6	672.	8.1	670.	2.45	678.
K+	5.5	673.	8.0	671.	2.4	686.
Na+	5.2	680.	7.9	671.	2.17	687.
Li+	4.9	684.	7.5	673.	2.05	687.
Ba^{2+}	3.3	685.	7.3	675.	1.10	687.
Sr^{2+}	3.1	689	5.7	677.	0.95	689.
Ca^{2+}	2.7	693.	5.4	678.	0.70	690.
Al^{3+}	1.4	695.	3.5	684.	0.28	692.
Ge^{4+}	0.67	697.	1.6	686.	-0.45	695.

calculation, two assumptions were made, (i) the Yb ion is surrounded by the nearest neighbor oxygen and the second nearest neighbor glass network cation, and (ii) one network cation was replaced by one modifier cation. In the calculation, the content of ytterbium oxide is 0.25% by weight, and the modifier content is 35% in silicate glass, 45% in.borate glass and 45% in phosphate glass respectively.

The Stark splitting of $^2F_{5/2}$ levels in silicate and phosphate glasses have similar behavior, i.e., Stark splitting decreases with increasing potential difference. For the cation modifiers, the Stark splitting increases in the order as shown:

$$Cs^+ < Rb^+ < K^+ < Na^+ < Li^+ < Ba^{2+} < Sr^{2+}$$
$$< Ca^{2+} < Al^{3+} < Ge^{4+}$$

Figure 3.25 represents the general trend for Stark splitting i.e., if the modifier cation produces a small positive potential, the Stark splitting due to co-dopant is small. This result is important in predicting the wavelength shift caused by the co-dopant. For example Al co-dopant blue shifts the emission spectrum and Ge co-dopant almost cause no shift in spectrum. Since glass anions are Yb ligands, anions have stronger influence on the Stark splitting than cations.

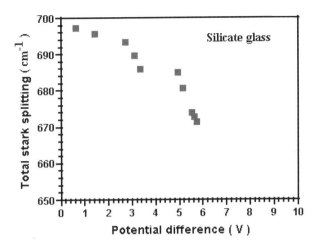

Fig. 3.25 Stark splitting of $^2F_{5/2}$ for Yb^{3+} with different co-dopants in silicate, glasses. Each point refers to different co-dopants. The potential difference seen by a Yb ion due to the presence of a co-dopant (Table 3.3) is plotted on the X-axis and the Stark splitting of the $^2F_{5/2}$ level is plotted on the Y-axis.[52] A similar plot is obtained for phosphate and borate glasses with different co-dopants.

However similar to the case for cations, the stark splitting is smaller for the smaller anion field strength.

The stimulated emission cross sections of the $^2F_{5/2}$ to $^2F_{7/2}$ transition in Yb-doped silica based fiber are shown in Fig. 3.26. The figure shows the stimulated emission cross sections for several silica fibers with co-dopants.

There is a peak around 975 nm and the cross section is 2.5 pm^2 (10^{-24} m^2), for all cases shown. From these graphs, it follows that the shift in spectrum by co-dopants is small. The maximum amount of dopant may be limited by the onset of clustering of the Yb ions Also at high concentration the non-radiative decay due to concentration quenching can decrease the pump absorption efficiency.

Previous sections describe in detail the co-doping effects in Er and Yb-doped fibers. Similar results have been obtained for Nd-doped fibers.[53] Using a method of calculation similar to that described earlier, the spectrum of stimulated emission cross section for the $^4F_{3/2}$ to $^4I_{9/2}$ transition of Nd^{3+} in Al co-doped and B co-doped silica fiber is shown in Fig. 3.27. The measured data is shown in Sec. 3.5.

Fiber Amplifiers and Fiber Lasers

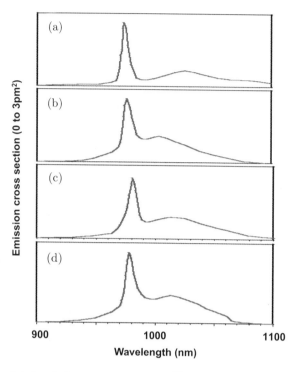

Fig. 3.26 Stimulated emission cross section of Yb^{3+} in silica glass fiber. The main peak is near 975 nm with a smaller peak at 1025 nm. (a) pure silica, (b) Al-co-doped silica (c) B co-doped silica, (d) P co-doped silica.[52] The Y-axis scale is 0 to 3 pm^2 for each case.

For Nd dopant in glass, the clustering of Nd (at high concentrations) causes a fast decay component with a very short lifetime ($\sim 0.34\,\mu s$) in the fluorescence spectrum, which decreases the total radiative lifetime. The clustering effect can be reduced significantly in Nd-doped fibers by introducing co-dopants such as Al, P and B, so that Nd concentrations far beyond the solubility can be obtained. The required Al concentration to reduce clustering is quite small, and it is found that an Al to Nd ratio of roughly 8:1 is sufficient. Similar phenomenon is expected in Yb-doped fibers. The co-doped high Yb concentration fibers are good candidates for high power double-clad amplifier.

Rare earth dopants in silica fibers with or without co-dopants provide a gain medium for amplifiers operating in a wide wavelength

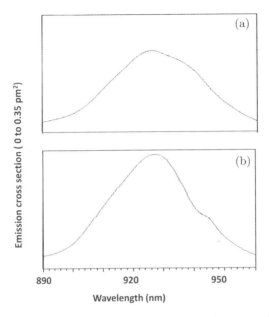

Fig. 3.27 Stimulated emission cross section for the $^4F_{3/2}$–$^4I_{9/2}$ of Nd^{3+} in (a) Al co-doped silica fiber, and (b) B co-doped silica fiber.[53] The Y-axis scale is 0 to 0.35 pm^2 for each case.

range. The operating wavelength is mainly determined by the energy levels of the rare earth ions. The glass matrix modifies the energy levels somewhat through Stark splitting. The spectrum of the stimulated cross section is affected by the presence of co-dopants.

References

1. M.J.F. Digonnet, *Rare earth doped fiber lasers and amplifiers*. New York: Marcel Dekker Inc. 1993.
2. E. Desurvire, *Erbium-Doped Fiber Amplifiers*. New York: Wiley. 1994.
3. L.D. Deloach, S.A. Payne, L.L. Chase, L.K. Smith, W.L. Kway and W.F. Krupke, *IEEE. J. Quantum Electron.*, **29** (1993) 1179.
4. J.Y. Allain, M. Monerie, H. Poignant and T. Georges, *J. Non-Cryst. Solids.* **161** (1993) 270.
5. S.E. Stokowski, R.A. Saroyan and M.J. Weber, *Nd-doped laser glass, spectroscopy, and physical properties*. **1** and **2**. Lawrence Livermore national Labortory, University of California, Livermore, CA, 1981.
6. R.R. Jacobs and M.J. Weber, *IEEE J. Quantum Electron.* QE-**12** (1976) 102.
7. J.M. Pellegrino, W.M. Yen and M.J. Weber, *J. Appl. Phys.* **51** (1980) 6332.

8. M.J. Weber, D.C. Ziegler and C.A. Angell, *J. Appl. Phys.* **53** (1982) 4344.
9. M.J. Weber, J.E. Lynch, D.H. Blackburn and D.J. Cronin, *IEEE. J. Quantum Electron.* QE-**19** (1983) 1600.
10. H. Takebe, T. Murata and K. Morinaga, *J. Am. Ceram. Soc.* **79** (1996) 681.
11. M.M. Mann and L.G. DeShazer, *J. of Appl. Phys.* **41** (1970) 2951.
12. G.H. Dieke, *Spectra and energy levels of rare earth ions in crystals.* New York Interscience Publishers Inc. 1968.
13. A.K. Przhevuskii, *Opt. Spectrosc.* **53** (1982) 414.
14. A.K. Przhevuskii, *Opt. Spectrosc.* **53** (1982) 499.
15. B.R. Judd, *Phys. Review.* **127** (1962) 750.
16. G.S. Ofelt, *J. of Chem. Phys.* **37** (1962) 511.
17. B. Henderson and R.H. Bertram, *Crystal field engineering of solid state laser materials*, Chapter 1. Cambridge: Cambridge University Press 2000, pp. 13.
18. P.C. Becker, N.A. Olsson and J.R. Simpson Erbium doped fiber amplifiers. Academic Press. 1997.
19. J. Becquerel, *C.R. Acad. Sci.* **142** (1906) 775.
20. M. Meyer, *Phys. Rev.* **60** (1941) 184.
21. M. Shimizu, M. Yamada, M. Horiguchi, T. Takeshita and M. Okayasu, *Electron. Lett.* **20** (1990) 1641.
22. J. L. Zyskind, D.J. DiGiovanni, J.W. Sulhoff, P.C. Becker and C.H. Brito Cruz, CA: *IEEE/LEOS Top. Meet. Opt. Amplifiers*, Monterey, Paper PDP6. 1990.
23. E. Desurvire, J.L. Zyskind and C.R. Giles, *J. Lightwave Technol.* **8** (1990) 1730.
24. C.R. Giles and E. Desurvire, *J. Lightwave Technol.* **9** (1991) 271.
25. A.A.M. Saleh, R.M. Jopson, J.D. Evankow and J. Aspell, *IEEE Photon. Technol. Lett.* **2** 1990.
26. S. Shimoda and H. Ishio (Ed.), *Optical amplifiers and their applications.* John Wiley and Sons. 1994.
27. M.J.F. Digonnet, *Rare earth doped fiber lasers and amplifiers*, Chapter 2. New York: Marcel Dekker Inc. (1993).
28. C.D. Marshall, L.K. Smith, R.J. Beach, M.A. Emanuel, K.I. Schaffers, J. Skidmore, S.A. Payne and B.H.T. Chai, *IEEE J. Quantum Electron.* **32** (1996) 650.
29. L.D. DeLoach, S.A. Payne, L.L. Chase, L.K. Smith, W.L. Kway and W.F. Krupke, *IEEE J. Quantum Electron.* **29** (1993) 1179.
30. H. Bruesselbach and D.S. Sumida, *Opt. Lett.* **21** (1966) 480.
31. U. Brauch, A. Giesen, Karszewski, C. Stewen and A. Voss, *Opt. Lett.* **20** (1995) 713.
32. C. Bibeau, R.J. Beach, S.C. Mitchell, M.A. Emanuel, C.A. Ebbers, S.B. Sutton and K.S. Jancaitis, *IEEE J. Quantum Electron.* **34** (1998) 2010.
33. Z. Burshtein, Y. Kalisky, S.Z. Levy, P. Le Boulanger and S. Rotman, *IEEE, JQE,* **36** (2000) 1000.
34. R. Paschotta, J. Nilsson, A.C. Tropper and D.C. Hanna, *IEEE, JQE.* **33** (1997) 1049.

35. H. Takebe, T. Murata and K. Morinaga, *J. Amer. Ceram. Soc.* **79** (1996) 681.
36. M.J. Weber, J.E. Lynch, D.H. Blackburn, and D.J. Cronin, *IEEE J. Quantum Electron.* QE-**19** (1983) 1600.
37. E. Snitzer, *Phys. Rev. Lett.* **7** (1961) 444.
38. C.J. Koster and E. Snitzer, *Appl. Opt.* **3** (1964) 1182.
39. B. Ross and E. Snitzer, *IEEE JQE.* QE-**6** (1970) 361.
40. J. Stone and C.A. Burrus, *Appl. Phys. Lett.* **23** (1973) 388.
41. T.Y. Fan and R.L. Byer, *J. Opt. Soc. Am. B.* **3** (1986) 1519.
42. A.D. Pearson, S.P.S. Porto and W.R. Northover, *J. Appl. Phys.* **35** (1964) 1704.
43. R.D. Mauer, *Appl. Opt.* **2** (1963) 87.
44. P.I. Alcock, A.I. Ferguson, D.C. Hanna and A.C. Tropper, *Opt. Commun.* **58** (1986) 405.
45. S. Zemon *et. al. IEEE Photonic Tech. Lett.* **4** (1992) 244.
46. M.L. Dakss, W.J. Miniscalco, *IEEE Photonic Tech. Lett.* **2** (1990) 650.
47. M.L. Dennis, J.W. Dixon and I. Aggarwal, *Electronics Letters* **30** (1994) 136.
48. D.N. Messias, M.V.D. Vermelho, M.T. de Araujo, A.S. Gouveia-Neto and J.S. Aitchison, *IEEE J. Quantum Electronics.* **38** (2002) 1640.
49. P.R. Watekar, S. Ju and W.T. Han, *Proc. CLEO, paper OWF5.* 2005.
50. O. Mahran, M. Shahat and W. Hagar, *Int. J. Scientific and Industrial Res.* **4** (2013) 1815.
51. Q. Wang and N.K. Dutta, *J. of Applied Physics.* **95**, (2004) 4025.
52. K. Lu and N.K. Dutta, *J. Appl. Phys.* **91** (2002) 576.
53. K. Lu and N.K. Dutta, *J. of Appl. Phys.* **89** (2001) 3079.

Chapter 4

Amplifier Fiber Fabrication

4.1. Introduction

Rare earth-doped fibers can be fabricated by several methods. The principles among them are MCVD (modified chemical vapor deposition), PCVD (plasma assisted chemical vapor deposition), VAD (vapor axial deposition) and OVD (outside vapor deposition). Rare earth dopants for silica fibers are often introduced during the growth of the fiber itself. Thus the fabrication of rare earth-doped fiber is very much linked to the fabrication of the regular low loss transmission fiber. The concentration of rare earth dopants can vary considerably. It can be as much as 1000 ppm in multicomponent glasses, to as small as <100 ppm in Erbium (Er)-doped fibers. In distributed Er-doped fibers it can be a few ppm. The back ground losses in rare earth-doped fibers (particularly Er-doped fiber) are comparable to that of transmission grade silica fiber.

The rare doped fibers often needed to be connected (spliced) to regular transmission grade silica fiber. Thus it is desirable to use conventional fusion splicing (with little modification) for low insertion loss optical connection. Thus, there is a strong practical incentive to maintain the compatibility for cleaving and splicing between the rare earth-doped amplifier fiber and the conventional low loss transmission fiber (made of silica). Although other glass hosts such as phosphate, tellurite, sulfide glass and/or fluorozirconate (ZBLAN: ZrF_4-BaF_2-LaF_3-AlF_3-NaF) glass may have higher gain or bandwidth, silica is the preferred host glass for reasons described earlier in addition to its low loss and low dispersion.

The optical fiber used for transmission has a core about $10\,\mu$m in diameter which is surrounded by a cladding about $100\,\mu$m in diameter. The core region has a slightly higher index ($\sim0.3\%$) which allows the light to be guided in the core. The cladding is further surrounded by a polymer jacket which provides both protection from the environment and strength.

4.2. Transmission Optical Fiber Fabrication

The optical fiber used in optical transmission systems is based on silica (SiO_2) material. Low loss silica fibers were first proposed in 1966[1] and by early $\sim$1970s low loss fibers had an attenuation of $20\,$dB/km. Since then the manufacturing processes have been refined and developed so that transmission fibers have typical losses of <0.15 dB/km in the 1550 nm region of the optical spectrum.[1–8]

The principle methods of optical fiber fabrication are (i) MCVD, (ii) PCVD, (iii) VAD and (iv) OVD. These methods are described here. The methods for the creation of SiO_2 are hydrolysis (reaction with H_2O) or oxidation (reaction with O_2) from $SiCl_4$. The hydrolysis and oxygen reactions are:

$$SiCl_4 + 2H_2O = SiO_2 + 4HCl, \tag{4.1}$$

$$SiCl_4 + O_2 = SiO_2 + 2Cl_2, \tag{4.2}$$

The hydrolysis method is accomplished by flowing $SiCl_4$ vapor into a hydrogen flame and the resulting silica particles get deposited on a rotating target. The oxidation method involves a reaction of oxygen and chloride inside a substrate tube heated to $1200°$C. Other materials such as GeO_2 can be incorporated in the silica by using a reaction of $GeCl_4$ with the hydrogen flame or oxygen.

4.2.1. MCVD Process

The MCVD process was invented around 1980.[3] It involves vapor deposition of high purity material on the inner surface of a tube. The tube may provide part of the cladding and the additional materials for the cladding and core get deposited on the inner surface of the tube. In the MCVD process, first a tube of suitable dimension and

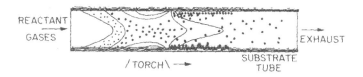

Fig. 4.1 Schematic of a MCVD reactor.[4]

purity is chosen. The tube is mounted on a lathe, which rotates the tube. It has a chemical (chlorides) delivery system at one end and at the other end is the exhaust. A heat torch traverses along the tube which causes the entrants to react forming SiO_2 and depositing it on the walls of the tube.

The deposition process is a high temperature gas phase oxidation of chlorides which creates SiO_2 (oxides) and deposition of these oxides as submicron particles on the tube.[4,7,8] These particles are converted to a clear glass film by a process called fusion. The entrants into the tube are controlled amounts of chemical reagents which are generated by passing (O_2 or He) through liquid sources such as $SiCl_4$, $GeCl_4$ or $POCl_3$. Sometimes gaseous sources such as SiF_4 are also mixed. In MCVD, first a high quality cladding is deposited and then the core is deposited. The total number of deposited layers and their composition depends on the fiber design. The schematic of a MCVD process is shown in Fig. 4.1.

4.2.2. PCVD Process

The PCVD was invented in 1975.[9] It uses an approach similar to MCVD, i.e., the chlorides react in a tube in the presence of oxygen and the oxide formed gets deposited in the walls of the tube. A non-rotating silica tube is held in a furnace at a temperature of 1000–1250°C.[9–11] The heating is provided by a microwave generator which generates a plasma in the tube. The generator moves back and forth along the furnace at speeds of 8 m/min. Appropriate proportions of the reagents ($SiCl_4$, $GeCl_4$ etc) and carrier gas (O_2) are injected into the tube using mass flow controllers. A large number of layers ($\sim$1000) are deposited in this process which allows accurate control of composition. The schematic of a PCVD furnace is shown in Fig. 4.2.

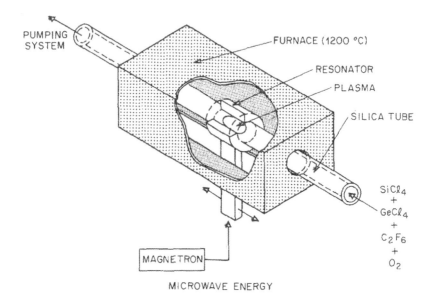

Fig. 4.2 Schematic of a PCVD reactor.[9]

4.2.3. *OVD Process*

The OVD process was invented around 1973.[12] It is based on flame hydrolysis, which is used to generate submicron size glass particles which get deposited on a rotating mandrel.[12–14] The flame traverses the length of the mandrel and soot is deposited and built up, layer by layer into a cylindrical porous boule. The composition of the deposited material is controlled by changing the gas composition with time in order to build up the desired the refractive index profile. The schematic of an OVD apparatus is shown in Fig. 4.3.

4.2.4. *VAD Process*

The VAD process was invented around 1977.[15] It is based on flame hydrolysis. It uses a flame to react the halides with oxygen and water to form oxide submicron particles.[15–17] The deposition occurs at the end of a rotating cylindrical rod. The deposition takes place within an enclosed glass container, which provides a controlled flow of reactants

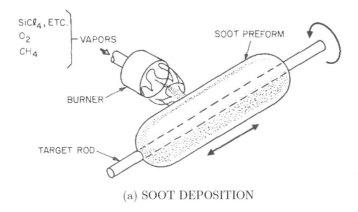

(a) SOOT DEPOSITION

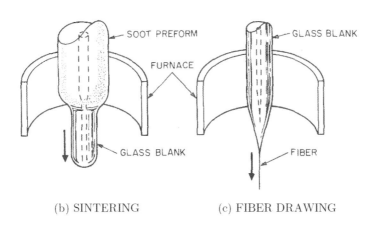

(b) SINTERING   (c) FIBER DRAWING

Fig. 4.3 Schematic of an OVD apparatus.[14]

and a clean environment. The schematic of a VAD apparatus is shown in Fig. 4.4.

4.2.5. *Doping and Fiber Drawing*

It is necessary to add dopants to the primary glass component SiO_2, to change its index. This allows fabrication of different waveguide designs. Index raising dopants such as germanium, phosphorus and aluminum and index lowering dopants such as boron and fluorine are introduced as halides or inert gases in the reaction chamber. The halides are carried by oxygen and inert gas. The oxidation process

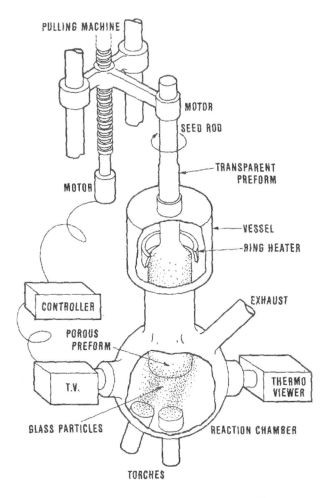

PULLING MACHINE

MOTOR

SEED ROD

TRANSPARENT
PREFORM

MOTOR

VESSEL

RING HEATER

CONTROLLER

EXHAUST

POROUS
PREFORM

T.V.

THERMO
VIEWER

GLASS PARTICLES

REACTION CHAMBER

TORCHES

Fig. 4.4 Schematic of a VAD apparatus.[16]

is controlled by the thermodynamic equilibrium established during
the doping reaction, deposition and sintering. Typical index profiles
that have been produced are shown in Fig. 4.5.

A major step in the fabrication of optical fiber is fiber drawing and the associated fiber coating with polymer.[4,18,19] This step
is important in determining the resultant optical, dimensional and
mechanical properties of the final lightguide. Figure 4.6 shows the
essential features of a fiber drawing facility for drawing silica based

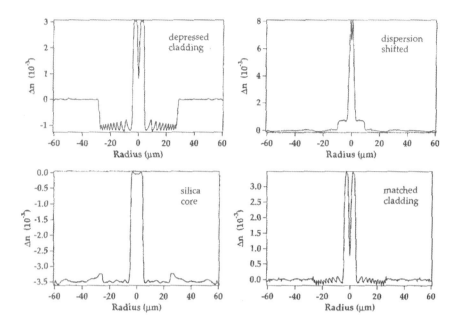

Fig. 4.5 Schematic of various index profiles that have been fabricated.

fiber from preforms. The preform is essentially the collapsed and drawn tube in the MCVD process after the deposition of the core and cladding materials. A tall structure is used for supporting the control equipment. The glass preform is fed into a high temperature furnace by a preform feed mechanism where it is aligned and centered with respect to the furnace. For silica fiber drawing, the temperature of the furnace is set in the 1950–2300°C range. This allows proper viscosity for drawing. The tip of the preform softens as it is fed to the high temperature region and both gravity and an applied tensile force causes it to shrink to small diameter. A controlled tensile force is provided by a fiber pull mechanism (capstan). The preform feed rate and the capstan rotation rate determines the ratio of the drawn down radius of fiber to preform. Typically preforms with diameter in the 10 to 70 mm range are drawn down to a fiber 100 to 225 μm in diameter. 125 μm is the diameter of a typical fiber. In line coating is a key step in fiber drawing process. Both glass fiber diameter and coated fiber diameter are measured and controlled by feedback loops.

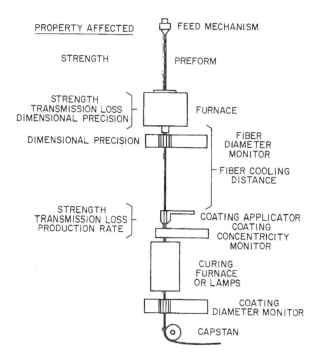

Fig. 4.6 Schematic of a fiber drawing and coating apparatus.[4]

4.3. Rare Earth Doping

Methods of incorporating rare earth dopants in the preform have been developed for all the deposition techniques.[20-23] The rare earth dopants are sent to the reaction region along with the index controlling dopants. Rare earths generally have a low vapor pressure. This is usually compensated by placing the vapor source close to the reaction zone or by delivering the material as an aerosol or high vapor pressure organic compound (Fig. 4.7).

The heated frit source (A) is made by soaking a previously deposited porous soot in a rare earth chloride solution (Fig. 4.7). For the heated source, the rare earth chloride is directly injected (after dehydration) close to the reaction chamber (B). An attractive feature of the heated source injector (C) is the rare earth source (in the small ampoule) is isolated from potential wanted reaction with other chlorides. The aerosol delivery method does not require

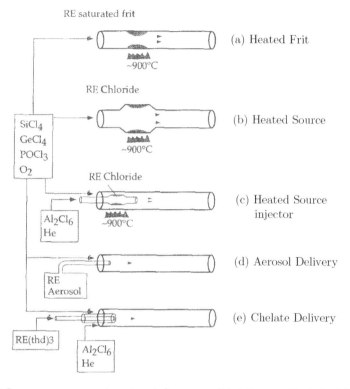

Fig. 4.7 Low vapor pressure dopant such (as rare earth) delivery methods for MCVD.[21]

a heated source compounds by generating vapor at the reaction site (D). Organic compound of rare earths (E) provides higher vapor pressure for rare earths than the chlorides.

Rare earth dopants have also been incorporated for the VAD or OVD process. Rare earth vapor, aerosol and solution transport has been used. The schematic for vapor and aerosol deposition is shown in Fig. 4.8. The doping can be achieved during soot deposition or after soot boule has been created while it is still porous (Fig. 4.9).

4.4. Alternate Glass Host Fabrication

So far, silica based fiber fabrication has been described. There are several reasons to consider other types of glass host. These glass hosts are selenides, tellurites, germinates, fluorides, chlorides, iodides, and

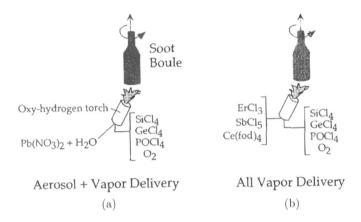

Aerosol + Vapor Delivery   All Vapor Delivery

(a)   (b)

Fig. 4.8 Schematic of rare earth incorporation via vapor phase transport and aerosol deposition during soot deposition in VAD process.[21]

sulfides.[24-26] The glass host determines the nonradiative recombination rates which generally involves phonon participation and the phonon energies are different in different glass hosts. Thus the nonradiative recombination rates are different which affects the amplifying properties of the rare earth dopant. The host material affects the transition rates and hence the gain. Also, energy splitting of the levels is determined by the local field around the rare earth ion which affects the broadening of the levels by Stark splitting and hence spectral width and spectral shape of emission and absorption. The excited stimulated emission cross sections are also modified by the host. Co-dopants in the host are often used to modify the spectral shapes.

As an example in a fluoride host, Er has a much flatter gain spectrum compared to a silica host. Pr is an effective amplifier in a fluoride host and not in silica host. Many more of the host materials can be made in the form of a bulk crystalline or amorphous material, so many early studies on rare earths were made using these types of materials. With the recognition of the advantage of "fiber form" for producing gain and associated coupling of pump and signal light, fabrication of fibers using different hosts continue to be investigated.

Glass fibers made using other halides (Fl, Cl, Br) have been considered as potential replacement of silica based fibers. Flouride based fibers were predicted to have very low losses $\sim 10^{-2}$ to 10^{-3} dB/km

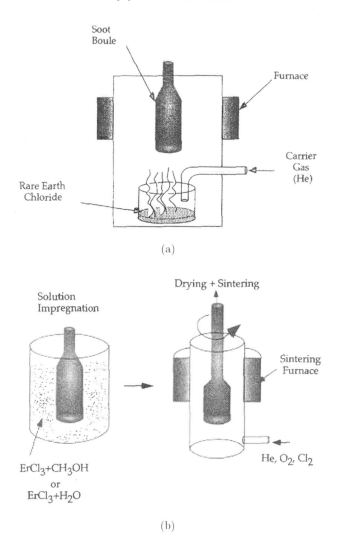

Fig. 4.9 Shows two schemes of rare earth doping after soot deposition.[21]

at wavelengths near $3\,\mu$m at very low impurity levels (<0.1 parts per billion). Predictions were based on lower Rayleigh scattering loss than silica and a longer wavelength infrared absorption edge.

Fabrication of these alternate glass host fibers is considerably more difficult than that for silica. They are not as stable as silica and often the working temperature range for fiber draw is very small. For example, ZBLAN as ZrF_4 based glass may be drawn into a fiber over a temperature range of 30°C.

A typical single mode silica fiber has 125 μm diameter cladding and about 10 μm diameter core. For fluoride fibers, the core region (core and some cladding — called preform here) is separately fabricated and is surrounded by a glass jacket. The first step in the fabrication of fiber is the fabrication of a preform which is material with a cladding to core ratio of at least 5:1. Unlike the case of silica fiber, the jacket, i.e., the material surrounding the preform is fabricated separately. The schematic of a fabrication process is shown in Fig. 4.10. The process used involves molten materials of appropriate composition.

The step index perform is made separately, by pouring the middle portion of the cladding glass casting out (upsetting in Fig. 4.10). This occurs because the temperature of the interior of the melt is hotter and stays molten longer. A jacket is fabricated independently by casting the glass in a mold and making sure (by the upsetting process) that the cylindrical hole left behind fits the preform. The close fit is often achieved by ultrasonically polishing. Smooth and clean surfaces are needed to prevent crystallization and bubble formation during drawing. Drawing of the halide glass fiber perform is accomplished by a process similar to that of silica. The draw temperature is lower, ~300°C to 350°C vs. >1000°C for silica fibers. Also, the draw rates are lower ~10 m/min vs. ~20 m/s for silica fibers.

Other methods, such as rotational casting or suction casting for creating the perform and jacket exists.[27, 28] These are modifications of the methods described.

Another method involves pulling the fiber directly from molten mixtures of core and cladding glasses. This is called a double crucible method. The method is shown in Fig. 4.11. The melts are created in Au crucibles (Au reacts little with flourides) in an inert gas atmosphere. Then the melts are transferred to a suitably designed concentric reservoir from which the fiber is drawn. The draw temperature is ~320°C and the draw rate is ~15 m/min. Thus the methods for other types of hosts are quite different than that for silica fibers and they generally have much less dimensional control and are not well developed.

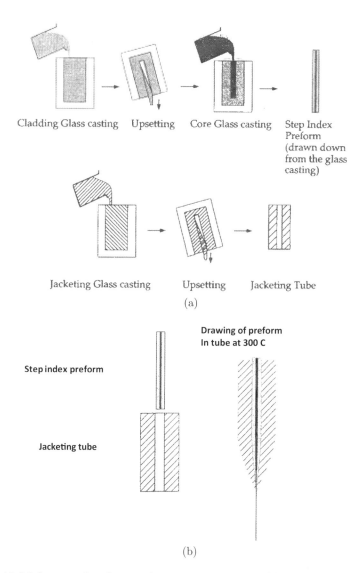

Cladding Glass casting   Upsetting   Core Glass casting   Step Index
Preform
(drawn down
from the glass
casting)

Jacketing Glass casting   Upsetting   Jacketing Tube

(a)

Drawing of preform
In tube at 300 C

Step index preform

Jacketing tube

(b)

Fig. 4.10 (a) Steps used to form perform core and cladding (b) The jacketing method and fiber draw used to make a fluoride single mode fiber.[26]

4.5. Photonic Crystal Fiber Fabrication

Photonic crystal fibers (PCF) also known as microstructure fibers (PCF) have been studied since the mid 1990's.[29–37] Nonlinear optics studies such as supercontinuum generation and amplification using

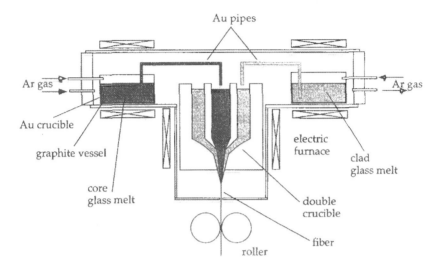

Fig. 4.11 The double crucible method for fiber fabrication.[28]

rare earth doping have been reported. Although much of these studies have been carried out using silica based fiber, the photonic crystal fiber fabrication (described in the next paragraph) is, in principle, applicable to a wide range of materials.

The fabrication of PCF involves a process by which an arranged macroscopic structure is multiply thinned using high temperatures. In the first step individual capillaries are created using standard glass capillary fabrication procedures. Then they are manually organized (arranged) to form a multicapillary structure of required symmetry. In the middle there is a glass rod in which the light propagates or, there could be a hole for fibers with photonic band gap. Capillaries with different aspect ratios (ratio of inner to outer diameter) can be chosen. The rods are positioned in the structure. Extra glass rods may be added to create a structure of sufficient mechanical integrity and desired dimensions. The structure is then fused in a furnace to create an intermediate preform a few mm in diameter. The preform is fused and drawn using a fiber drawing tower (described previously) to create the microstructured fiber. Figure 4.12 shows the schematic of the process. The fiber cross section for various types of microstructure fibers is shown in Fig. 4.13. One of the capillaries could be rare

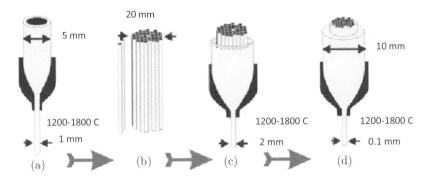

Fig. 4.12 Schematic of the microstructure fiber fabrication. (a) Creation of individual capillaries, (b) Perform creation, (c) Drawing of preform with cladding — intermediate preform, (d) Drawing of microstructured fiber.[33]

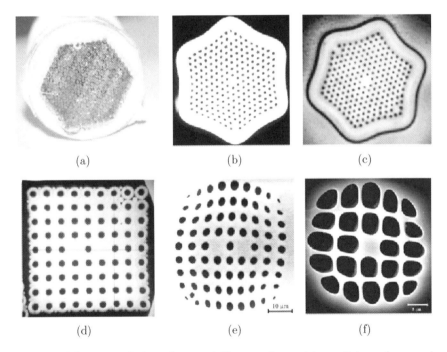

Fig. 4.13 Fabrication of photonic crystal fibers: preforms, intermediate preforms and final fibers (a) The preform of fiber with holes spaced 1 mm with hexagonal lattice (b) The intermediate preform with air holes spaced 250 μm with hexagonal lattice (c) The fiber diameter of 120 μm, air holes diameter $d = 3\,\mu$m; (d) the intermediate preform of double core fiber with square lattice; (e) a double core fiber with a square lattice, diameter of the 250 μm, air holes diameter $d = 2.5\,\mu$m; (f) a multimode fiber with a square lattice; diameter of the fiber 160 μm, air holes diameter 3 μm.[33]

earth-doped for amplifier fiber fabrication. The process is very general and could be applicable to wide range of materials choices. In principle, many types of glasses (silica, fluorides, germinates, etc.) can be used.

References

1. C.K. Kao and G.A. Hockmann, *Proc. IEEE.* **133** (1966) 1151.
2. D.B. Keck, *IEEE Comm. Mag.* **23** (1985) 17.
3. J.B. MacChesney and P.B.O'Conner, US Patent 4,217, 027 (1980).
4. S.R. Nagel, In Optical Fiber Telecommunications, Chapter 4, II Edition, S.E. Miller and I.P. Kaminow (Eds.).
5. K.J. Beales and C.R. Day, *Phys. Chem. Glasses.* **21** (1980) 5.
6. K.J. Beales, S.F. Carter, PW. France and S. Partington, *J. Non-crystalline solids.* **70** (1985) 253.
7. K.L. Walker, G.M. Hornsy and F. T. Geyling, *J. of Colloidal and Interface Science* **69** (1979) 138.
8. K.L. Walker, F.T. Geyling and S.R. Nagel, *J. Amer Cer. Soc.* **63** (1980) 552.
9. J. Koenings, D. Kuppers, H. Lydtin and H. Wilson, *Proc. 5th International Conference. CVD.* **270** (1975).
10. P. Geittner, H.J. Hagemann, J. Warnier and H. Wilson, *J. Lightwave Tech.* LT-4 (1986) 818.
11. H. Lydtin, *J. Lightwave, Tech.* LT-4. (1986) 1034.
12. D. B. Keck, P.C. Shultz and F. Zimar, US patent 3,737,292 (1973).
13. D.B. Keck, R.D. Maurer and P.C. Shultz, *Appl. Phys. Lett.* **22** (1973) 307.
14. P.C. Shultz, *Appl. Opt.* **18** (1979) 3684.
15. T. Izawa, T. Miyashita and F. Hanawa, US Patent 4,062,655 (1977).
16. T. Izawa and N. Inagaki, *Proc. IEEE.* **68** (1980) 1184.
17. F. Hanawa, S. Sudo, M. Kawachi and M. Nakahara, *Electron Lett.* **16** (1980) 299.
18. L.L. Blyler and F.V. DiMarcello, *Proc. IEEE.* **68** (1980).
19. F.V. DiMarcello, C.R. Kurkjian and J.C. Williams, Chapter 4. In *Optical Drawing and Strength Properties: Optical Fiber Communications*, T. Li (Ed) New York: Academic Press. (1985).
20. P.C. Becker, N.A. Olsson and J.R. Simpson, *Erbium doped fiber amplifiers.* Academic Press. 1997.
21. J. Simpson. In *Fiber Laser Sources and Amplifiers*, M. J. F. Digonnet (Ed) *Proc. SPIE.* **1171** 2 (1989).
22. D.J. DiGiovanni. In *Fiber Laser Sources and Amplifiers* M. J. F. Digonnet (Ed) Proc. SPIE. **1373** 2 (1990).
23. B.J. Ainslie, *J. Lightwave Tech.* **9** (1991) 220.
24. P.W. France, S.F. Carter, M.W. Moore and C.R. Day, *Br Telecom Tech. J.* **5** (1987) 28.

25. S. Takanashi and H. Iwasaki, Chapter 5. In *Flouride Glass Fiber Optics*, I.D. Agrawal and G. Lu (Eds), New York: Academic Press. 1991.

26. Y. Ohishi, S. Mitachi ans S. Takahashi, *J. Lightwave Tech.* LT-**2** (1984) 593.

27. D.C. Tran, C.F. Fisher and G.H. Sigel, *Electron Lett.* **18** (1982) 657.

28. H. Tokiwa, Y. Mimura, T. Nakai and O. Shinburi, *Electron Lett.* **22** (1986)1034.

29. J.C. Knight, T.A. Birks, P.St.J. Russell and D.M. Atkin, *Opt. Lett.* **21** (1996) 1547.

30. J.C. Knight, J. Broeng, T.A. Birks and P.S. Russell, *Science.* **282** (1998) 1476.

31. P.St. Russel, *Science* **299** (2003) 358.

32. R.F. Cregan, B.J. Mangan, J.C. Knight, T.A. Birks, P.S. Russell, P.J. Roberts and D.C. Allan, *Science* **285** (1999) 1537.

33. R. Buczynski, *Acta Physica Polonica.* **106** (2004) 141.

34. T. Monro, Y. West, D. Hevak, N. Broderick and D. Richardson, *Electron. Lett.* **36** 1998 (2000).

35. V. Ravi Kanth Kumar, A. George, J. Knighr and P. Russell, *Opt. Expr.* **11** (2003) 2641.

36. F. Fogli, G. Bellanca, P. Bassi, I. Madden and W. Johnstone, *IEEE J. Lightwave Tech.* **17** (1999) 136.

37. Z. Zhu and T.G. Brown, *Opt. Expr.* **10** (2002) 853.

Chapter 5

Amplifier Design — Model and Results

5.1. Introduction

Erbium-doped optical fiber amplifier is an important device for both terrestrial and submarine optical communication systems and next generation all-optical networks. As the name implies, it is a device that amplifies an input optical signal. The amplification factor or gain can be higher than 1000 ($>30\,$dB) in some devices. For a fiber amplifier, the light propagates through a glass (SiO_2 based) fiber which is doped with Er to a level $\sim 10\,$ppm. The dopant atoms (Er) are excited to a higher energy state by the absorption of a pump light (typically from a diode laser) and when they make a transition to a lower energy state, photons (light) near 1550 nm is emitted. The stimulated emissions of photons are responsible for the amplification of an input signal near 1550 nm.

Since the late 1980's there has been an interest in using Er-doped fiber amplifier as in line amplifiers in telecommunication systems.[1-9] Their high gain, multiwavelength operation capability, high saturation power, ability to amplify high speed data, and ease of operation makes them an attractive alternative to regenerators. As mentioned in previous chapters, the core region of the amplifier fiber (typically 5 to 10 μm in diameter) is doped with $\sim 10\,$ppm of Er. This region is surrounded by a cladding region about 100 μm in diameter. The two regions form a waveguide through which the light travels and undergoes amplification. Optical fiber amplifiers (OFAs) are typically ~ 10 to 30 m in length. The operating principals, design, and model of Er-doped optical amplifiers are described in this chapter.

The amplification in Er-doped amplifier arises due to the stimulated emission from excited Er ions. The excitation is caused by the absorption of pump laser light. These amplifiers have been studied using different pump wavelengths in order to find the most suitable pump laser wavelength. Although pump lasers operating at 980 nm or 1480 nm, fabricated using semiconductors have been the pump laser of choice for Er- doped amplifiers for many years, initial studies were carried out using pump laser at other wavelengths (such as 800 nm).

5.2. Er-Doped Fiber Characterization

The fabrication of Er-doped fiber (EDF) is described in Chapter 4. It is important to characterize its absorption and emission characteristics at least at the initial stages of amplifier fiber development.

The EDF absorption spectrum is obtained by cutback measurement (i.e., absorption measurements on progressively shorter length of fiber) using a white light source. The fluorescence spectrum is obtained by pumping a short length (<1 m) of EDF with light from an Ar ion laser (514 nm). Figure 5.1 shows the cross section of the absorption and emission spectrum obtained using

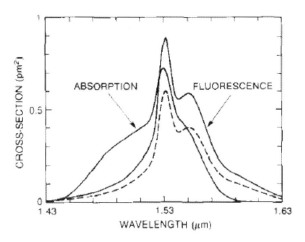

Fig. 5.1 Absorption and emission cross sections obtained from the measured absorption and fluorescence spectrum. The dashed line is a scaling of the emission cross section using the measured ratio of gain to loss at 1.532 μm.[8, 9]

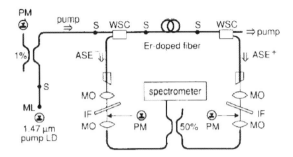

Fig. 5.2 Experimental set up for Er-doped fiber (EDF) measurement. PM: Power meter, WSC: Wavelength selective filter, MO: Microscope Objective, S: Splice, IF: Filter.[9]

Fuchtbauer–Landenberg relationship and an upper state lifetime of 10 ms. The absorption/gain measurement at a signal wavelength near 1.55 μm as a function of input power is an important characterization measurement for EDF. A typical experimental set up is shown in Fig. 5.2. The output of a 1.47 μm diode pump laser is fiber coupled and launched into the EDF.

The EDF used is a germeno–silicate fiber with 0.1% mole fraction of Al_2O_3, and has Er concentration in the core of 0.5×10^{19} cm^{-3}. The EDF has a waveguide power mode diameter (1/e) of 3.9 μm at $\lambda = 1.50$ μm. The EDF absorption coefficients are 1.04 dB/m at 1.47 μm, 4.8 dB/m at 1.532 μm, and 2.5 dB/m at 1.55 μm respectively. The set up shown in Fig. 5.2. is also used to measure the EDF transmission as a function of pump power. The result is shown in Fig. 5.3. At pump power of 15 dBm the EDF is nearly transparent at signal wavelength of 1.532 μm. At higher pump power it has gain.

A simple model for Er-doped amplifier has been developed.[10,11] The model has been used to predict the CW gain saturation performance of amplifiers. The small signal gain as a function of output power for Er-doped amplifiers of 5 and 7 m in length (for different pump power inputs) are shown in Fig. 5.4. The data points are measured values and the solid line is the calculated result.

An important issue in spectral gain profile of amplifier is if the gain spectrum is homogeneously or inhomogeneously broadened.[12–17] This has been investigated in Ref. 16, using a combination of experimental results and modeling. For an inhomogeneously broadened

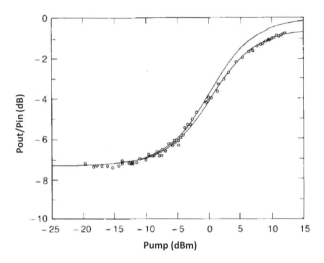

Fig. 5.3 The ratio of 1532 nm signal transmitted power to input power as a function of pump power with a pump wavelength of 1.47 μm. Solid curve is from a model.[9]

gain medium, the total emission or absorption cross section $(\sigma^T(\nu))$ can be written as an integral of the homogeneously broadened $(\sigma^H(\nu))$ lineshape:

$$\sigma^T_{e,a}(\nu) = \int d\nu' f(\nu - \nu') \sigma^H_{e,a}(\nu'), \qquad (5.1)$$

where $f(\nu - \nu')$ is distribution function for inhomogeneous broadening.

This broadening is represented by a Gaussian, whose $1/e$ width is $\Delta\nu$. The quantity $\Delta\nu = c\Delta\lambda/\lambda^2$ where $\Delta\lambda$ is the inhomogeneous linewidth. The derived emission and absorption cross sections using Fuchtbauer–Landenberg relationship and the measured absorption and fluorescence spectrum is shown in Fig. 5.5(a). The deconvoluted homogeneously broadened spectra derived using Eq. (5.1) and the total spectrum for Fig. 5.5(a) using a $\Delta\lambda = 11$ nm for the inhomogeneously broadened linewidth is shown in Fig. 5.5(b) A model and measurement of the saturated amplified spontaneous emission spectrum is used to investigate the inhomogeneous nature of the linewidth. The experimental set up for measuring ASE under saturation is shown in Fig. 5.6. The relative high power ($\sim$6 mW) tunable

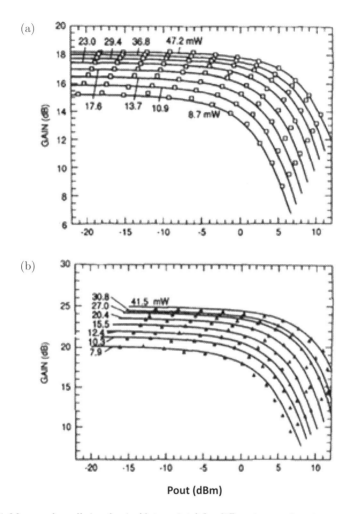

Fig. 5.4 Measured small signal gain (data points) for different pump input powers plotted as a function of signal output power for Er-doped fiber amplifier. The solid lines are the calculated result. (a) Amplifier length = 5 m, (b) Amplifier length = 7 m.[11]

signal with a spectral width of $\sim$0.1 nm is generated by pumping a Er-doped fiber laser with a 514 nm Ar laser. This laser light is combined with a light from a 1.48 μm laser and injected into an EDF. The ASE generated is measured using a spectrometer.

The measured ASE and the modeled ASE spectrum in the presence of a 1.53 μm saturating signal is shown in Fig. 5.7. The modeling

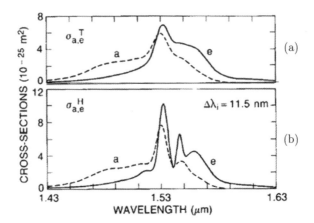

Fig. 5.5 (a) Total emission and absorption cross section of EDF. (b) Deconvoluted homogeneously broadened spectrum using $\Delta\lambda = 11.5$ nm.[16]

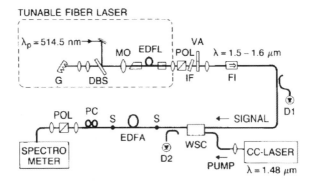

Fig. 5.6 Experimental set up for measuring ASE spectrum under saturated conditions.[16]

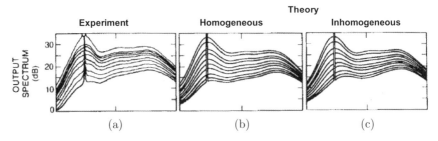

Fig. 5.7 Amplified spontaneous emission (ASE) spectrum. The various curves are for signal input (at $1.53\,\mu$m) powers of 1, 5, 10, 25, 50, 100, 250, 500 and $1000\,\mu$W respectively.[16] The theoretical results for both homogeneous ($\Delta\lambda = 0$ nm) and inhomogeneous ($\Delta\lambda = 11.5$ nm) assumptions are shown.

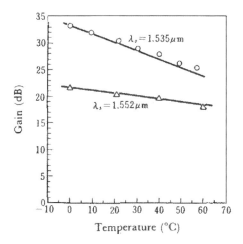

Fig. 5.8 Gain as a function of temperature for an Er-doped fiber amplifier.[18]

is carried both for a homogeneously broadened spectrum ($\Delta = 0$) and for a inhomogeneously broadened spectrum with $\Delta\lambda = 11$ nm. The emission and absorption cross section used in the model is shown in Fig. 5.5. A comparison of the three sets of curves show that the homogeneous broadening is a good approximation for describing amplifier saturation in the signal power range considered in this experiment, i.e., <5 dBm. For higher signal powers, inhomogeneous broadening is a better approximation.

Temperature dependence of gain of a Er-doped amplifier has been reported. The gain decreases with increasing temperature. The data shown in Fig. 5.8 is for two signal wavelengths. The gain decreases faster for the longer wavelength.

5.3. Single Mode Amplifier Model

Extensive model and results on Er-doped fiber amplifier is described in the book by Desuvire.[17] A simple model of Er-doped amplifier was developed in Refs. 19, 20. The work described here follows the three-level laser model described earlier (Chapter 2). Instead of a single level as shown in Fig. 2.2, the energy levels in Er-doped fiber (or any rare earth-doped glass) are broadened to multiple levels due to stark

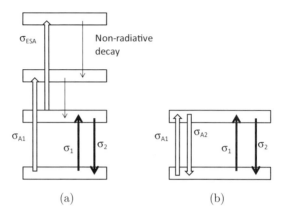

(a)   (b)

Fig. 5.9 Energy levels of Er showing relevant arrows for pump (open) and for signal (bold) transitions for (a) 980 nm and 800 nm pump and (b) 1480 nm pump.[19]

splitting (Fig. 3.3). These levels are shown as a group of broad levels in Fig. 5.9.

The figure shows the presence of an excited state absorption for 800 nm and 980 nm pumping which was not taken into account in previous three-level laser model. Using the following change of notations, $P = \sigma I_p/h\nu$ where I_p is the pump intensity and $h\nu$ is the pump photon energy, $A_{21} = \tau^{-1}$ where, τ is the lifetime of the upper laser level, σ is the absorption cross section, the previous Eq. (2.8) can be modified to yield:

$$\frac{N_2}{N} = \frac{I_P(\sigma_{A1}\tau/h\nu)}{I_P(\sigma_{A1}\tau/h\nu + \sigma_{A2}\tau/h\nu) + 1}, \tag{5.1}$$

where N_1, N_2 are population densities of the lower and upper laser level, $N = N_1 + N_2$ is the total population density. σ_{A1}, σ_{A2} are absorption and emission cross sections from the relevant levels in the band for the pump. The quantities σ_1, σ_2 are similar transition cross sections for signal.

For the analysis in this section, any transverse mode profile issues have been neglected, i.e., the complication due to radial field distribution have been ignored and overlap of pump, signal and dopant profiles are assumed to be 100%. The mode profiles are taken into account in later sections. Hence the conclusions reached here will indicate a trend. Under these assumptions, the pump propagation equation is given by:

$$\frac{dI_P}{dz} = -(N_1\sigma_{A1} + N_2\sigma_{ESA} - N_2\sigma_{A2})I_p, \qquad (5.2)$$

The resulting small signal gain $G(\lambda)$ is as follows:

$$\ln[G(\lambda)] = \sigma_2(\lambda)\int_0^L N_2(z)dz - \sigma_1(\lambda)\int_0^L N_1(z)dz, \qquad (5.3)$$

The absorption cross sections used in the model are obtained from measurements on doped fibers using a white light source. The emission cross sections are calculated using Fuchtbauer–Landenberg relationship using measured fluorescence spectrum and fluorescence lifetimes. The relationship is as follows:

$$\sigma_{a,e}(\lambda) = \frac{\lambda_{a,e,\text{peak}}^4 I_{a,e}(\lambda)}{8\pi c n^2 \tau \int I_{a,e}(\lambda)d\lambda}. \qquad (5.4)$$

where $\lambda_{a,e,\text{peak}}$ is the wavelength at the absorption (emission) peak, τ is the lifetime of the metastable level (upper energy level), n is the refractive index, and c is the velocity of light.

Both fluorescence lifetimes and spectra varies slightly with the exact host, i.e., fraction of Ge, Al or P in the primarily silica host. These materials are needed to create suitable index profiles for waveguiding. Equations (5.2) and (5.3) are solved numerically to obtain the gain spectrum. Equation (5.3) shows that the gain depends on the fraction of Er population in the upper laser level. Figure 5.10 shows the spectral shape of gain for different inversion. The shape of the gain spectrum can be altered by varying fiber length, pump power and pump wavelength. Figure 5.11 shows the calculated gain spectrum for various pump levels for optimized fiber lengths when pumped at 977 nm.

Conceptually, stimulated emission in a fiber amplifier arises from atomic transition in the doped core region, and the light generated is confined and guided by a circular waveguide consisting of the core and cladding regions (Fig. 2.3). A fraction of the optical mode is confined in the core which is doped. The single mode amplifier model described here has been generalized including, the distribution of

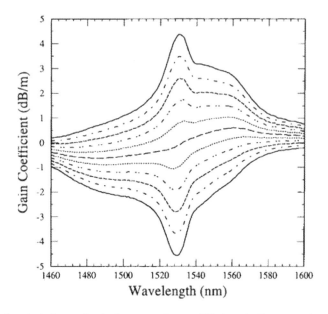

Fig. 5.10 Spectral shape of gain for percentages of Er ions in the upper laser group of levels. The inversion increases from 0% for the lowest line to 100% for the topmost line in 10% increments. The EDF is Al and Ge co-doped.[21] Ref. 19, has a similar figure.

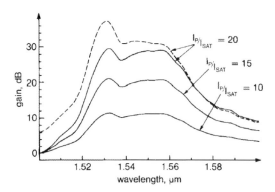

Fig. 5.11 Calculated gain spectrum when pumped at 977 nm for optimized fiber lengths for different pump powers. The dashed line is for a fiber optimized in length for maximum gain at 1532 nm.[19]

dopant atoms, the radial and angular distribution of the populations of the atomic levels, and the radial distribution and angular distribution of the pump intensity and stimulated emission intensity. Thus unlike the previous case where a plane wave assumed, the loss or gain

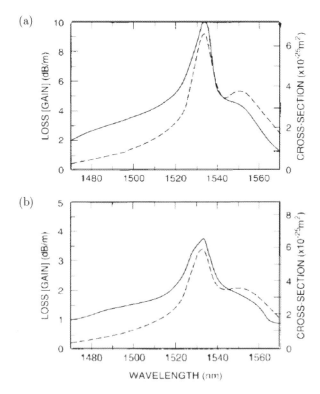

Fig. 5.12 The absorption (solid line) and gain spectra (dashed line) of (a) Ge:silicate and (b) Al:Ge:silicate fiber amplifiers. The cross sections are calculated using Fuchbauer–Landenberg relationship.[22]

at a given wavelength λ are given by:

$$\alpha(\lambda) = \sigma_a(\lambda)\Gamma(\lambda)n_1, \tag{5.5}$$

$$g(\lambda) = \sigma_e(\lambda)\Gamma(\lambda)n_2, \tag{5.6}$$

where $\Gamma(\lambda)$ is the overlap integral between the optical mode and the Er ions and n_1, n_2 are the density of the Er ions in the lower and upper state respectively. $\sigma_a(\lambda)$ and $\sigma_e(\lambda)$ are the absorption and emission cross sections respectively. Figure 5.12 shows the absorption (solid line) and gain spectra (dashed line) of (a) Ge: silicate and (b) Al:Ge:silicate fiber amplifiers. The cross sections are calculated using Fuchtbauer-Landenberg relationship [Eq. (5.4)].

Now a set of equations are written down and solved numerically using the procedure of Refs. 17, 22. The light generated and propagating in the amplifier can be thought of as a number of optical signals of frequency bandwidth $\Delta\nu_k$ centered at ν_k, the optical wavelength being $\lambda_k = c/\nu_k$. This scheme describes both narrow line beams such as pump and signal sources when $\Delta\nu_k \sim 0$, and broadband ASE where $\Delta\nu_k$ equals the frequency steps used in the simulation to resolve the ASE spectrum. Then integration over optical frequency is approximated by a summation over k. Integrating the light intensity distribution of the kth beam $I_k, (r, \phi, z)$ over the radial and angular coordinates gives the beam's total power $P_k(z)$ at position z in the fiber amplifier[22]:

$$P_k(z) = \int_0^{2\pi} \int_0^\infty I_k(r, \phi, z) r\, dr\, d\phi, \qquad (5.7)$$

The normalized optical intensity is defined as:

$$i_k(r, \phi) = I_k(r, \phi, z)/P_k(z), \qquad (5.8)$$

The rate equations for population of upper (n_2) and lower (n_1) laser levels and the equation for signal propagation (P_k) are[22]:

$$\frac{dn_2}{dt} = \sum_k \frac{P_k i_k \sigma_{ak}}{h\upsilon_k} n_1(r, \phi, z) - \sum_k \frac{P_k i_k \sigma_{ek}}{h\upsilon_k} n_2(r, \phi, z) - \frac{n_2(r, \phi, z)}{\tau},$$
$$(5.9)$$

$$n_t(r, \phi, z) = n_1(r, \phi, z) + n_2(r, \phi, z), \qquad (5.10)$$

where $n_t(r, \phi, z)$ is the local total Er density:

$$\frac{dP_k}{dz} = u_k \sigma_{ek} \int_0^{2\pi} \int_0^\infty i_k(r, \phi) n_2(r, \phi, z) r\, dr\, d\phi \times (P_k(z) + mh\upsilon_k\Delta\upsilon_k)$$

$$- u_k \sigma_{ak} \int_0^{2\pi} \int_0^\infty i_k(r, \phi) n_1(r, \phi, z) r\, dr\, d\phi (P_k(z)), \qquad (5.11)$$

If the beam is traveling in the forward direction $(u_k = 1)$ or in the reverse direction $(u_k = -1)$. The quantity $mh\upsilon_k\Delta\upsilon_k$ is the contribution of spontaneous emission from the local n_2 population which grows in the amplifier. These equations have been numerically solved.[22] The amplifier gain, gain coefficient, and amplified spontaneous emission (ASE) power as function of pump power for a Al:silicate Er-doped amplifier has been calculated. The results are

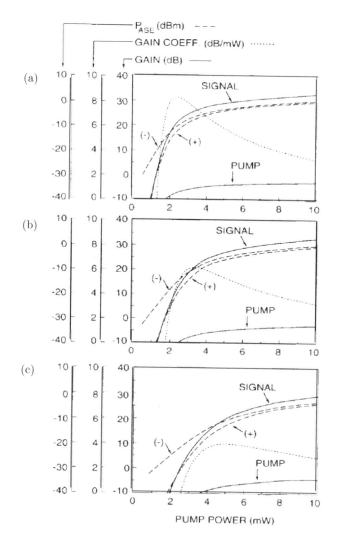

Fig. 5.13 Amplifier gain, gain coefficient and ASE power as a pump power for a fiber with uniformly doped-Er core.[22] The results for three core diameters are shown (a) 0.6 μm, (b) 1.2 μm, (c) 1.8 μm. The parameters used are in Table 5.1.

shown in Fig. 5.13. The parameters of the fiber are noted in Table 5.1. The fiber has a uniformly doped (with Er) core.

The optimum fiber length for maximum gain can be calculated using this model when the fiber is pumped at one end. For too long a fiber length, the pump depletion will cause the far end to have losses

Table 5.1 Fiber parameters used in the model of Fig. 5.13.

Index core radius	$a = 1.2\,\mu\text{m}$		Amplifier length L = 18.8 m
Index step	$\Delta n = 0.035$		Metastable lifeime $\tau = 10\,\text{ms}$
Er core radius	$b = 1.2\,\mu\text{m}$		ASE bandwidth 10 nm

	Pump	Signal
Wavelength	1480 nm	1550 nm
Absorption coefficient	1.6 dB/m	2.6 dB/m
Gain coefficent	0.5 dB/m	3.6 dB/m
Excss loss	0.03 dB/m	0.03 dB/m
Absorption, σ		$3 \times 10{-}25\,\text{m}^2$
Input power	0–10 mW	100 nW

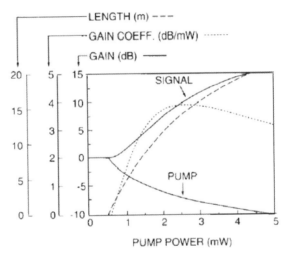

Fig. 5.14 Amplifier gain, gain coefficient and length (with the length optimized to produce maximum gain) for a given pump power.[22]

and for too short a fiber length the pump power is not completely utilized. Hence an optimum fiber length produces maximum gain for a given pump power. Figure 5.14 shows the calculated result.

The amplifier model can be used to calculate gain saturation for two input signals. Consider the spectral modeling of the saturation of an amplifier by two wavelength-multiplexed signals at 1545 and 1555 nm.[22] The amplifier parameters and operating conditions are listed in Table 5.2. The ASE spectrum is resolved to 1 nm. Calculated

Table 5.2 Fiber parameters for the model of Fig. 5.15.

Amplifier length	10 m
Saturation parameter	$4.2 \times 10E15 \, \text{m}^{-1} \text{s}^{-1}$
Pump wavelength	1480 nm
Pump power	50 mW
Signal #1 wavelength	1545 nm
Signal #2 wavelength	1555 nm

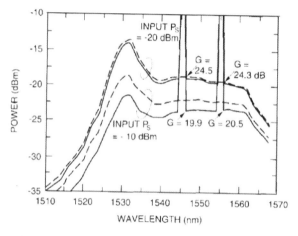

Fig. 5.15 Amplifier spectrum when two input signals at 1545 and 1555 nm are present at the input. The amplifier parameters are listed in Table 5.2. The solid and dashed lines are forward and backward propagating ASE power.[22]

results are shown in Fig. 5.15 for equal input signal powers of either -20 or -10 dBm. At $P = -20$ dBm, the amplifier gains were 24.5 and 24.3 dB at 1545 and 1555 nm, respectively.

5.4. Photonic Crystal Fiber Amplifier

The technology of Photonic Crystal Fibers (PCF) has been studied over the last several years.[23-30] This technology is of interest for potentially high nonlinearity and high saturation powers for PCF based amplifiers. Also, the PCF technology can improve the performance of standard rare-earth-doped fiber amplifiers and lasers due to the possibility of better control of the overlap between pump and

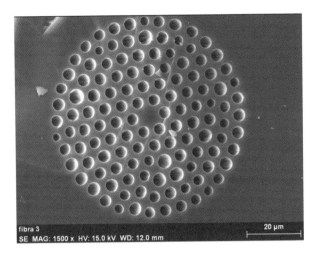

Fig. 5.16 Scanning electron photomicrograph of an Er-doped photonic crystal fiber.

signal modes. For instance, this allows the design of Er-doped PCF amplifiers and lasers with very low pump threshold and high slope-efficiency.[23,24]

The PCF amplifier is fabricated using Er-doped silica glass. Many capillaries are fused and drawn to make the Er-doped PCF as described in Chapter 4. Figure 5.16 show scanning electron microscope (SEM) images of a PCF with an outer diameter of $105\,\mu$m, a pitch of $4.8\,\mu$m, an average hole diameter of $d = 3.15\,\mu$m, and a core diameter of $6.1\,\mu$m. The gain is measured using 980 nm pump lasers. The fiber is pumped simultaneously in both the co-propagating and counter-propagating configuration. The mode field diameters of the pump and signal are $6.3\,\mu$m and $6.4\,\mu$m respectively. The gain as a function of length for 31 mW of input power is shown in Fig. 5.17. The gain is 15 dB for a 4 m long fiber. High gain (>35 dB) is achieved at fiber lengths in the range of 9 to 17 m. The gain decreases for longer fiber lengths due to lack of pump power for inversion.

PCFs can have high losses due to residual water concentration. The measured passive loss coefficient is $<0.1\,\text{m}^{-1}$. The gain spectrum using different signal wavelengths has been measured. The data is shown in Fig. 5.18. The pump power is 31 mW and fiber length is $\sim$10 m. The Er-doped PCF has been used to form a ring laser

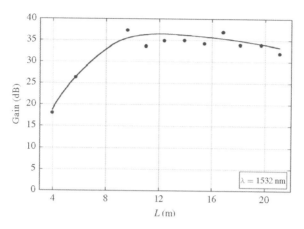

Fig. 5.17 The measured gain 1532 nm for an Er-doped PCF as a function of fiber length. The input power is 31 mW.

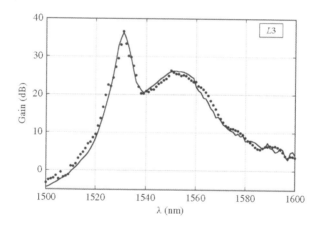

Fig. 5.18 The measured gain spectrum for ~10 m long fiber with 31 mW of pump power.

(Fig. 5.19). A filter is used in the ring cavity to choose the laser wavelength. The threshold pump power for 1550 nm emission is ~3 mW and that for 1532 nm emission is ~1.8 mW. This is due to higher gain at 1532 nm. The fiber length is ~10 m. These results show that lasers based on Er-doped PCF can have very low threshold current.

Other rare earth dopants, for example Yb, have been used to make PCF lasers.[25] Also, photonic crystal fiber lasers have been used for

Fiber Amplifiers and Fiber Lasers

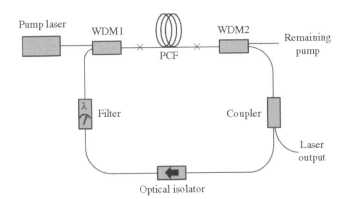

Fig. 5.19 Schematic of a ring fiber laser cavity. The wavelength division multiplexers (WDM1 and WDM2) are used for injecting the pump. A coupler is used to couple the light out and a filter is used for choosing the operating wavelength.

short pulse generation using active or passive mode locking schemes. These are discussed in Chapter 14.

References

1. R.J. Mears, L. Reekie, I.M. Jauncey and D.N. Payne. *Electron. Lett.*, **23** (1987) 1096.
2. E. Desurvire, J.R. Simpson and P.C. Becker, *Opt. Lett.* **12** (1987) 888.
3. A.A.M. Saleh, R.M. Jopson, J.D. Evankow and J. Aspell, *IEEE Photon. Technol. Lett.* **2** (1990) 714.
4. M. Peroni and M. Tamburini, *Opt. Lett.* **15**, (1990) 842.
5. E. Desurvire and J.R. Simpson, *J. Lightwave Technol.* **7** (1989) 835.
6. E. Desurvire, *ZEEE Photon. Technol. Lett.* **1** (1989) 293.
7. J.G. Edwards, *Brit. J. Appl. Phys. (J. Phys. D).* **1** (1968) 449.
8. W.L. Barnes, R.I. Laming, P.R. Morkel and E.J. Tarbox. In *Proc. Conf. Lasers Electro-Opt., CLEO 1990, Optical Society of America.* Paper JTUA3. 1989.
9. E. Desurvire, M. Zirngibl, H.M. Presby and D. DiGiovanni, *IEEE Photonic Tech. Lett.* **3** (1991) 127.
10. A.A.M. Saleh, R.M. Jopson, J.D. Evankow and J. Aspell, *IEEE Photonic Tech. Lett.* **2**, (1990) 714.
11. I.M.I. Habib, A.A.M. Saleh and P.K. Runge, *J. Lightwave Tech.* **13** (1995) 33.
12. E. Desuvire, J.L. Zyskind and J.R. Simpson, *IEEE Photonic Tech. Lett.* **2** (1990) 246.
13. K. Inoue, H. Toba, N. Shibata, K. Iwatsuki and A. Takada, *Electron Lett.* **25** (1989) 594.
14. J.R. Armitage, *Appl. Opt.* **27** (1988) 4831.

15. P.R. Morkel and R.I. Laming, *Opt. Lett.* **14** (1989) 1062.
16. E. Desuvire, J.W. Sulhoff, J.L. Zyskind and J.R. Simpson, *IEEE Photonic Tech. Lett.* **2** (1990) 653.
17. See for example, E. Desurvire, *Erbium doped fiber amplifiers.* John Wiley and Sons. 1994.
18. S. Shimoda and H. Ishio (Ed), Optical amplifiers and their applications. John Wiley and Sons. 1994.
19. J.R. Armitage, *IEEE JQE.* **26** (1990) 423.
20. J.R. Armitage, *Appl. Optics.* **27** (1988) 4831.
21. A. Srivastava and Y. Sun, Chapter 12. In Guided Wave Optical Components and Devices, B.P. Pal (Eds). Elsevier Academic Press, 2006.
22. C.R. Giles and E. Desuvire, *J. Lightwave Tech.* **9** (1991) 271.
23. K.G. Hougaard, J. Broeng, and A. Bjarklev, *Electron. Lett.* **39** (2003) 590.
24. K. Furusawa, T. Kogure, J. K. Sahu, J.H. Lee, T.M. Monro and D.J. Richardson, *IEEE Technol. Lett.* **17** (2005) 25.
25. W.J. Wadsworth, J.C. Knight, W.H. Reeves, P.S.J. Russell and J. Arriaga, *Electron. Lett.* **36** (2000) 1452.
26. B.T. Kuhlmey, R.C. McPhedran and C.M. de Sterke, *Opt. Lett.* **27** (2002) 1684.
27. J.A. Sanchez-Martin, M.A. Rebolledo, J.M. Alvarez, J.A. Valles, A. Diez and M.V. Andres, *IEEE J. Quantum Electron.* **46** (2010) 1145.
28. J.H. Chong and M.K. Rao, *Opt. Express.* **11** (2003) 1365.
29. L.M. Xiao, W. Jin, and M.S. Demokan, *Opt. Lett.* **32** (2007) 115.
30. J.A. Sánchez-Martín, J.M. Álvarez Abenia, M.Á. Rebolledo, M.V. Andrés and A. Díez, *IEEE J. Quantum Electrom.* **48** (2012) 338.

Chapter 6

Amplifier Dynamic Characteristics

6.1. Introduction

Er-doped optical fiber amplifier (EDFA) is an important device for both terrestrial and submarine optical communication systems and next generation all-optical networks because it amplifies signals in the 1550 nm range which is also the region of low loss in silica optical fibers. The amplification factor or gain can be higher than 1000 (>30 dB) in some devices. In recent years, the emphasis has been on lightwave networks including multiwavelength networking using add/drop multiplexing of channels and optical cross-connects in addition to point to point communications. Erbium-doped amplifiers are key elements in these wavelength division multiplexed (WDM) systems. Several laboratory experiments have demonstrated >10 Tb/s transmission capacity[1] and commercial systems with Tb/s capacity are available. The multiwavelength networks require EDFAs with high output power and low noise and flat gain spectrum over a large spectral width.[2,3]

6.2. Gain Dynamics

The gain dynamics of the Er-doped amplifier (EDFA) has been studied by several authors.[4–8] The temporal change in gain to an input optical pulse determines the performance of the EDFA in amplifying high data rate signals and also crosstalk among different input signal wavelengths in WDM system application. As discussed in previous chapters, the EDFA can be represented by a three-level laser system. The decay time constant from the upper laser level to the lower laser

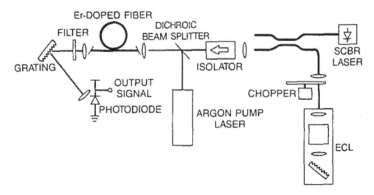

Fig. 6.1 Experimental setup.[8] ECL is external cavity laser. SCBR laser is a silicon chip Bragg reflector (SCBR) laser which emits in a single wavelength.

level is ∼10 ms. But in the presence of a saturating signal and high pump power, the response time for transient gain is expected to be lower. The transient gain response has been experimentally measured using the setup shown in Fig. 6.1.

The setup uses an Ar ion laser ($\lambda \sim 514$ nm) as a pump laser and an external cavity laser (ECL) and another wavelength stabilized diode laser serve as probe and saturating lasers. Various fiber coupled optical elements are used for optical pump and signal input to EDFA and for separately measuring the saturating signal and probe signal response. The fiber core radius is 2.2 μm, with a N.A. = 0.18, the fiber length is 1m, and, the Er^{3+} concentration is 6.9×10^{19} cm^{-3}. An unsaturated optical gain of 30 dB is obtained in the fiber amplifier with a pump power of 210 mW launched into the fiber.[8]

The response of a pulsed signal is measured by injecting an optical signal tuned to fiber amplifier's gain peak ($\lambda = 1531$ nm). The measured signal power as a function of time is shown in the inset of Fig. 6.2. The figure shows the output at $\lambda = 1531$ nm and hence the gain saturates after a certain duration. The unsaturated gain of this amplifier is 30.1 dB. The saturated gain and time constant for gain saturation is shown in Fig. 6.2 as a function of input signal power. At higher signal power, the saturation time constant is shorter.

An important measurement for system application is saturation induced crosstalk time constant, i.e., how fast does the gain of a

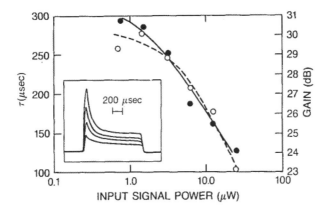

Fig. 6.2 The saturated gain and the gain saturation time plotted as a function of input signal power.[8]

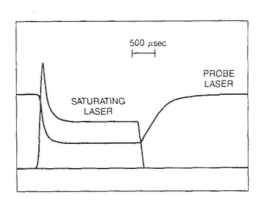

Fig. 6.3 The saturating signal and the weak probe signal is plotted as a function of time.[8]

weak signal recovers when the gain is saturated by a strong signal. Figure 6.3 shows the result of an experiment. The saturating signal (at 1531 nm) has a power of 34 μW and the weak (probe) signal (at 1537 nm) has a power of 3.5 μW. The data (Fig. 6.3) show the measured saturating signal power and weak probe signal power as a function of time at the output of the EDFA.[8] The figure shows that the probe signal gain recovers in a time of ~400 μs. The recovery time constant is inversely proportional to the pump rate (R, defined earlier in Chapters 2 and 5); $R = \Gamma_p \sigma_p P / (\pi a^2 h \nu_p)$ where Γ_p is the

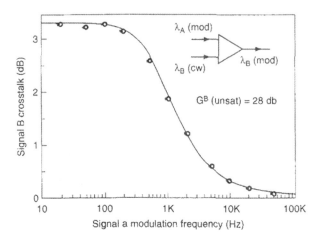

Fig. 6.4 Modulation response of the probe signal. The strong signal is sinusoidally modulated and the sinewave modulation amplitude is measured on the probe signal.[9]

pump mode confinement, σ_p is the pump absorption cross section, P is the pump power, $h\nu_p$ is the pump photon energy, and a is the core radius. The above expression is valid for pump power much larger than $P_t \gg \pi a^2 h\nu_p/(\Gamma_p\sigma_p\tau_{21})$ where τ_{21} is the decay time from upper laser level (2) to lower laser level (1). The frequency response of the cross talk (i.e., gain saturation of a weak probe signal by another strong input signal) is measured by modulating the strong signal (at 1531 nm) and measuring the modulation response on the CW probe signal (at 1537 nm). The data are shown in Fig. 6.4.

The above set of figures illustrates the essence of transient gain dynamics in the presence of gain saturation in an EDFA. In the absence of saturation, the transient response of gain has a time constant of ∼350 μs, and in the presence of saturation the value decreases to ∼100 μs. Transient gain effects in single channel amplification causes signal distortion in single channel amplification and cross talk in multichannel (e.g., in WDM systems) amplification. However, these effects occur at relatively low frequencies, i.e., relative to a few Gb/s data rates of optical signals in transmission systems, the response time constant of gain is slow. The saturation induced crosstalk begins to roll-off at frequencies of ∼250 Hz and beyond ∼5 kHz the crosstalk is simply a reduction in gain. Thus, in comparison to semiconductor optical amplifier (SOAs) which have sub-ns response times, the EDFA exhibits much less signal distortion and crosstalk in fiber transmission systems. The effect of gain saturation is present in the event of a channel drop-off or channel addition for multichannel transmission. This is discussed in the Sec. 6.3.

6.3. Multichannel Amplification

EDFA is used as an amplifier in multichannel WDM systems and also in dynamic optical networks where the number of channels (each channel has signals at different wavelengths) are changed. For multichannel WDM transmission systems operating at data channel rate of 2.5 Gb/s or higher data rate, the EDFA operates in a saturated mode, the crosstalk between the channel is negligible, the problem arises when the number of channels are being changed, or one/many of the channels stops working. For dynamic networks, the channel add/drop process causes a decrease/increase of gain of previous channels or the surviving channel. Addition of a channel can cause errors by reducing the power of all the channels needed for the required bit-error-rate (BER). Dropping of channels can introduce errors in the surviving channel by an increase in power so that threshold for nonlinear effects such as stimulated Brillouin scattering is surpassed. Consider an eight-channel system, addition of a single channel (when seven are already present and operating) generally has a much lower effect than the dropping of all channels (i.e., seven channels dropped and one operating) except one. The response needed for surviving channel protection (e.g., by altering the pump laser current) depends on the transient response of the EDFA.

An experimental setup for measuring the results of channel add/drop on surviving channels is shown in Fig. 6.5. Two lasers are used to simulate a multichannel system. The distributed feedback (DFB) laser is used to mimic the dropped channel. It can be modulated if needed. The ECL has a booster EDFA for higher power output. When both lasers are on, the input power to EDFA is 7 dBm, which corresponds to 8 WDM channels at −2 dBm each. The gain of the EDFA is 9 dB which corresponds to the requirement for a typical 40 km transmission link. The output power of EDFA is 16 dBm.

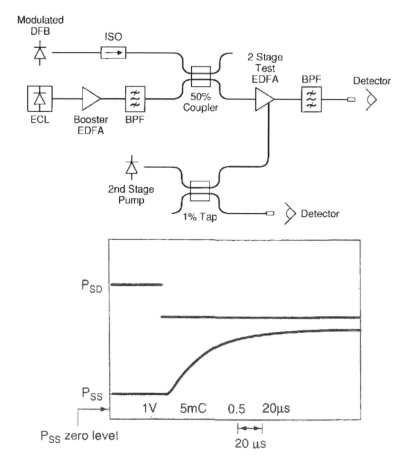

Fig. 6.5 (Top) Experimental setup. (Bottom) Oscilloscope trace showing the power dependence of the surviving channel power when all other seven channels are dropped.[10]

The transient behavior of surviving channel when all the other channels are dropped is shown in Fig. 6.5b. An optical filter is used to remove the amplified spontaneous emission (ASE). Figure 6.5 shows that the surviving channel power increases to 90% of its final value in $\sim 80\,\mu$s. The upper trace shows the drop in power of all the other channels combined. Similar experiments have been carried out for one and four channel drop. The data for the power of surviving channels when one, four and seven channels are dropped are shown in Fig. 6.6. The power transient behavior $(P(t))$ is approximated by

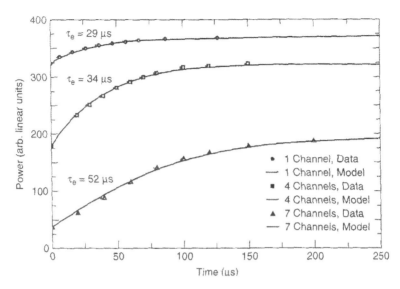

Fig. 6.6 The trace of the total surviving channel powers for one, four and seven channel loss is shown.[10]

the formula.[9, 10]

$$P(t) = P_s[(P(0)/P_s]^{(-t/\tau_e)}, \qquad (6.1)$$

where P_s is the power at infinite time. The quantity τ_e is the decay time of the upper laser level averaged over fiber length, and can be used as a fitting parameter for the data. The above equation can be used to deduce power excursions for channel drop.

The time required for a feedback circuit (such as through pump current control) to limit the power excursion to 1 dB for 4 channel and 7 channel drop are 18 and 8 μs, respectively. Experiments have been carried out using two-stage EDFA using the same setup. The results are shown in Fig. 6.7. The figure shows the effect of channel drop after the two EDFAs on power excursion on the surviving channels.

Power transients in long EDFA links using an eight-channel WDM system has been reported.[9] The system had 12 EDFAs. In the experiment, four of the eight channels are turned off and the power transient after EDFA is measured using taps. All EDFAs in this case are operating in the gain saturated regime. When four of the eight channels are suddenly removed ($t = 0$ in Fig. 6.8), the input power of the first

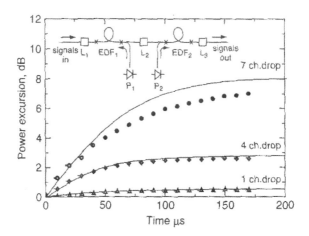

Fig. 6.7 Power excursions of the surviving channels after the two-stage EDFA shown in the insert. The solid lines are from a model calculation.[11]

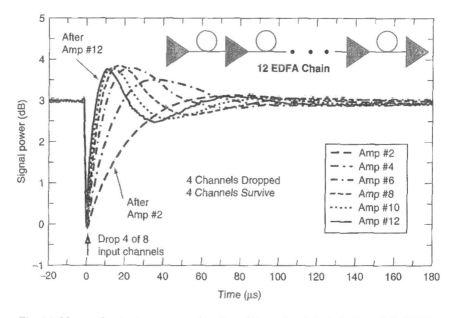

Fig. 6.8 Measured output power as a function of time after 0, 2, 4, 8, 10, and 12 EDFAs in a 12 EDFA amplifier link originally carrying 8 WDM channels.[9]

EDFA decreases by 3dB, the output power of each surviving channel increases toward double the original channel power to conserve the original saturated power.

It is important to limit or control the power excursions due to channel add/drop in an actual transmission system. The gain of the EDFA varies with pump current. Thus, one means of controlling the output power of the EDFAs in a link is by varying the pump current. The pump current needs to be altered in a time scale comparable to that of the power excursions. The scheme involves making measurements of the input and output power of the EDFA using power taps at the input and output and photodiodes. The signals from the photodiodes are fed to a gain control circuit which adjusts the pump current. The pump power is adjusted using a fast algorithm to maintain constant gain. With fast gain control, the overshoot is reduced from 4 dB to less than 0.5 dB.[9] The power excursions are significantly reduced with the gain control circuit on.

It is important that the delay between the pump current control and the add/drop events be sufficiently small. The result of an experiment is shown in Fig. 6.9. In this experiment, the pump delay was varied. The least excursion was observed for the shortest delay ($\sim 7\,\mu$s).

The method described would require control for all EDFAs in a link. Generally add/drop occurs at the beginning of every link which may have a series (4 to 16) of EDFAs. The constant loading of all EDFAs in these cases is maintained by adding a control channel at the beginning of the link and it is stripped off after the first EDFA. This control channel is an idle compensation channel (optical input) operating at low frequencies. The control channel gets amplified by the first EDFA along with the data channels. Using feedback after the first EDFA, the power of the control channel and that the remaining data channels are held constant following add/drop events. This maintains constant power loading of all the downstream EDFAs and hence the link operates properly.

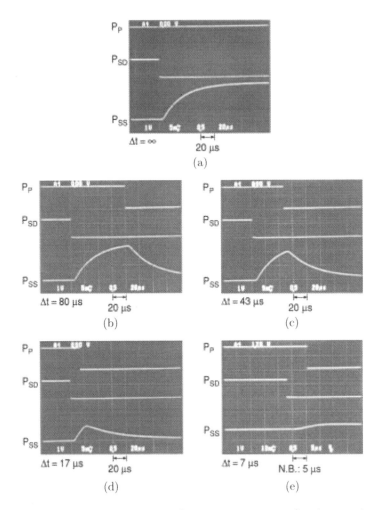

Fig. 6.9 The surviving channel excursion (using oscilloscope traces) is shown as the pump power is reduced after channel drop. The quantity Δt is the delay between channel drop and pump current reduction.[10] P_p — Pump power, P_{so} — Signal power, P_{ss} — Surviving channel power.

6.4. Amplifier Noise

Amplifiers degrade the signal to noise ratio (SNR) of the amplified signal primarily because of ASE which adds noise to the signal.[12] The effect of spontaneous emission is to add fluctuations in the signal which adds noise to the detected photocurrent. The SNR degradation is generally characterized by a quantity called noise figure, NF which is defined as

$$NF = \frac{(\text{SNR})_{\text{in}}}{(\text{SNR})_{\text{out}}}, \tag{6.2}$$

where SNR refers to the signal to noise ratio of the electrical power generated when the signal is converted to current by a photodetector. The SNR of the photodetector is determined by both the thermal noise and the shot noise. For an ideal detector, considered below, shot noise is the only noise. In this case, simple expressions can be obtained.

The following analysis assumes the Er-doped fiber amplifier is a lumped element with gain and it has a certain amount of spontaneous emission which also undergoes amplification. Consider an amplifier with an input optical power P_{in}, amplifier gain G, a detector with a responsivity R, and, with an electrical bandwidth B. The responsivity R is the ratio of the photocurrent (Amp) per unit power (W). For an ideal detector $R = (e/h\nu)$ where e is the charge of the electron and ν is the frequency of the incident optical signal. The photocurrent generated is given by

$$I_i = RP_{\text{in}} \tag{6.3}$$

and the r.m.s (root mean square value of the photocurrent) due to shot noise is

$$\sigma^2 = 2e(RP_{\text{in}})B. \tag{6.4a}$$

Thus, the input SNR is given by

$$(\text{SNR})_{\text{in}} = \frac{\langle I_i \rangle^2}{\sigma^2} = \frac{P_{\text{in}}}{2h\nu B}. \tag{6.4b}$$

In order to determine the output SNR, the spontaneous emission must be added. The spectral density of spontaneous emission induced noise (white noise) is given by

$$S(\nu) = (G - 1)N_{\text{sp}}h\nu, \tag{6.5}$$

where G is the gain of the amplifier and N_{sp} is the spontaneous emission factor or the population inversion factor. For a two-level atom, it is given by

$$N_{sp} = \frac{N_2}{N_2 - N_1}, \tag{6.6}$$

where N_2 and N_1 are the number of atoms in the upper and lower state, respectively. Thus, for high population inversion, $N_2 \gg N_1$, $N_{sp} \sim 1$. However, for low population inversion, N_{sp} could be much larger. Various sources of noise in an optical amplifier are discussed later. For the discussion here, only the dominant contribution is considered i.e., the variance of the photocurrent arises mainly from the beating of the spontaneous emission with the signal. The spontaneous emission mixes coherently with the signal at the photodetector and produces a fluctuating photocurrent within the bandwidth B. The signal and the variance of the photocurrent after amplification is given by

$$I = RGP_{in}, \tag{6.7}$$

$$\sigma^2 = 2qIB + 4IRSB. \tag{6.8}$$

The variance in Eq. (6.8) is the sum of the shot noise and spontaneous–signal beat noise. All other noise contributions (discussed later) have been neglected. Thus, the SNR at the output is given by

$$(\text{SNR})_{out} = \frac{\langle I \rangle^2}{\sigma^2} \approx \frac{GP_{in}}{4SB}, \tag{6.9}$$

where the last relation is obtained by neglecting shot noise and assuming $G \gg 1$, the amplifier excess NF can then be written as

$$NF = 2N_{sp}(G - 1)/G$$
$$\approx 2N_{sp}. \tag{6.10}$$

The equation shows that the SNR of the amplifier is degraded by a factor of 2 (3 dB) for the ideal case of $N_{sp} = 1$. For an Er-doped amplifier pumped by 980 nm laser, this ideal value of 3 dB has been reported. However, for most practical amplifiers the NF is in the 3.5 to 6 dB range. The noise in Er-doped amplifier is discussed following the general analysis in Sec. 6.4.1.

6.4.1. *Noise Analysis for Optical Transmission*

The following analysis follows the procedure of Ref. 13. Assume an optical amplifier with unity coupling efficiency, uniform gain G, over an optical bandwidth B_o, and an input power of P_{in} at optical frequency ω_0 centered in the optical pass band B_o. The spontaneous emission power in the optical bandwidth B_o is given by (using Eq. (6.5)):

$$P_{\text{sp}} = N_{\text{sp}}(G - 1)h\nu B_o. \tag{6.11}$$

Writing the electric field E_{sp}, representing the spontaneous emission as sum of cosine terms:

$$E_{\text{sp}} = \sum_{k=(-B_o/2\delta\nu)}^{B_o/2\delta\nu} \sqrt{2N_{\text{sp}}(G - 1)h\nu\delta\nu}$$
$$\cdot \cos((\omega_0 + 2\pi k\delta\nu)t + \Phi_k), \tag{6.12}$$

where Φ_k is a random phase for each component of spontaneous emission. Using

$$N_{\text{sp}}(G - 1)h\nu = N_0 \quad \text{and} \quad \frac{B_o}{2\delta\nu} = M \tag{6.13}$$

the total electric field at the output of the amplifier is

$$E(t) = \sqrt{2GP_{\text{in}}} \cos(\omega_0 t) + \sum_{k=-M}^{M} \sqrt{2N_0\delta\nu}$$
$$\cdot \cos((\omega_0 + 2\pi k\delta\nu)t + \Phi_k). \tag{6.14}$$

The photocurrent $i(t)$ generated by a unity quantum efficiency photodetector is proportional to the intensity. It is given by

$$i(t) = \overline{E^2(t)} \frac{e}{h\nu}, \tag{6.15}$$

where the bar indicates time averaging over optical frequencies. Hence

$$i(t) = GP_{\text{in}}\frac{e}{h\nu} + \frac{4e}{h\nu}\sum_{k=-M}^{M}\sqrt{GP_{\text{in}}N_0\delta\nu}$$

$$\cdot\cos(\omega_0 t)\cos((\omega_0 + 2\pi k\delta\nu)t + \Phi_k) + \frac{2eN_0\delta\nu}{h\nu}$$

$$\cdot\left[\sum_{k=-M}^{M}\cos((\omega_0 + 2\pi k\delta\nu)t + \Phi_k)\right]^2 \qquad (6.16)$$

The three terms in (6.16) represent, signal, signal–spontaneous beat noise, and spontaneous–spontaneous beat noise, respectively. Note that the noise within the electrical bandwidth is important. The signal–spontaneous beat noise term from Eq. (6.16) is given by

$$i_{s-\text{sp}}(t) = \frac{4e}{h\nu}\sum_{k=-M}^{M}\sqrt{GP_{\text{in}}N_0\delta\nu}\cdot\cos(\omega_0 t)\cos((\omega_0 + 2\pi k\delta\nu)t + \Phi_k)$$

$$= \frac{2e}{h\nu}\sqrt{GP_{\text{in}}N_0\delta\nu}\sum_{k=-M}^{M}\cos(2\pi k\delta\nu t + \Phi_k) \qquad (6.17)$$

where terms $\sim\cos(2\omega_0 t)$, which average to zero, have been neglected. For each frequency, $2\pi k\delta\nu$, in (6.17), the sum has two components but with a random phase. Hence, the power spectrum of $i_{s-\text{sp}}(t)$ is uniform in the frequency interval $0\sim B_o/2$ with a density of

$$N_{s-\text{sp}} = \frac{4e^2}{(h\nu)^2}GP_{\text{in}}N_0\cdot\frac{1}{2}\cdot 2$$

$$= \frac{4e^2}{h\nu}P_{\text{in}}N_{\text{sp}}(G-1)G \qquad (6.18)$$

The spontaneous–spontaneous beat noise term from Eq. (6.16) is

$$i_{s-\text{sp}}(t) = 2N_0\frac{\delta\nu e}{h\nu}\left[\sum_{k=-M}^{M}\cos((\omega_0 + 2\pi k\delta\nu)t + \Phi_k)\right]^2$$

$$= 2N_0\frac{\delta\nu e}{h\nu}\left[\sum_{k=-M}^{M}\cos(\beta_k)\sum_{j=-M}^{M}\cos(\beta_j)\right], \qquad (6.19)$$

where

$$\beta_k = (\omega_0 + 2\pi k \delta \nu)t + \Phi_k \quad \text{and} \quad \beta_j = (\omega_0 + 2\pi j \delta \nu)t + \Phi_j.$$
$$(6.20)$$

Equation (6.19) can be written as

$$i_{\text{sp-sp}}(t) = 2N_0 \frac{\delta \nu e}{h\nu} \sum_{k=-M}^{M} \sum_{j=-M}^{M} \frac{1}{2} \cos(\beta_k - \beta_j) + \frac{1}{2} \cos(\beta_k + \beta_j).$$
$$(6.21)$$

The terms $\sim \cos(\beta_k + \beta)$ have frequencies $\sim 2\omega_0$ and average to zero. Rewriting Eq. (6.21) gives:

$$i_{\text{sp-sp}}(t) = \frac{N_0 \delta \nu e}{h\nu} \sum_{k=-0}^{2M} \sum_{j=0}^{2M} \cos((k-j)2\pi\delta\nu \cdot t + \Phi_k - \Phi_j).$$
$$(6.22)$$

The dc term is obtained for $k = j$ and there are $2M$ such terms:

$$I_{\text{sp}}^{\text{dc}} = \frac{e}{h\nu} N_0 \delta \nu 2M = N_{\text{sp}}(G-1)eB_o. \qquad (6.23)$$

A list of the various terms according to their frequencies is shown below:

frequency	# terms
$-(2M-1)\delta\nu$	1
$\vdots$	$\vdots$
$-l\delta\nu$	$2M - l$
$\vdots$	$\vdots$
$-1\delta\nu$	$2M - 1$
$1\delta\nu$	$2M - 1$
$\vdots$	$\vdots$
$-l\delta\nu$	$2M - l$
$\vdots$	$\vdots$
$(2M-1)\delta\nu$	1

The terms with same absolute frequency but of opposite sign add in phase. Therefore, the power spectrum of the spontaneous–spontaneous beat noise extends from 0 to B_o, with a triangular shape and a power density near dc of

$$N_{\text{sp}-\text{sp}} = \frac{4N_0^2\delta\nu e^2}{h\nu^2}\left(\frac{B_o}{\delta\nu} - 1\right)\cdot\frac{1}{2} = 2N_{\text{sp}}^2(G-1)^2e^2B_o \qquad (6.24)$$

Using Eq. (6.60) the photo current equivalent of the spontaneous emission power is:

$$I_{\text{sp}} = P_{\text{sp}}e/h\nu = N_{\text{sp}}(G-1)eB_o \qquad (6.25)$$

I_{sp} may be called the photocurrent equivalent of the spontaneous emission power. In the following, many of the parameters are defined as photocurrent equivalents. According to square law detection in the receiver, the received signal power is given by:

$$S = (GI_s\eta_{\text{in}}\eta_{\text{out}}L)^2, \qquad (6.26)$$

where G is the optical gain of the amplifier, L is the optical loss between the amplifier and receiver, I_s is the photocurrent equivalent of the amplifier input power defined in the same way as Eq. (6.25). The quantities η_{in} and η_{out} are amplifier input and output coupling efficiencies.

The noise terms are:

$$N_{\text{shot}} = 2B_e e\eta_{\text{out}}L(GI_s\eta_{\text{in}} + I_{\text{sp}}), \qquad (6.27)$$

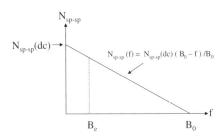

Fig. 6.10 Schematic of the spontaneous–spontaneous beat noise spectrum. F is the frequency. The dc value $N_{\text{sp}-\text{sp}}$ is given by Eq. (6.72). The equation for the line is written above.[13]

$$N_{s-\text{sp}} = 4GI_s\eta_{\text{in}}\eta_{\text{out}}^2 I_{\text{sp}}L^2 B_e/B_o, \tag{6.28}$$

$$N_{\text{sp-sp}} = (I_{\text{sp}}\eta_{\text{out}}L)^2 B_e(2B_o - B_e)/B_o^2, \tag{6.29}$$

$$N_{\text{th}} = I_{\text{th}}^2. \tag{6.30}$$

The total noise is given by

$$N_{\text{tot}} = N_{\text{shot}} + N_{s-\text{sp}} + N_{\text{sp-sp}} + N_{\text{th}}, \tag{6.31}$$

where N_{shot}, $N_{s-\text{sp}}$, $N_{\text{sp-sp}}$ and N_{th} are the shot noise, signal–spontaneous beat noise, spontaneous–spontaneous beat noise and thermal noise, respectively. N_{tot} is the total noise. The quantity I_{th} is the equivalent thermal noise induced photocurrent and B_e is the electrical bandwidth. The quantity $N_{\text{sp-sp}}$ in Eq. (6.31) is obtained by integrating $N_{\text{sp-sp}}(f)$ from 0 to B_e and taking the average (per unit bandwidth) of the result as follows:

$$N_{\text{sp-sp}} = \frac{1}{B_e} \int_0^{B_e} N_{\text{sp-sp}}(f)df. \tag{6.32}$$

For an amplitude modulated signal of average power P_{in}, with a 50% duty cycle and an extinction ratio of r ($= I_s(1)/I_s(0)$), the photo current equivalents of the input powers for a mark ($I_s(1)$) and a space ($I_s(0)$) are:

$$I_s(1) = eP_{\text{in}}2r/(h\nu(r+1)), \tag{6.33}$$

$$I_s(0) = eP_{\text{in}}2/(h\nu(r+1)), \tag{6.34}$$

using $r = I_s(1)/I_s(0)$ and $(I_s(1) + I_s(0))/2 = eP_{\text{in}}/h\nu$ is the average photocurrent.

For a transmission experiment, the measure of performance is determined by the BER, i.e., the number of errors per transmitted bit.[14] For a digital ON/OFF keying transmission system, a random sequence of "1" s and "0" s are transmitted. The receiver (generally a photodiode) receives the transmitted 1's and 0's with some noise. The received currents are labeled as I_1 when a 1 is received and I_0 when a 0 is received. There is some noise (i.e., variation in I_1 and I_0) in the received signal as schematically shown in Fig. 6.11. The determination of "1" or "0" of a bit is a result of a decision process for which a threshold I_d is set. If $I_1 < I_d$, then the bit is recognized as

Fiber Amplifiers and Fiber Lasers

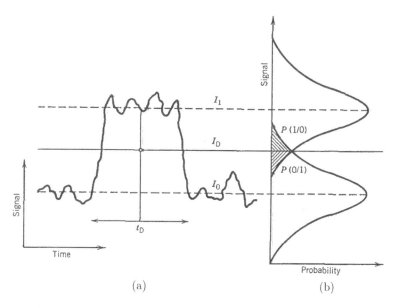

Fig. 6.11 Schematic of one bit with noise (level fluctuations). The Gaussian distributions of the "1" and "0" level are also shown.[14]

1 and if $I_0 > I_d$, the bit is recognized as 0. Clearly I_d is set between I_1 and I_0. In the following, I_d is determined by minimizing BER.

The noise for the "1" and "0" state is assumed to be Gaussian. The noise distribution is plotted in Fig. 6.11. For both the "1" and "0" state, σ_1 and σ_0 are standard deviations of the noise of the "1" and "0" state, respectively. The shot noise form of σ is given by Eq. (6.4a). The error probability is determined by the cross hatched region of Fig. 6.11. Consider $p(1)$ is the probability of "1" and $p(0)$ is the probability of "0" in the bit stream, and $P(0/1)$ is the probability of detecting "0" when the actual value is "1" and $P(1/0)$ is the probability of detecting "1" when the actual value is "0", then BER is given by

$$\text{BER} - p(1)P(0/1) + p(0)P(1/0) \tag{6.35}$$

For a pseudo random data stream $p(1) = p(0) = 0.5$. Thus,

$$\text{BER} = (P(0/1) + P(1/0))/2. \tag{6.36}$$

The quantities $P(0/1)$ and $P(1/0)$ are given by

$$P(0/1) = \frac{1}{\sigma_1\sqrt{2\pi}} \int_{-\infty}^{I_d} \exp\left(-\frac{(I-I_1)^2}{2\sigma_1^2}\right) dI = \frac{1}{2}erfc\left(\frac{I_1 - I_d}{\sigma_1\sqrt{2}}\right),$$

$$P(1/0) = \frac{1}{\sigma_0\sqrt{2\pi}} \int_{I_d}^{\infty} \exp\left(-\frac{(I-I_0)^2}{2\sigma_0^2}\right) dI = \frac{1}{2}erfc\left(\frac{I_d - I_0}{\sigma_0\sqrt{2}}\right),$$

$$(6.37)$$

where erfc is the complementary error function given by

$$erfc(x) = \frac{2}{\sqrt{\pi}} \int_x^{\infty} \exp(-y^2)dy. \qquad (6.38)$$

Hence,

$$\text{BER} = \frac{1}{4}\left[erfc\left(\frac{I_1 - I_d}{\sigma_1\sqrt{2}}\right) + erfc\left(\frac{I_d - I_0}{\sigma_0\sqrt{2}}\right)\right]. \qquad (6.39)$$

The quantity I_d is chosen to minimize BER. The minimum of BER occurs when I_d is chosen such that[14]

$$(I_1 - I_d)/\sigma_1 = (I_d - I_0)/\sigma_0 = Q \qquad (6.40)$$

i.e.,

$$I_d = \frac{\sigma_0 I_1 + \sigma_1 I_0}{\sigma_0 + \sigma_1}$$

When $\sigma_1 = \sigma_0 = \sigma$, $I_d = (I_1 + I_0)/2$, for minimum BER. This is the situation for most p-i-n receivers where the noise is determined by thermal noise i.e. noise in both 1 and 0 state are same. In this case BER is given by

$$\text{BER} = \frac{1}{\sqrt{2\pi}}\frac{\exp\left(-\frac{Q^2}{2}\right)}{Q}, \qquad (6.41)$$

where Q is given by

$$Q = \frac{I_1 - I_0}{\sigma_1 + \sigma_0}. \qquad (6.42)$$

BER varies with the Q parameter. Receiver sensitivity generally corresponds to a BER value of 10^{-9} (i.e., 1 error in 10^9 bits). For

BER $= 10^{-9}$, the value of Q is 6. For large extinction ratio $(I_1 \gg I_0)$, $Q = I_1/\sigma$. Equation (6.41) shows log(BER) is approximately proportional to Q^2. For $I_1 \gg I_0$, log (BER) is proportional to I_1^2 and hence P^2 where P is the average power on the receiver. Thus, a plot of log (log (BER)) versus log (P) should yield a straight line in the absence of other effects such as pulse broadening. This type of a plot is called a bit-error-rate plot or BER plot or BER curve. Since, the electrical power is proportional to square of photocurrent, I_1 is proportional to $(S(1)^{1/2})$ where $S(1)$ is the electrical power in the photodiode for a "1". Thus, Q is given by

$$Q = \frac{\sqrt{S(1)} - \sqrt{S(0)}}{\sqrt{N_{\text{tot}}(1)} + \sqrt{N_{\text{tot}}(0)}} \qquad (6.43)$$

The quantities $S(1)$, $S(0)$ and $N_{\text{tot}}(1)$, $N_{\text{tot}}(0)$ are the signal and total noise for a mark (1) and space (0), respectively. A BER of 10^{-9} requires $Q = 6$. Some results of the amplifier noise on receiver sensitivity calculations are now presented. The amplifier parameters are gain (G), NF (N_{sp}) and optical bandwidth (B_o).

6.4.2. Er-doped Amplifier Noise

Equation (6.6) for N_{sp} is valid for atomic transitions where the absorption and emission probabilities (and hence cross sections) are equal. However, for rare earths, including Er, the absorbing and emitting levels are degenerate and are broadened by Stark splitting. The distribution of atoms in the Stark-split group level is determined by Boltzmann distribution. The absorption and emission cross sections depend on the wavelength. For Er-doped alumina–silicate fiber the absorption and emission cross sections derived from fluorescence and absorption measurements are shown in Fig. 6.12. The emission rate is proportional to $\sigma_e(\lambda)N_2$ and the absorption rate is proportional to $\sigma_a(\lambda)N_1$. Thus, the quantity N_{sp} depends on the inversion of the amplifier and also the emission and absorption cross sections and is given by

$$N_{\text{sp}} = \sigma_e(\lambda)N_2/(\sigma_e(\lambda)N_2 - \sigma_a(\lambda)N_1) \qquad (6.44)$$

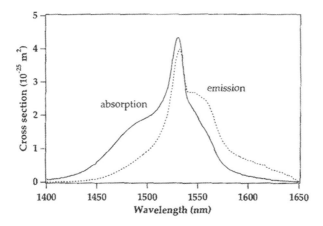

Fig. 6.12 Emission and absorption cross section in Al–Ge–Er–SiO$_2$ (alumina–silicate) fiber obtained from fluorescence and absorption measurements.[15]

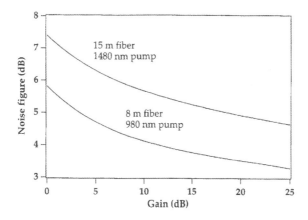

Fig. 6.13 NF at 1550 nm for 980 nm and 1480 nm pump wavelengths.[15]

The two common wavelengths for pump laser that are used in Er-doped amplifiers are 980 nm and 1480 nm. In an Er-doped amplifier, complete inversion can be achieved by using 980 nm pump laser. Thus, 980 nm pumped amplifier can achieve a lower NF than a 1480 nm pumped amplifier.

Figure 6.13 show the dependence of NF on gain for both 980 nm pump and 1480 nm pumped amplifier. The amplifier gain per unit

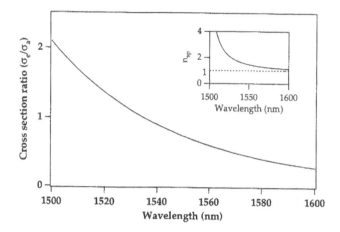

Fig. 6.14 The ratio of emission to absorption cross section as function of wavelength using the data of Fig. 6.11. The inset shows the dependence of N_{sp} on wavelength.[16]

length is generally smaller for 1480 nm pump than that for 980 nm pump and hence the 1480 nm pumped amplifier is longer than the 980 nm pumped amplifier. For Fig. 6.13, the fiber is 8 m long for 980 nm pump and it is 15 m long for 1480 nm pump.

Equation (6.44) shows that N_{sp} depends on the wavelength. Figure 6.14 show a plot of the ratio of emission and absorption cross section as a wavelength. The inset shows N_{sp} as a function of wavelength. At longer wavelength the ratio is close to 1. Thus lower noise figure is feasible for longer wavelength operation.

The equations of the previous section are rewritten in a different form to calculate the NF for a preamplifier application. It is assumed that the coupling factors are unity. For Eq. (6.4), I is the signal current, the SNR at the input are

$$(SNR)_{in} = \frac{\langle I_i \rangle^2}{\sigma^2} = \frac{I}{2eBe}, \tag{6.45}$$

where e is the charge of an electron and B_e is the electrical bandwidth at the photodetector. The SNR at the output

$$(SNR)_{out} = \frac{(GI)^2}{N_{tot}} \tag{6.46}$$

with $N_{tot} = N_{s-sp} + N_{sp-sp} + N_{shot}$

N_{tot} is the total noise, the thermal noise has been neglected. Using Eqs. (6.27)–(6.29) the NF can thus be written as

$$\text{NF} = 2N_{\text{sp}}\frac{(G-1)}{G} + \frac{1}{G} + \frac{N_{\text{sp}}(G-1)^2 e(2B_o - B_e)}{G^2 I}$$

$$+ \frac{2(G-1)N_{\text{sp}}eB_o}{G^2 I}, \tag{6.47}$$

where the first term is the dominant term in Eq. (6.47). The total ASE power (P_{ASE} in a gain bandwidth $\Delta\nu$) and the total current (I_{sp} in an optical bandwidth B_o) are given by

$$P_{\text{ASE}} = 2N_{\text{sp}}h\upsilon\Delta\upsilon(G-1)$$
$$I_{\text{sp}} = 2N_{\text{sp}}(G-1)eB_o. \tag{6.48}$$

Considering only the first two terms in Eq. (6.47), the NF is

$$\text{NF} = \frac{P_{\text{ASE}}}{h\upsilon\Delta\upsilon G} + \frac{1}{G} \tag{6.49}$$

For an Er-doped preamplifier, assuming a large extinction ratio (infinite), and neglecting all noise sources other than signal–spontaneous beat noise, The Q-factor using Eq. (6.43) for infinite extinction ratio is $Q = (S(1)/N_{\text{tot}}(1))^{1/2}$. For large gain, $G \gg 1$, this becomes

$$Q = \sqrt{\frac{P_{\text{in}}}{h\upsilon 2B_e N_{\text{sp}}}}. \tag{6.50}$$

The quantity $\beta = P_{\text{in}}/2h\nu B_e$ is the average number of photons per bit in bandwidth B_e. Thus, $Q = (\beta/N_{\text{sp}})^{1/2}$. For a BER of 10^{-9}, the quantity $Q \sim 6$. Thus for the ideal case $N_{\text{sp}} = 1$, the minimum number of photons per bit required for a BER of 10^{-9} is 36.

6.4.3. *Noise Measurements*

NF measurements on Er-doped amplifier have been reported by several researchers. The experimental setup for noise measurement is shown in Fig. 6.15. The fiber amplifier is 47 m long and it has core diameter of 3.6 μm. The core composition is 15% mole fraction of $Al_2O_3 \cdot GeO_2$ with an Er dopant concentration of 50 ppm. A tunable F-center laser was used as a signal source and an external cavity

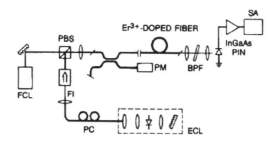

Fig. 6.15 Experimental setup for noise measurements.[16] ECL: External cavity laser, pump source, PBS: polarization beam splitter, PC: polarization controller, PM: power meter, BPF: band pass filter, SA: spectrum analyzer, FCL: F-center laser (tunable).

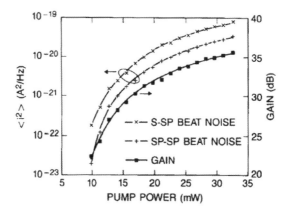

Fig. 6.16 signal–spontaneous (*s*–sp) and spontaneous–spontaneous (sp–sp) beat noise and gain as a function of pump power.[16]

semiconductor laser as a pump source. The signal amplified by the amplifier is measured using a InGaAs photodiode followed by an amplifier. The receiver noise is primarily signal–spontaneous (*s*–sp) beat noise, spontaneous–spontaneous (sp–sp) beat noise, and receiver circuit noise. The beat noise depends on the pump, through amplifier gain (G), and ASE power. The beat noises and the gain are plotted as a function of pump power in Fig. 6.16. The input signal wavelength is 1.531 μm and the input signal power is -40 dBm. For this setup, the circuit noise is 1×10^{-21} A^2/Hz and is the largest source of noise for pump power <13 mW. At high gain ($G > 27$ dB) *s*–sp (signal–spontaneous) beat noise is largest source of noise.

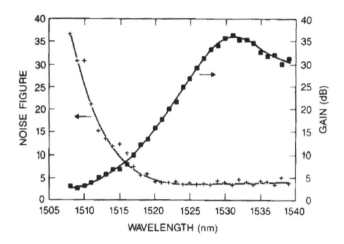

Fig. 6.17 NF and gain at a pump power of 34 mW as a function of wavelength.[16]

The NF is calculated using NF $= i^2/(2\eta e(G-1)\ I_s$ where i^2 is the average square noise current, η (=0.26) is the photodetector quantum efficiency, e is the electron charge, G is the amplifier gain and I_s is the average signal current. Using this formula, NF = 5.2 dB at $\lambda = 1.531\,\mu$m, and $G = 37$ dB. As mentioned in the previous section, NF is smaller at long wavelengths. The data on NF and gain as a function of wavelength at a constant pump power are shown in Fig. 6.17.

Higher NF is associated with saturated gain. The measured data using a 1480 nm pump laser is shown in Fig. 6.18. The top trace is gain and the bottom trace is noise figure. With higher signal power output the gain saturates and the NF goes up.

6.5. Preamplifier Results

One of the applications of optical amplifier is as a preamplifier in front of the receiver. The low noise and high gain of a Er-doped fiber amplifier makes them suitable as a preamplifier. The schematic of a preamplifier circuit along with various noise terms is shown in Fig. 6.19. The EDFA preamplifier is in front of the photodiode and the latter is followed by an electrical amplifier. The signal-dependent noise, i.e.,

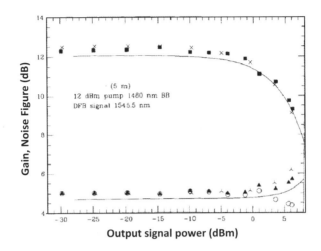

Output signal power (dBm)

Fig. 6.18 Gain and NF as a function of output signal power.[17] The Er-doped amplifier is 5 m long. Pump wavelength = 1480 nm, Pump power = 12 dBm, Signal wavelength = 1545.5 nm from a DFB laser.

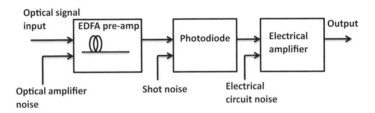

Fig. 6.19 Schematic of an EDFA preamplifier.[18]

the signal–spontaneous beat noise is the dominant noise term at high signal level (>-40 dBm), as mentioned earlier. At low received power (<-45 dBm), the spontaneous emission noise is dominant.

The BER data when Er-doped fiber is used as a preamplifier has been obtained at a data rate of 1.8 Gb/s and is generated using a directly modulated single mode laser. The receiver electrical bandwidth is 1.4 GHz and the receiver sensitivity (power needed for 10^{-9} BER is -21 dBm). The measured error rate as a function of received power with Er-doped preamplifier is shown in Fig. 6.20. The receiver sensitivity (power needed for 10^{-9} BER) is -43 dBm. The EDFA has also been used as a preamplifier in front of an avalanche

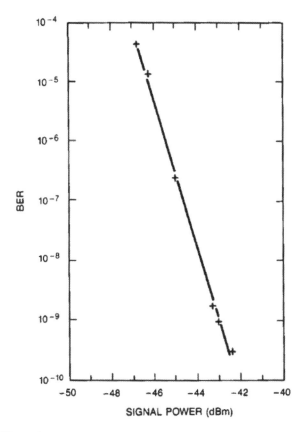

Fig. 6.20 BER as a function of signal power for a Er-doped preamplifier-based receiver.[16]

photodiode (APD). The results for an experiment at 1.8 Gb/s is shown in Fig. 6.21. The EDFA is pumped by a 1480 nm pump laser and the ASE in front of the APD is reduced using a bandpass filter whose pass-band width is 2 nm. About 7 dB improvement in receiver sensitivity (for BER = 10^{-9}) is observed using EDFA as preamplifier.

6.6. Pulse Propagation

Pulse propagation in optical fibers has been extensively studied. For long lengths of transmission fiber, dispersion effects and nonlinearity play an important role in pulse propagation. These nonlinear effects include four wave mixing, stimulated Brillouin scattering and

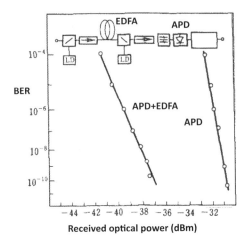

Fig. 6.21 Measured BER (Bit-error-rate as a function of received power. About 7 dB improvement is observed using EDFA as preamplifier.[18] Data rate (RZ) = 1.8 Gb/s, signal wavelength = 1552 nm.

in some instances stimulated Raman scattering. The EDFA is a relatively short fiber compared to a transmission fiber. However, it has gain and somewhat higher nonlinearity due to smaller cross section. EDFA is primarily a silica glass-based fiber. The silica has inversion symmetry, thus the second-order nonlinearity $\chi^{(2)}$ in a silica fiber is 0. Thus, second harmonic generation and sum and difference frequency generation do not occur in silica fibers. Before considering pulse propagation in EDFAs, it is useful to discuss pulse propagation in regular transmission fiber. Most of the same considerations apply, except EDFA has gain and less nonlinearity due to its short length (typically <25 m *versus* >40 km for transmission fibers).

6.6.1. *Pulse Propagation in Regular Fibers*

The basic equations for pulse propagation in fibers is derived in this subsection. For an analysis starting with Maxwell's equations, please see Ref. 19. Consider the propagation of a plane light wave at frequency ω through a medium having third-order $(\chi^{(3)})$ nonlinearity. The polarization generated in the medium is given by

$$P = \varepsilon_0 \chi E + \varepsilon_0 \chi^{(3)} E^3. \tag{6.51}$$

For a light at frequency ω propagating along the z-direction with propagation constant k the electric field is given by

$$E = E_0 \cos(\omega t - kz). \tag{6.52}$$

The polarization P is given by

$$P = \varepsilon_0 \chi E_0 \cos(\omega t - kz) + \varepsilon_0 \chi^{(3)} E_0^3 \cos^3(\omega t - kz). \tag{6.53}$$

For a plane wave given by Eq. (6.52), the intensity is

$$I = \frac{1}{2} c \varepsilon_0 n_0 E_0^2, \tag{6.54}$$

where n_0 is the refractive index of the medium at low intensity. From Eq. (6.53), the polarization at frequency ω is

$$P = \varepsilon_0 \left(\chi + \frac{3}{4} \chi^{(3)} E_0^2 \right) E_0 \cos(\omega t - kz). \tag{6.55}$$

Then

$$P = \varepsilon_0 \left(\chi + \frac{3}{2} \frac{\chi^{(3)}}{c \varepsilon_0 n_0} I \right) E. \tag{6.56}$$

The polarization P and electric field are related by

$$P = \varepsilon_0 (n^2 - 1) E, \tag{6.57}$$

where n is the refractive index of the medium. From Eqs. (6.56) and (6.57), n^2 is given by (with $n_0^2 = 1 + \chi$)

$$n^2 = n_0^2 + \frac{3}{2} \frac{\chi^{(3)}}{c \varepsilon_0 n_0} I. \tag{6.58}$$

The last term in Eq. (6.58) is usually very small, n can be written as,

$$n \approx n_0 + n_2 I, \tag{6.59}$$

where

$$n_2 = \frac{3}{4} \frac{\chi^{(3)}}{c \varepsilon_0 n_0^2}. \tag{6.60}$$

The quantity n_2 is the nonlinear coefficient. The above equation shows that the refractive index of the medium becomes intensity dependent and the coefficient n_2 represents the strength of the intensity dependence.

For silica $n_0 \approx 1.47$, $n_2 \approx 3.2 \times 10^{-20}\,\text{m}^2/\text{W}$. For a fiber with a cross section of 100 μm^2 and with a power of 100 mW, the change in refractive index is $\Delta n = n_2 I = 3.2 \times 10^{-11}$. For an EDFA, the cross section is smaller by as much as a factor of 10, hence the nonlinear index is higher.

For fibers, the nonlinear effect is expressed in terms of the propagation constant β. It is represented by

$$\beta_{NL} = \beta + \frac{k_0 n_2}{A_{\text{eff}}} P, \qquad (6.61)$$

where $k_0 = 2\pi/\lambda_0$, and P is the power carried by the mode. The quantity A_{eff} represents the effective transverse cross-sectional area of the mode. For the Gaussian approximation of the mode profile (Sec. 2.4),

$$A_{\text{eff}} = \pi w_0^2. \qquad (6.62)$$

It is usual to describe the nonlinear characteristic of an optical fiber by the coefficient γ given by

$$\gamma = \frac{k_0 n_2}{A_{\text{eff}}}. \qquad (6.63)$$

Thus, for the same input power and same wavelength, smaller values of A_{eff} lead to greater nonlinear effects in the fiber. Typically $A_{\text{eff}} \approx 20\,\mu\text{m}^2$ for EDFA and $\gamma \approx 10\,\text{W}^{-1}\text{km}^{-1}$. The nonlinear effects are higher in high gain EDFAs due to increase in power. The electric field in an optical pulse can be written as:

$$E(x, y, z, t) = \frac{1}{2}[A(z, t)\psi(x, y)e^{i(\omega_0 t - \beta_0 z)} + cc], \qquad (6.64)$$

where $A(z, t)$ represents the slowly varying complex envelope of the pulse, $\psi(x, y)$ represents the transverse electric field distribution of the mode, ω_0 represents center frequency, and β_0 represents the propagation constant at ω_0. In the presence of optical loss or gain, second-order dispersion, and third-order nonlinearity, (by using Maxwell's equations) the complex envelope $A(z, t)$ can be shown to satisfy the following equation[19]:

$$\frac{\partial A}{\partial z} = -\frac{\alpha}{2} A - \beta_1 \frac{\partial A}{\partial z} + i\frac{\beta_2}{2}\frac{\partial^2 A}{\partial t^2} - i\gamma |A|^2 A, \qquad (6.65)$$

where

$$\beta_1 = \left.\frac{d\beta}{d\omega}\right|_{\omega=\omega_0} = \frac{1}{v_g}, \qquad (6.66)$$

$$\beta_2 = \left.\frac{d^2\beta}{d\omega^2}\right|_{\omega=\omega_0} = -\frac{\lambda_0^2}{2\pi c} D, \qquad (6.67)$$

where D represents the group velocity dispersion (measured in ps/nm-km). The quantity α is negative for gain. The various terms on the right-hand side of Eq. (6.65) represent the attenuation/gain, group velocity, dispersion and nonlinearity, respectively. Changing to the time frame defined by $T = t - \beta_1 z$, Eq. (6.65) becomes,

$$\frac{\partial A}{\partial z} = -\frac{\alpha}{2} A + i\frac{\beta_2}{2}\frac{\partial^2 A}{\partial t^2} - i\gamma |A|^2 A. \qquad (6.68)$$

In the absence of loss ($\alpha = 0$), the following equation is obtained:

$$\frac{\partial A}{\partial z} = i\frac{\beta_2}{2}\frac{\partial^2 A}{\partial t^2} - i\gamma |A|^2 A. \qquad (6.69)$$

The above equation has a solution (optical pulse) given by

$$A(z, t) = A_0 \sec h(\sigma T) e^{-igz} \qquad (6.70)$$

with

$$A_0^2 = -\frac{\beta_2}{\gamma}\sigma^2 \quad g = -\frac{\sigma^2}{2}\beta_2. \qquad (6.71)$$

In terms of pulse peak power $P_0 = A_0^2$, the pulse can be written as

$$A(z, t) = \sqrt{P_0} \sec h\left(\sqrt{\frac{P_0\gamma}{|\beta_2|}}T\right) e^{-i\gamma P_0 z/2}. \qquad (6.72)$$

Equation (6.72) represents a soliton and has the property that it propagates undispersed through the medium. The full width at half-maximum (FWHM) of the pulse envelope is given by $\tau_f = 2\tau_0$ where

$$\sec h^2 \sigma \tau_0 = \frac{1}{2}$$

which gives the FWHM τ_f

$$\tau_f = 2\tau_0 = \frac{2}{\sigma}\ln(1+\sqrt{2}) \approx \frac{1.76}{\sigma}. \tag{6.73}$$

The peak power of the pulse is:

$$P_0 = |A_0|^2 = \frac{|\beta_2|}{\gamma}\sigma^2. \tag{6.74}$$

Replacing σ by τ_f, we obtain

$$P_0\tau_f^2 \approx \frac{\lambda_0^2}{2\pi c}D. \tag{6.75}$$

The above equation gives the required peak power for a given τ_f for the formation of a soliton pulse. For a typical transmission fiber, $\tau_f = 10\,\mathrm{ps}$, $\gamma = 2.4\,\mathrm{W}^{-1}\mathrm{km}^{-1}$ $\lambda_0 = 1.55\,\mu\mathrm{m}$, $D = 2\,\mathrm{ps/nm\text{-}km}$, and the required peak power is $P_0 = 33\,\mathrm{mW}$. Soliton pulses are being extensively studied for application to ultra-long distance optical communication. Since optical loss is neglected for soliton formation, in actual systems, the pulses have to be optically amplified at regular intervals to compensate for the loss suffered by the pulses.

Soliton transmission experiments over transoceanic distances have been carried out. It has been shown that effects of soliton–soliton interaction and polarization mode dispersion can be reduced and error-free transmission over long distances can be obtained.[20] This is discussed further in Chapter 10. Figure 6.22 shows the measured waveforms before and after 10,000 km transmission at 40 Gb/s. The experiment is carried out in a recirculating loop (see Chapter 10) with erbium-doped fiber amplifiers for loss compensation. The result shows negligible pulse distortion.

6.6.2. *Pulse propagation in EDFA*

The pulse propagation in the optical fiber can be described by non-linear Schrodinger equation (NLSE). Other than soliton solution in the dispersive fiber, the parabolic pulses are exact asymptotic solutions of the NLSE with gain (in the optical fiber amplifier). The self-similar propagation and amplification of parabolic pulses

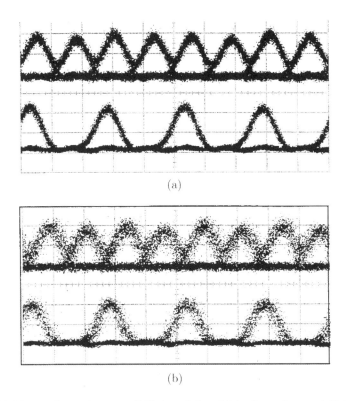

(a)

(b)

Fig. 6.22 Measured waveforms at 40 Gb/s and demultiplxed waveforms at 20 GB/s (a) before transmission i.e., at ∼0 km and (b) after 10,000 km transmission.[20]

in optical fibers has been experimentally and numerically demonstrated in 2000.[22] It has attracted considerable interest because the self-similar amplified pulses are able to propagate over substantial fiber lengths without optical wave breaking, the chirp remains linear and it is easy to achieve large temporal compression using a fiber-grating pair or a fiber amplifier.[23-25] The generation of self-similar parabolic pulses has been demonstrated in erbium-doped fiber amplifier (EDFA),[23] ytterbium-doped fiber amplifier (YDFA),[22, 26, 27] and Raman-amplifiers.[28, 29] The NLSE with gain is given by (Eq. (6.68) multiplied by i):

$$i\frac{\partial A}{\partial z} - \frac{ig}{2}A - \frac{\beta_2}{2}\frac{\partial^2 A}{\partial T^2} + \gamma|A|^2A = 0 \qquad (6.76)$$

with

$$A(z,t) = \sqrt{P_0}U(z,t),$$

$$U(0,t) = \exp\left(-\frac{t^2}{2T_0^2}\right), \qquad (6.77)$$

where $A(z,t)$ is the slowly varying pulse envelope in a retarded time frame, β_2 is the group-velocity-dispersion parameter, γ is the nonlinear parameter, and g is the gain coefficient. The assumption that initial pulse is a chirp free Gaussian pulse with a pulse energy of $U(0) = 30\,\text{pJ}$ has been made during the analysis. The erbium-doped fiber amplifier has the following parameters, $\beta_2 = 30\,\text{ps}^2\text{km}^{-1}$ $\gamma = 5.8\,\text{W}^{-1}\text{km}^{-1}$, and $g = 3\,\text{dBm}^{-1}$ and the operating wavelength resides in the telecom wavelength range ($\sim$1550 nm).

For an amplifier with constant distributed gain, an exact asymptotic solution has been found. This solution corresponds to a parabolic pulse. The asymptotic pulse characteristics are not influenced by the shape or width of the input pulses.

Only the initial pulse energy determines the final pulse amplitude and width. The parabolic solution is defined as follows[22]:

$$A_p(z,T) = A_0\left[1 - \left(\frac{T}{T_0}\right)^2\right]\exp[i\varphi(z,T)], |T| \le T_0(z) \qquad (6.78)$$

otherwise, $A_p(z,T) = 0$

$$A_0(z) = \frac{1}{2}(gE_{\text{in}})^{1/3}\left(\frac{\gamma\beta_2}{2}\right)^{-1/6}\exp\left(\frac{gz}{3}\right) \qquad (6.79)$$

$$T_0(z) = 3(g)^{-2/3}\left(\frac{\gamma\beta_2 E_{\text{in}}}{2}\right)^{1/3}\exp\left(\frac{gz}{3}\right). \qquad (6.80)$$

Equation (6.78) gives the exact high-intensity parabolic solution to NLSE. The pulse amplitude and pulse width are shown in Eqs. (6.79) and (6.80).

The NLSE simulations using split step Fourier method (shown in Fig. 6.23) have confirmed these results. Figure 6.23 shows a 0.8-ps-duration FWHM Gaussian pulse at the input and its spectrum.

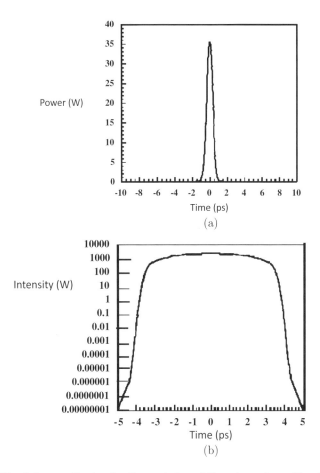

Fig. 6.23 Simulation results showing the evolution of Gaussian pulses with width 0.8 ps in 8.5 m fiber amplifier (a) initial pulse profile (b) output pulse intensity profile on a logarithmic scale.

The output pulse shape and its spectrum after propagation through an 8.5 m long fiber amplifier are also shown. The amplification and reshaping of the input pulse to a pulse with a parabolic intensity profile after 8.5 m of propagation are very apparent. The low-amplitude wings on the parabolic pulse have been shown in Fig. 6.23b. The wings are predicted to vanish and have infinite slope in the limit $z \to \infty$.

Experimental results are now described.[23] The erbium-doped amplifier was pumped using a 1480 nm laser with the pump co-propagating with the input pulses. The input pulse has a FWHM of 1.4 ps and a pulse energy of 100 pJ. The pulses are nearly transform limited and are generated using a mode locked fiber laser. The pulse intensity as a function of time and spectrum was measured for different propagation distances through an Er-doped fiber amplifier. When the Er-doped fiber is 9 m long, it has a gain of 13.6 dB using 140 mW of pump power. The pulse intensity profiles are measured for several different fiber lengths. The experimental results are shown in Fig. 6.24. The figure shows that after about 4 m of propagation in the amplifier parabolic pulses appear.

The parabolic pulses train has been generated in all-optical communication systems.[30,31] To investigate the optical SNR during the pulse propagation, a numerical analysis of the quality of pulse train

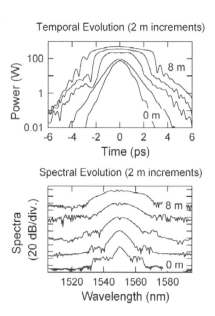

Fig. 6.24 (Top) Experimental results on pulse profile plotted on a logarithmic scale to illustrate temporal broadening. (Bottom) Experimental results on evolution of spectrum.[23]

has been carried out. The Q factor is defined as before:

$$Q = \frac{\overline{P_1} - \overline{P_0}}{\sigma_1 + \sigma_2},$$ (6.81)

$$\text{BER} = \frac{1}{2} erfc\left(\frac{Q}{\sqrt{2}}\right).$$ (6.82)

In the above, BER is the bit-error rate, P_1, P_0 are the average optical power of "1" and "0", and σ_1, σ_2 standard deviation of power of "1" and "0", respectively.

A model for pulse propagation using 2^7-1 pseudo-random input pulses has been carried out.[30] The Q factor as a function of the propagation distance in the optical amplifier has been calculated. From the formula in Sec. 6.4, for BER $>10^{-9}$, Q must be more than 6. For the calculation, the input pulse widths are 0.4 ps (for 200 Gb/s) and 0.8 ps (for 100 Gb/s), respectively. The pulse period is 12.5 times the initial pulse width. The model uses an amplifier gain of 20 dB for a 10 m long amplifier. High Q factors ($Q > 6$), corresponding to BER $>10^{-9}$ is feasible for long propagation distances (20 m or less) in the amplifier at 100 Gb/s but at 200 Gb/s the propagation distance in the amplifier is found to be less than 9 m for Q not to exceed 6. The result shows that about 200 Gb/s is the speed limit for pseudo random input pulse train width of 0.4 ps. Higher data rate is feasible for shorter pulses.

Erbium-doped optical amplifiers (EDFA) pumped by laser diodes are one of the key components in fiber networks. Transient gain effects in single channel amplification can cause signal distortion in single channel amplification and cross talk in multichannel (e.g., in WDM systems) amplification. However, due to slow decay time of the high energy state of Er, these effects occur at relatively low frequencies, i.e., gain dynamics simply results in lower gain. EDFAs also have high saturation power. These unique properties make EDFA an important element in multichannel WDM networks.

References

1. K. Fukuchi, *Proceedings, Optical Fiber Communications*, Paper THX5 (2002).

2. R. Ramaswami and K.N. Sivarajan, *Optical networks*, San Francisco: Morgan Kaufman. 1998.
3. A.K. Srivastava and Y. Sun, In *Optical fiber telecommunication*, Chapter 4, IVA, I. Kaminow and T. Li (Eds.) London: Academic Press. 2002, p. 174.
4. R.J. Mears, Y.L. Reekie, J.M. Jauncey and D.N. Payne, *Electron. Lett.* **23** (1987) 1026.
5. E. Desuvire, J.R. Simpson and P.C. Becker, *Opt. Lett.* **12** (1987) 888.
6. T. Mukai, K. Inoue and T. Saitoh, *Electron. Lett.* **23** (1987) 396.
7. G. Grasskopf, R. Ludwig and H.J. Weber, *Electron. Lett.* **22** (1986) 900.
8. C.R. Giles, E. Desuvire and J.R. Simpson, *Opt. Lett.* **14** (1989) 880.
9. A. Srivastava and Y. Sun, In *Guided wave optical components and devices*, Chapter 12, B.P. Pal (Ed.) Elsevier Academic Press. 2006.
10. A.K. Srivastava, Y. Sun, J.L. Zyskind and J.W. Sulhoff, *IEEE Photonics Technol. Lett.* **9** (1997) 386.
11. Y. Sun, G. Luo, J.L. Zyskind, A.A.M. Saleh, A.K. Srivastava and J.W. Sulhoff, *Proceedings, optical fiber communication*, paper THM3 (1997).
12. G.P. Agrawal and N.K. Dutta, In *Semiconductor lasers*, Chapter 11, van Nostrand Reinhold. 1992.
13. N.A. Olsson, *J. Lightwave Technol.* **LT-7** (1989) 1071.
14. G.P. Agrawal, *Fiber optic communication systems*, Chapter 4, John Wiley. 1997.
15. P.C. Becker, N.A. Olsson and J.R. Simpson, *Erbium doped fiber amplifiers*, Academic Press. 1997.
16. C.R. Giles, E. Desurvire, J.L. Zyskind and J.R. Simpson, *IEEE Photonics Technol. Lett.* **1** (1989) 367.
17. I.M.I. Habib, A.A.M. Saleh, N.J. Frigo and G.E. Bodeep, *IEEE J. Lightwave Technol.* **10** (1992) 1281.
18. S. Shimoda and H. Ishio (Eds.), *Optical amplifiers and their applications*, John Wiley and Sons, 1994.
19. G.P. Agrawal, *Nonlinear fiber optics*, Chapter 2, Academic Press. 1989.
20. I. Morita, K. Tanaka, N. Edagawa and M. Suzuki, *IEEE J. Lightwave Technol.* **17** (1999) 2506.
21. D. Anderson, M. Desaix, M. Karlson, M. Lisak and M.L. Quiroga-Teixeiro, *J. Opt. Soc. Am. B* **10** (1993) 1185.
22. M.E. Fermann, V.I. Kruglov, B.C. Thomsen, J.M. Dudley and J.D. Harvey, *Phys. Rev. Lett.* **84** (2000) 6010–6013.
23. C. Billet, J.M. Dudley, N. Joly and J.C. Knight, *Opt. Express* **13** (2005) 3236.
24. C. Finot, F. Parmigiani, P. Petropoulos and D.J. Richardson, *Opt. Express* **14** (2006) 3161.
25. J.M. Dudley, C. Finot, D.J. Richardson and G. Millot, *Nat. Phys.* **3** (2007) 597.
26. J. Limpert, T. Schreiber, T. Clausnitzer, K. Zollner, H.J. Fuchs, E.-B. Kely, H. Zellmer and A. Tinnermann, *Opt. Express* **10** (2002) 628.
27. A. Malinowski, A. Piper, J.H.V. Price, K. Furusawa, Y. Jeong, J. Nilsson and D.J. Richardson, *Opt. Lett.* **29** (2004) 2073.

28. C. Finot, G. Millot, C. Billet and J.M. Dudley, *Opt. Express* **11** (2003) 1547.
29. C. Finot, G. Millot and J.M. Dudley, *Opt. Lett.* **29** (2004) 2533.
30. Z. Chen, S. Ma and N.K. Dutta, To be published.
31. C. Finot, L. Provost, P. Petropoulos and D.J. Richardson, *Opt. Express* **15** (2007) 852.

Chapter 7

High Power Amplifiers

7.1. Introduction

For a regular single mode amplifier the pump co-propagates and/or counter propagates with the signal in the rare earth-doped core. Since the confinement factor of the pump and signal are not significantly different, a large fraction of the pump interacts with the rare earth and produces gain for the signal as the signal propagates through the amplifier. The power output of such an amplifier is limited by the pump power that can be coupled in the small core which is typically few μm (3 to 6 μm) in diameter. The pump power is generally produced by a single mode pump laser. The output powers of single mode lasers are generally limited by catastrophic facet degradation (for short wavelength 800 or 980 nm lasers) or by leakage current (for long wavelength 1480 nm lasers). Use of multiple pumps such as using a co-propagating and counter propagating configuration, increases the output power somewhat but it is still limited to about 1 W.

For higher power ($\sim$10 W to many kWs) applications, larger amounts of pump light needs to be coupled into the fiber. The advantage of fiber amplifiers for such applications is that it produces a better quality beam at the desired wavelength. For free space communications, output powers of $\sim$10 W may be needed and for manufacturing applications kW level pulsed or CW powers may be needed. These fiber amplifiers therefore require coupling of >10 W and higher coupled pump power levels. One way of achieving higher coupled pump power is coupling the pump light into a large-area (typically 100 to 200 μm diameter) cladding region.

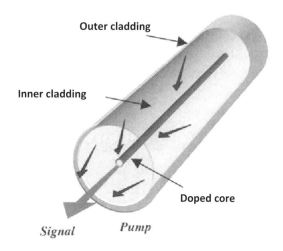

Fig. 7.1 Schematic of a DCF design.[10] The coupled pump power in the multimode pump waveguide can reach kW levels.

A second cladding region (generally polymer based) is used around this large-area cladding to produce a multimode pump waveguide. The schematic of a double clad fiber (DCF) is shown in Fig. 7.1. The core is doped with the rare earth such as Yb, Nd, or Tm. For single mode DCF, the core is sufficiently small so that only the fundamental mode of the fiber is amplified. DCFs with single mode core are generally limited to lower power than that for large area multimode (LMA) fibers. The LMA fibers typically have core regions 20 to $50\,\mu$m in diameter so that kW level powers are produced.

Several methods of coupling pump light into a large core fiber has been studied.[1–17] In this type of design, the fraction of the pump power in the core interacts with the rare earth in the core and produces a gain for the signal. The pump light transfers its power to the signal light (i.e., one pump photon creates one signal photon for 100% efficiency) as it propagates along the amplifier. The signal output can thus be much higher than ~ 1 W, generally feasible for single mode amplifiers described earlier (Chapters 5 and 6). A large cladding fiber is also suitable for coupling pump laser light from multiple semiconductor diode laser bars each of which have a typical emitting area size of $100 \times 0.2\,\mu$m (Chapter 8).

A 100 μm wide diode bar produces >10 W of power. The output power of many such laser diodes could be coupled into the cladding of a DCF fiber using suitable pump coupling mechanisms described later.[1-5] The DCF-based lasers and amplifiers essentially provide an efficient means of increasing the brightness of semiconductor sources. Various types of cladding pumped high-power amplifiers have been used along with different pump coupling procedures. These are discussed in this chapter.

7.2. Waveguide Designs and Pumping

The pump travels along a large-area multimode fiber waveguide. Several types of pump waveguide designs have been studied. These are shown in Fig. 7.2. Enhanced pump coupling from diode laser bars is an important consideration for pump waveguide design.

The simplest pump waveguide is circular in shape. It consists of a large area ($\sim$100 μm or more in diameter) Ge-doped silica fiber, surrounded by another cladding layer typically 10 to 20 μm in thickness. For single mode DCF used in somewhat low-power systems (10 to

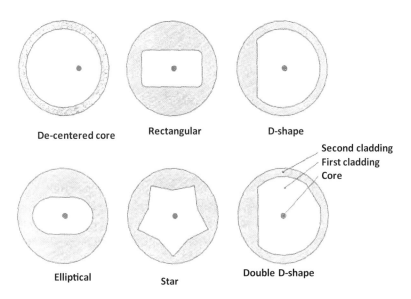

Fig. 7.2 Various pump waveguide cross sections. The central dot is the core.[18]

20 W), the rare earth-doped core design is similar to that described earlier but with the cladding diameter that matches the pump fiber for end pumping.

7.2.1. *End Pumping*

The schemes that have been developed for coupling pump light into a large-area DCF are end pumping and side pumping.[1-5] The tapered fiber bundle (TFB scheme) for end pumping[2,19] is discussed in this section. The TFB allows the coupling of light from many semiconductor lasers into the large-area cladding (or large-area fiber).

This type of end pumping coupler is made by splicing a TFB of N fibers (each of which carry pump light) into a single output fiber. By optimizing the length of the tapered region, high coupling efficiency from all N-input fibers to a single output fiber can be achieved.

The schematic of a 7×1 TFB is shown in Fig. 7.3. In use, the output of six semiconductor pump lasers are input to the six outer fibers and the inner fiber carries the signal. The TFB couples the output into a single fiber. The TFB coupler is fused to the output fiber, thus it is stable against mechanical vibrations. Note the seven fibers naturally fill up a larger circular region (Fig. 7.2). This is the key to the choice of the number of fibers in the coupler, although all of them need not be used. The fabrication technology for the TFB end-pumping coupler has four successive steps: bundle the individual fibers, followed by adiabatic tapering to the area of a large core fiber, and, cleaving and splicing to the large-area fiber. The coupling efficiency of the TFB depends on the taper length. The coupling efficiency of TFBs as a function of coupling length (taper length) has been calculated. The results are shown in Fig. 7.4.

Since the pump fibers are multimode fibers, the calculated coupling efficiency is for 30 modes in the fiber starting with the lowest order mode. The calculation shows the coupling efficiency when the total power is evenly distributed in the mode and when the power is distributed in a Gaussian form, i.e., more power in lower order modes. 7×1 does not represent a limit of the TFB, the next set of close packed structure has 19 fibers and such TFBs have also

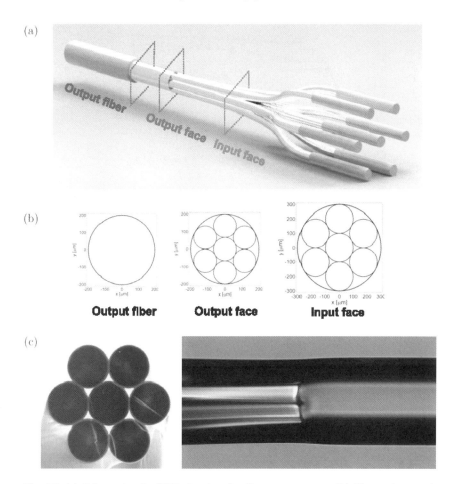

Fig. 7.3 (a) Schematic of a TFB showing the fiber arrangement. (b) Photomicrograph of the cross section of a fabricated TFB (c) Side view of the coupling to a single fiber.[19]

been fabricated. A coupling experiment has been carried out using a TFB of the following design.[19] The pump fibers are seven multimode fibers with the core/clad diameter of $200/220\,\mu$m, and the numerical aperture (NA) of core of 0.22. The output fiber is a DCF fiber with core/inner clad/outer clad diameter of $20/400/550\,\mu$m. The NA of core/inner clad is $0.06/0.46$. The core in this case is not doped with rare earth but for a DCF amplifier it would be. The input fiber is coupled to semiconductor laser each of which can be driven to produce

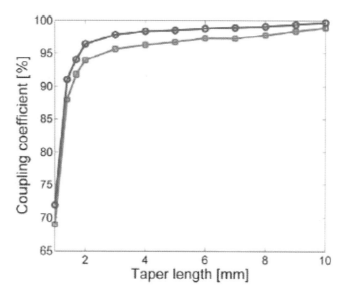

Fig. 7.4 Calculated coupling efficiency as a function of tapering length. The upper curve is for even distribution and the lower Gaussian distribution of modes.

a power of 430 W. The total coupled output power of TFB is plotted as a function of total input power of all seven lasers in Fig. 7.5.

The results show 3 kW power output of TFB with >99% coupling efficiency. In the particular TFB, and, the experiment of Fig. 7.4, the large area of the DCF allows very high coupling. High coupling efficiencies (>95%) have also been reported using 100/125 μm pump fibers and 10/12/100 μm DCF for 7 × 1 TFBs.

The 7 × 1 TFB has been used in a DCF amplifier configuration where the signal light is injected into the central fiber which has a single mode core (8 μm inner core/125 μm cladding) and the outer fibers are multimode fibers (100/125 μm inner/outer cladding) for pump injection from a broad area semiconductor laser. The DCF in this case also has a core (8 μm diameter) to match the signal light. The pump is mostly in the inner cladding of the DCF due to its large area (100 μm diameter). This configuration has been used in Er–Yb co-doped (Sec. 7.4) single mode amplifier which produces ~10 W of amplified power. Such design will be discussed further in sections that follow.

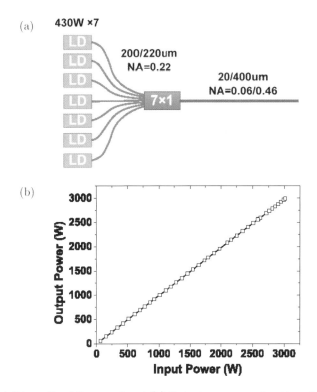

Fig. 7.5 (a) Schematic of the experiment (b) Output power as a function of total input power of a 7×1 TFB.

Another method for end pumping a DCF amplifier is attaching the single mode signal fiber and multimode mode fiber to the end of the DCF.[20] An important requirement here is that the DC-fiber shape has to resemble the cross section of the two input fibers as much as possible. This requirement is met by grinding the initial round preform to almost rectangular shape, as shown in Fig. 7.6.

The TFBs have been widely used in many relatively low power (10 to 30 W) amplifiers for applications and for system demonstrations.

7.2.2. *Side Pumping*

The advantage of side pumping over end pumping is that it can be repeated along the DCF and thus very high pump powers can be coupled which can lead very high output. Several schemes for side

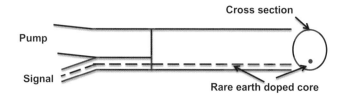

Fig. 7.6 Schematic of an end pumping method.[20]

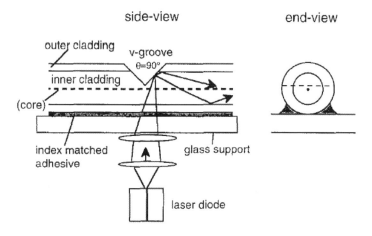

Fig. 7.7 Pump coupling using the V-groove technique.[5, 25]

pumping have been demonstrated.[5, 20–36] One side pump technique involves forming a V-groove in the DCF and the total internal reflection of the pump light couples and propagates the light along the length of the DCF. Efficient coupling has been demonstrated using a 90° V-groove, oriented transversely to the fiber axis, and imbedded into the fiber side-wall as shown in Fig. 7.7. The bottom of the V-groove does not go past the core as a result the single mode is unaffected by the V-groove. Mechanical support for the fiber is often provided near the V-groove. 80% power coupling from 10 mm wide diode laser bars into the inner cladding of a DCF has been demonstrated using this method.

Multiple V-grooves on the same fiber has been demonstrated for pump light coupling for Nd-doped DCF laser. The results of an experiment is shown in Fig. 7.8. The diameter of the core and first cladding

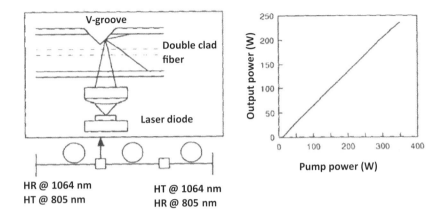

Fig. 7.8 Coupling of light using multiple V-grooves[26] for a Nd-doped DCF.

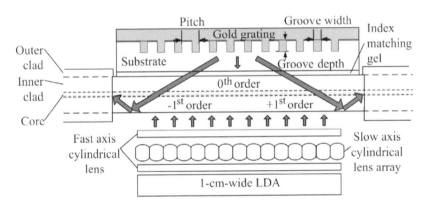

Fig. 7.9 Schematic of pump coupling using grating reflectors.[27]

are 7 and 400 μm, respectively. A total conversion efficiency of 68%, i.e., conversion of 805 nm pump laser power to Nd laser power at 1064 nm, has been achieved. The laser power output is $\sim$240 W.

Pump coupling using a grating coupler which is fabricated on silica and is attached to the side of the fiber has been demonstrated. The metal grating reflects the light back into the fiber where it gets guided longitudinally by total internal reflection (Fig. 7.9). Coupling efficiencies of $\sim$50% has been achieved using 1cm wide laser diode array (LDA).

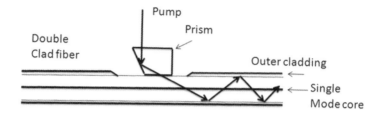

Fig. 7.10 Side pumping with a portion of outer cladding etched off.[28]

Another scheme where a portion of the second cladding is etched off (Fig. 7.10) and a reflector is put in its place to couple the pump light has been reported.[28] More than 90% pump coupling has been achieved.

Another method uses a mirror or prism positioned in the DCF after etching. The method is self-explanatory from Fig. 7.11. Pump coupling efficiency of as high as 80% has been demonstrated. Clearly the mirror design and placement is critical in achieving high efficiency. A commercially successful technology for side pumping is shown in Fig. 7.12.[4] In this scheme, the fiber carrying the multimode pump light is fused along the side of the doped fiber and the pump light then gets coupled to the DCF through internal reflection.

7.3. DCF Laser and Amplifier Results

High-power fiber laser or amplifier has been extensively studied using a DCF fiber with a Yb-doped core.[37–42] The V-groove scheme for side pumping described in Sec. 7.2.2 has been used to demonstrate high-power amplification from Yb-doped DCF. The amplifier used is a 12 m long DCF with a rectangular inner cladding ($100 \times 200\,\mu$m) and a $10\,\mu$m diameter Yb-doped core. The absorption coefficients are 1.6 and 0.55 dB/m at 975 and 915 nm light propagating in the inner cladding, respectively. The amplifier is seeded with 100 mW light at 1064 nm, the output as a function of pump power is shown in Fig. 7.13. Small signal gain for different wavelength has been measured for a pump current of 3A i.e., $\sim$1.4 W coupled power in inner cladding (Fig. 7.14). $\sim$50 dB of small signal gain is observed at 1070 nm.

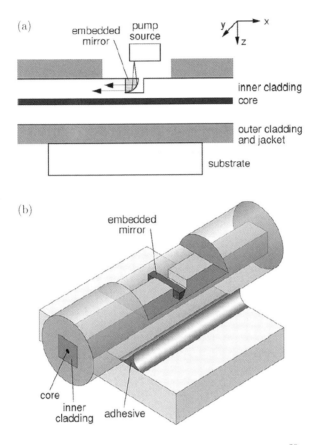

Fig. 7.11 Side pumping with mirror in the etched DCF.[29]

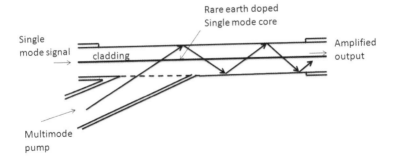

Fig. 7.12 Fused fiber method for coupling pump light.[4]

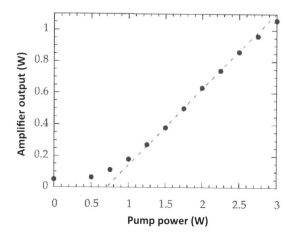

Fig. 7.13 Amplified power output as a function of pump diode current. The maximum pump power coupled to the inner cladding is estimated to be 1.4 W. The seed power is 100 mW.[41]

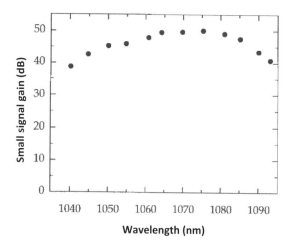

Fig. 7.14 Small signal at various input signal wavelengths.[41]

Laser results from a single transverse mode Yb-doped DCF is discussed now. An experimental result using bending losses to reduce/eliminate stimulated Raman scattering (SRS) and higher order modes is described below.[42] The fiber is a DCF. It has a 20 μm diameter Yb-doped core region, and has an inner cladding of 400 μm in diameter. The experimental setup for high power demonstration

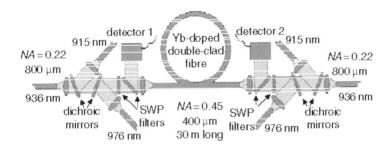

Fig. 7.15 Schematic of the experimental setup.[42]

is shown in Fig. 7.15. The fiber used is 30 m long. It has dichroic mirrors (transmits pump and reflects signal) and pump coupling elements at both ends. The pumps are coupled into 800 μm diameter (pump delivery) fibers, the output of which is coupled to the DCF.

The fiber laser cavity is formed by Fresnel reflections (~3.5%) at both ends of the fiber. Thus, the fiber laser has nearly equal output from both ends which are then added to get the total output power in Fig. 7.16. The fiber supports only two modes (LP01 and LP11), it is possible to suppress the higher order mode by coiling the fiber with a 15 cm diameter coil. This has been verified experimentally. The estimated SRS threshold for the fiber is 900 W. The SRS phenomenon is discussed in detail in Chapter 10. A plot of total laser power as a function of coupled pump power is shown in Fig. 7.16. Although circular cross section for the pump waveguide is most common, other cross sections such as that shown in Fig. 7.2 have been used for improving pump interaction with the doped core so that shorter DCF fiber lengths can be used. For example, the star shape and the double D-shape allows large pump interaction with the core, but the fabrication process (which can involve mechanical polishing) is more complicated.

7.4. Er–Yb Co-doped Cladding Pumped Amplifier

As discussed in Chapters 5 and 6, erbium-doped fiber lasers and amplifiers are important for their application in optical communication systems. High-power lasers and amplifiers are very important as

Fiber Amplifiers and Fiber Lasers

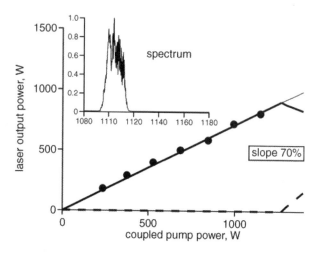

Fig. 7.16 Plot of total laser power (i.e., sum of both outputs) as a function of diode laser power input. The spectrum is shown in the inset. The calculated stimulated Raman power is shown by the dashed line.[42]

communication networks expand in capacity and distance. In order to get high power operation, it is necessary to use high erbium concentration for high gain and a DCF. However, the ion–ion interactions which causes pair-induced up-conversion[43] depletes the erbium metastable level and lowers the efficiency, for concentrations above a few hundred parts per million (ppm) of Er.[44] A means of addressing this issue is by co-doping the Er-doped fiber with Yb.[45,46] The presence of Yb reduces the formation of Er clusters and reduces the up-conversion rate from the Er upper level ($^4I_{13/2}$ level) significantly. This allows high erbium doping level needed for a high gain amplifier. In addition, an energy transfer from Yb to Er provides a means for indirect pumping mechanism of Er ions. This energy transfer mechanism is very efficient and thus for a Er–Yb co-doped amplifier the preferred pump wavelength corresponds to an Yb absorption transition.

Figure 7.17 shows the simplified energy level transitions for Er–Yb co-doped DCF amplifiers. Yb ions in silica fiber have one broadband laser transition, between 970 and 1200 nm. The absorption peak is at 975 nm. In the Er–Yb co-doped fiber, the Yb ions absorb the pump power, and, transfer the energy to Er as shown in Fig. 7.17.

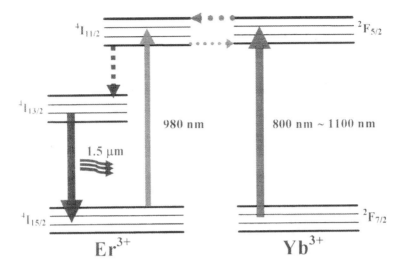

Fig. 7.17 Energy level diagram of Er and Yb in a Er–Yb co-doped fiber.[47]

The energy transfer efficiency from Yb to Er can be as high as 95% because of the large spectral overlap between Yb emission spectrum ($^2F_{5/2} - {}^2F_{7/2}$) and Er absorption spectrum ($^4I_{15/2} - {}^4I_{11/2}$).[48] This mechanism allows strong absorption of the pump by Yb without signal absorption due to high Er concentration, which helps to obtain high power amplifiers and lasers.[49,50]

The Er–Yb co-doped double clad amplifier (EYDCF) is schematically shown in Fig. 7.18. The 1550 nm input is from an Er-doped preamplifier. The pump lasers are at 970 nm corresponding to the Yb absorption peak. The output power from EYCDF for different Er–Yb co-doped fiber lengths has been measured. The result is shown in Fig. 7.19. For 12 m fiber length, nearly 4.5 W of amplified power is obtained for 12 W of pump power. The measured noise figure is ~6.

A model calculation of gain at 1550 nm for Er–Yb double clad amplifiers as a function of pump power and temperature is now described. A high-power Er–Yb co-doped DCF amplifier also exhibits high gain for Yb transition near 1060 nm. This is not unexpected since the input pump causes population inversion in Yb also. The laser action in Er (erbium) and Yb (ytterbium) co-doped fibers can

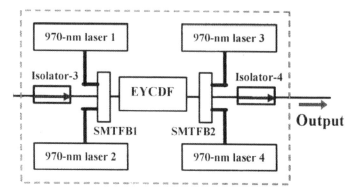

Fig. 7.18 Schematic of an Er–Yb co-doped fiber amplifier.[47] Four pump lasers at 970 nm create Yb ions in the upper state by absorption in Er–Yb doped fiber (EYDCF). The isolators are typical in most amplifier designs. They prevent reflection induced noise in amplified signal.

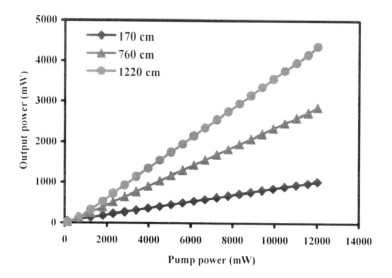

Fig. 7.19 Measured amplified power at 1550 nm as a function of pump power.[47]

be modeled as three-level laser system. The energy levels for these two ions along with possible transitions are shown in Fig. 7.20. The transitions involve both radiative and nonradiative energy transfer processes.

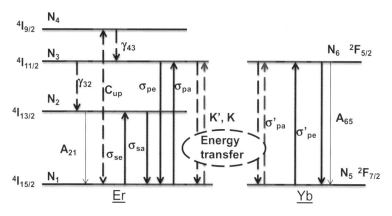

Fig. 7.20 Energy level diagram of Er-Yb (erbium–ytterbium) system. The dashed lines, and, the solid lines represent nonradiative transitions, and radiative transitions, respectively.[51]

On the basis of the energy level diagram, the rate equations for Er and Yb population densities can be written as[48–51]:

$$\frac{dN_4}{dt} = C_{\mathrm{up}}N_2^2 - \gamma_{43}N_4 \tag{7.1}$$

$$\frac{dN_3}{dt} = -N_3\sigma_{pe}\phi_p + N_1\sigma_{pa}\phi_p + KN_6N_1 - K'N_3N_5 - \gamma_{32}N_3 + \gamma_{43}N_4 \tag{7.2}$$

$$\frac{dN_2}{dt} = -A_{21}N_2 - 2C_{\mathrm{up}}N_2^2 + N_1\sigma_{sa}\phi_s - N_2\sigma_{se}\phi_s + \gamma_{32}N_3 \tag{7.3}$$

$$N_1 + N_2 + N_3 + N_4 = N_{\mathrm{Er}} \tag{7.4}$$

$$\frac{dN_5}{dt} = -KN_6N_1 + K'N_3N_5 - N_5\sigma'_{pa}\phi_p + N_6\sigma'_{pe}\phi_p + A_{65}N_6 \tag{7.5}$$

$$N_5 + N_6 = N_{\mathrm{Yb}} \tag{7.6}$$

The parameters in the rate equations are as follows. The quantities N_1, N_2, N_3, and N_4 (m^{-3}) are the Er^{3+} population density of the $^4\mathrm{I}_{15/2}$, $^4\mathrm{I}_{13/2}$, $^4\mathrm{I}_{11/2}$, and $^4\mathrm{I}_{9/2}$ level, respectively. The quantities N_5 and N_6 (m^{-3}) are the Yb^{3+} population density of the $^2\mathrm{F}_{7/2}$ and $^2\mathrm{F}_{5/2}$ level, respectively. σ_{sa} and σ_{se} (m^2) are the absorption and emission cross section of Er^{3+} at the signal wavelength, respectively, and, σ_{pa} and σ_{pe} (m^2) are the absorption and emission cross section of Er^{3+} at the pump wavelength, respectively. The quantities σ'_{pa} and σ'_{pe} (m^2) are the absorption and emission cross section of Yb at the pump wavelength. γ_{43} and γ_{32} (s^{-1}) are the nonradiative transition rate of Er^{3+}. A_{21} (s^{-1}) is the spontaneous emission rate of Er^{3+}. A_{65} (s^{-1}) is the spontaneous emission rate of Yb^{3+}. C_{up} (m^3s^{-1}) is up-conversion coefficient from $^4I_{13/2}$ to $^4I_{9/2}$ level of Er^{3+}, this process cannot be neglected when the signal power is high, which is the case in this application. K and K' (m^3s^{-1}) are the energy transfer coefficients.

It is assumed that the Er^{3+} ions are homogenously excited. This implies that they experience similar surroundings. The Er concentration is large enough to allow rapid energy migration in the Er subsystem. This energy migration can be expected to be higher than the up-conversion rate due to the poor spectral overlap for the up-conversion process.[49] Thus, the up-conversion may saturate in the kinetic limit. Therefore, homogenous up-conversion is modeled by a relaxation term which is quadratic in the concentration of excited Er^{3+}, with a concentration-independent up-conversion coefficient. This assumption is reasonable when Er^{3+} clusters are not present. However, if Yb^{3+} concentration is not high enough to dissolve the Er^{3+} clusters, they will act as quenching centers where rapid up-conversion occurs.[52] These quenching centers are extremely harmful in Er–Yb system because efficient pumping of quenching center will result in an efficient drain for the pump light.[53] From Eqs. (7.1) to (7.3), the following solution in steady state is obtained

$$N_4 = \frac{C_{up}N_2^2}{\gamma_{43}} \qquad (7.7)$$

and

$$N_3 = \frac{A_{21}N_2 + 2C_{up}N_2^2 - N_1\sigma_{sa}\phi_s + N_2\sigma_{se}\phi_s}{\gamma_{32}}. \qquad (7.8)$$

Since the nonradiative relaxation rates γ_{32} and γ_{43} are about $10^9\,s^{-1}$, for the parameters used in the calculation, it can be verified that N_3 and N_4 are much smaller than N_1 and N_2. Then with the approximation $N_1 + N_2 = N_{Er}$, the following equations result governing the ion density at $^4I_{11/2}$ and $^2F_{5/2}$ levels for Er^{3+} and Yb^{3+}, respectively:

$$\frac{dN_2}{dt} = -A_{21}N_2 - C_{\text{up}}N_2^2 - N_2\sigma_{se}\phi_s$$

$$+ (N_{Er} - N_2)(\sigma_{sa}\phi_s + \sigma_{pa}\phi_p + KN_6), \quad (7.9)$$

$$\frac{dN_6}{dt} = -KN_6(N_{Er} - N_2) + (N_{Yb} - N_6)\sigma'_{pa}\phi_p$$

$$- N_6\sigma'_{pe}\phi_p - A_{65}N_6. \quad (7.10)$$

Since the cross transfer coefficient K is much larger than C_{up},[53] if the up-conversion terms are neglected, the solutions of N_2 and N_6 in steady state are

$$N_6 = \frac{\phi_p N_{Yb}\sigma'_{pa}}{\phi_p\sigma'_{pa} + \phi_p\sigma'_{pe} + A_{65} + K(N_{Er} - N_2)}, \quad (7.11)$$

$$N_2 = \frac{N_{Er}(\sigma_{sa}\phi_s + \sigma_{pa}\phi_p + KN_6)}{A_{21} + \sigma_{se}\phi_s + (\sigma_{sa}\phi_s + \sigma_{pa}\phi_p + KN_6)}. \quad (7.12)$$

In the presence of crystal field, each atomic level are broadened into a band of energy levels. The population distribution of the atoms in a band is given by the Boltzmann distribution[54]:

$$N_a = \frac{N_0}{Z_a}\exp(-E_a/kT) = f_a N_0, \quad (7.13)$$

$$Z_a = \sum_i \exp\left(-\frac{E_i}{kT}\right). \quad (7.14)$$

The population of a level of energy E_a in the lower band is $N_a = f_a N_0$, where N_0 is the total lower level band population. Similarly, the upper laser level population, N_b is given by $f_b N_1$, where N_1 is the total upper manifold population. For the laser transition, $f_b = 0.67$ and $f_a = 0.0168$ at $T = 25°C$, and $f_b = 0.65$ and $f_a = 0.0192$ at $T = 40°C$, where T is the temperature.[55] Similarly, for the pump transition, $f'_b = 0.33$ and $f'_a = 0.72$ at $T = 25°C$, and $f'_b = 0.35$ and $f'_a = 0.70$ at $T = 40°C$. Including these fractions in the populations, the equations become:

$$N_6 = \frac{\phi_p N_{Yb} \sigma'_{pa} f'_a}{\phi_p \sigma'_{pa} f'_a + \phi_p \sigma'_{pe} f'_b + A_{65} + K(N_{Er} - N_2)}. \quad (7.15)$$

The total power P, propagating in a DCF is divided into two mode ensembles. The first mode ensemble is the power in the inner core, P_i, which can be absorbed by the active rare earth ions. The other mode ensemble is the power between the inner core and the first cladding, P_f. Then the following equations are obtained[56]:

$$P = P_i + P_f, \quad (7.16)$$

$$\frac{dP_i}{dz} = -\alpha_a P_i - \gamma_1 P_i + \gamma_2 P_f, \quad (7.17)$$

$$\frac{dP_f}{dz} = -\alpha_s P_f - \gamma_2 P_f + \gamma_1 P_i, \quad (7.18)$$

$$\alpha_a = \Gamma_p[\sigma'_{pa}(N_{Yb} - N_6) - \sigma'_{pe} N_6] + \Gamma_p[\sigma_{pa}(N_{Er} - N_2) - \sigma_{pe} N_2],$$

$$\frac{dS}{dz} = -S \iint_A [(N_{Er} - N_2)\sigma_{sa} - N_2 \sigma_{se}] \psi_s(x, y) dx dy + \alpha S,$$

$$(7.19)$$

where α_a is the absorption coefficient caused by the active rare earth ions in the inner core, γ_1 is the coupling constant from P_i to P_f, α_s is the scatter loss coefficient in the first cladding, and γ_2 is the coupling constant from P_f to P_i. Γ_p, Γ_s and Γ'_s are the proportions of the pump power, signal power (Er.) and signal power (Yb) propagating within the fiber core, respectively. S is the signal power at position z of the DCF. A numerical solution of Eqs. (7.12–7.19), provides the gain for the Er transition near 1550 nm and at Yb transition near 1060 nm. The fiber gain G at Er transition is given by

$$G = \exp\left(\int_0^L g(z) dz\right), \quad (7.20)$$

where $g(z)$ is the gain per unit length which depends on the position z, $g(z)$ is given by

$$g(z) = \Gamma_s[\sigma_{se} N_2 - \sigma_{sa}(N_{Er} - N_2)] \quad (7.21)$$

and the gain at Yb transition is also given by Eq. (7.20) with $g(z)$ given by

$$g(z) = \Gamma'_s[\sigma'_{se}N_6 f_b - \sigma'_{sa}(N_{Yb} - N_6)f_a] \qquad (7.22)$$

This section describes the results of the calculation. The parameters used in the calculation are as follows. The core is doped with both Er and Yb. The Yb concentration is $1.2 \times 10^{26}\,\mathrm{m}^{-3}$ and the Er concentration is $1.0 \times 10^{25}\,\mathrm{m}^{-3}$. The core radius is $3.5\,\mu\mathrm{m}$ and the first cladding radius is $125\,\mu\mathrm{m}$. The pump stimulated absorption cross section of Yb. $\sigma'_{pa} = 2.0 \times 10^{-24}\,\mathrm{m}^2$, the pump stimulated emission cross section of Yb. $\sigma'_{pe} = 1.5 \times 10^{-24}\,\mathrm{m}^2$, the pump stimulated absorption cross section of Er. $\sigma_{pa} = 5.5 \times 10^{-25}\,\mathrm{m}^2$, the pump stimulated emission cross section of Er. $\sigma_{pe} = 5 \times 10^{-25}\,\mathrm{m}^2$, the 1535 nm signal stimulated absorption cross section of Er. $\sigma_{sa} = 5.5 \times 10^{-25}\,\mathrm{m}^2$, the 1535 nm signal stimulated emission cross section of Er. $\sigma_{se} = 6.6 \times 10^{-25}\,\mathrm{m}^2$, the 1060 nm signal stimulated absorption cross section of Yb. $\sigma'_{sa} = 1.5 \times 10^{-25}\,\mathrm{m}^2$, the 1060 nm signal stimulated emission cross section of Yb. $\sigma'_{se} = 2.6 \times 10^{-25}\,\mathrm{m}^2$, transfer coefficient $K = 6 \times 10^{21}\,\mathrm{M}^3\mathrm{s}^{-1}$ the life time of the upper level of Yb is 1.5 ms, the life time of the upper level of Er is 1.1 ms. $\Gamma_p = \Gamma_s = \Gamma'_s = 1$. The results are shown in Figs. 7.21 and 7.22, respectively.

Measurements of optical gain at 1550 nm as a pump power has been carried out in an 8 m long Er/Yb DCF. The core of which is doped with Er and Yb has a diameter of $6\,\mu\mathrm{m}$, the first cladding has a diameter of $110\,\mu\mathrm{m}$ and the outer cladding has a diameter of $125\,\mu\mathrm{m}$. The pump at 970 nm propagates in the first cladding. The Yb concentration is $1.2 \times 10^{26}\,\mathrm{m}^{-3}$ and the Er concentration is $1.0 \times 10^{25}\,\mathrm{m}^{-3}$. The measured data are shown in Fig. 7.23. The bottom curve is for 50 mW input power and the top curve is for 4 W input power.

The calculated gain is $\sim 20\,\mathrm{dB}$ for 6 W pump for 20 mW input signal at 25°C. More than 10 W of amplified power can be obtained using 8 m long fiber with $\sim 25\,\mathrm{W}$ of pump power. The gain decreases with increasing input signal. A high-power Er–Yb co-doped DCF amplifier also exhibits high gain for Yb transition near 1060 nm. This is expected since the input pump also causes population inversion in Yb.

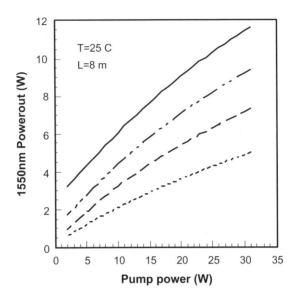

Fig. 7.21 The output power at 1550 nm as a function of the pump power with different 1550 nm signal input with 5 m long fiber. The dotted line is for 20 mW signal input. The dashed line is for 200 mW signal input. The double dot dash line is for 800 mW and the solid line is for 2 W input.

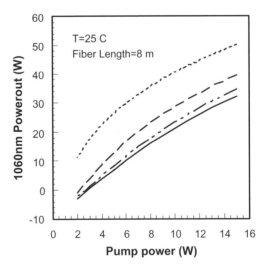

Fig. 7.22 1060 nm gain as a function of the pump power with different 1550 nm signal input for 8 m long fiber. The dotted line is for 20 mW signal input. The dashed line is for 200 mW signal input. The double dot dash line is for 800 mW and the solid line is for 2W input.

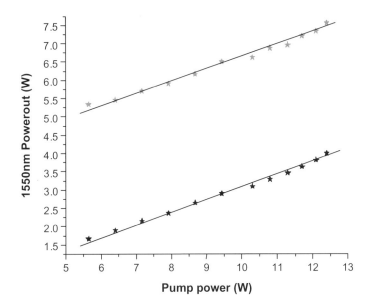

Fig. 7.23 Measured output power at 1550 nm as a function of input pump power at 970 nm. The bottom curve is for 50 mW input power and the top curve is for 4 W input power. The fiber length is 8 m.

7.5. DCF Model

A model of effective pump power absorption ratio in a DCF is discussed in this section. For this analysis, it is reasonable to divide the total power P propagating in a DCF into two mode ensembles. The first mode ensemble is the power in the inner core, P_i, which can be absorbed by the active rare earth ions. The other mode ensemble is the power between the inner core and the first cladding, P_f. Hence,

$$P = P_i + P_f. \tag{7.23}$$

When these two mode ensemble propagate along the DCF, they can be described by a system of two coupled differential equations

$$\frac{dP_i}{dz} = -\alpha_a P_i - \gamma_1 P_i + \gamma_2 P_f, \tag{7.24}$$

$$\frac{dP_f}{dz} = -\alpha_s P_f - \gamma_2 P_f + \gamma_1 P_i, \tag{7.25}$$

where α_a is the absorption coefficient caused by the active rare earth ions in the inner core, γ_1 is the coupling constant from P_i to P_f, α_s

is the propagation loss coefficient in the first cladding, and γ_2 is the coupling constant from P_f to P_i. By substituting the trial solution

$$P_i = A \exp(-\sigma z) \tag{7.26}$$

$$P_f = B \exp(-\sigma z) \tag{7.27}$$

to the coupled differential Eqs. (7.24) and (7.25), it follows

$$-\sigma A = -\alpha_a A - \gamma_1 A + \gamma_2 B \tag{7.28}$$

$$-\sigma B = -\alpha_s B - \gamma_2 B + \gamma_1 A \tag{7.29}$$

In order to have non-vanish solution, the determinant of the coupled Eqs. (7.28) and (7.29) must be zero.

$$\begin{vmatrix} \sigma - \alpha_a - \gamma_1 & \gamma_2 \\ \gamma_1 & \sigma - \alpha_s - \gamma_2 \end{vmatrix} = 0 \tag{7.30}$$

which leads to the eigenvalue equation

$$(\sigma - \alpha_a - \gamma_1)(\sigma - \alpha_s - \gamma_2) - \gamma_1 \gamma_2 = 0, \tag{7.31}$$

with the solution

$$\sigma_{1,2} = \frac{(\alpha_a + \alpha_s + \gamma_1 + \gamma_2)}{\pm\sqrt{(\alpha_a + \alpha_s + \gamma_1 + \gamma_2)^2 - 4(\alpha_a \alpha_s + \alpha_a \gamma_2 + \alpha_s \gamma_1)}}{2}.$$
$$\tag{7.32}$$

The coefficients $A_{1,2}$ and $B_{1,2}$ for the two solutions have the following relation

$$B_1 = \frac{-\sigma_1 + \alpha_a + \gamma_1}{\gamma_2} A_1 = \frac{\gamma_1}{-\sigma_1 + \alpha_s + \gamma_2} A_1, \tag{7.33}$$

$$B_2 = \frac{-\sigma_2 + \alpha_a + \gamma_1}{\gamma_2} A_2 = \frac{\gamma_1}{-\sigma_2 + \alpha_s + \gamma_2} A_2. \tag{7.34}$$

The general solution of the coupled differential equations can be expressed as a superposition of the two solutions

$$P_i(z) = A_1 \exp(-\sigma_1 z) + A_2 \exp(-\sigma_2 z), \tag{7.35}$$

$$P_f(z) = B_1 \exp(-\sigma_1 z) + B_2 \exp(-\sigma_2 z). \tag{7.36}$$

At the input of the fiber, the following boundary condition exists

$$P_i(0) = \gamma P(0), \tag{7.37}$$

$$P_f(0) = (1 - \gamma) P(0), \tag{7.38}$$

where γ is the fraction of the input power coupled into the core. Using these boundary conditions, we obtain

$$A_1 = \left[\frac{\gamma_2 + (\sigma_2 - \alpha_a - \gamma_1 - \gamma_2)\gamma}{\sigma_2 - \sigma_1} \right] P(0), \qquad (7.39)$$

$$A_2 = \gamma P(0) - A_1. \qquad (7.40)$$

The total power propagating along the fiber can be expressed as

$$\begin{aligned} P(z) &= P_i(z) + P_f(z) \\ &= (A_1 + B_1) \exp(-\sigma_1 z) + (A_2 + B_2) \exp(-\sigma_2 z), \qquad (7.41) \end{aligned}$$

where $A_{1,2}$, $B_{1,2}$, and $\sigma_{1,2}$ are given by (7.39) and (7.40), (7.33) and (7.34), and (7.32), respectively. Suppose the local effective attenuation coefficient is $\alpha(z)$, then for the total power propagating at the position z is

$$P(z) = P(0) \exp[-\alpha(z)z]. \qquad (7.42)$$

With Eqs. (7.41) and (7.42), the local effective attenuation coefficient is

$$\alpha(z) = -\frac{1}{z} \ln[(A_1 + B_1) \exp(-\sigma_1 z) + (A_2 + B_2) \exp(-\sigma_2 z)]. \qquad (7.43)$$

The total power absorbed by the active rare earth ions is

$$AbsorbedPower = \int_0^z \alpha_a P_i(z) dz. \qquad (7.44)$$

Hence the effective absorbed power ratio is

$$\mu = \frac{\int_0^z \alpha_a P_i(z) dz}{P(0)}. \qquad (7.45)$$

By using (7.39) and (7.40), the following expression for μ is obtained

$$\mu = \int_0^z \alpha_a \left\{ \begin{array}{l} \dfrac{\gamma_2 + (\sigma_2 - \alpha_a - \gamma_1 - \gamma_2)}{\sigma_2 - \sigma_1} \exp(-\sigma_1 z) \\ \\ + \left[\gamma - \dfrac{\gamma_2 + (\sigma_2 - \alpha_a - \gamma_1 - \gamma_2)}{\sigma_2 - \sigma_1} \right] \exp(-\sigma_2 z) \end{array} \right\} dz. \qquad (7.46)$$

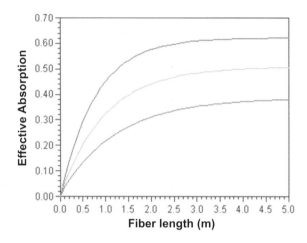

Fig. 7.24 The effective pump power absorption along the fiber for different coupling constants for the power in the first cladding to the inner core. The value of γ_2 for the four curves are 0.3, 0.5, $0.8 \, \text{m}^{-1}$. Note the pump absorption increases rapidly with increasing γ_2. The pump propagation loss in the first cladding is $0.5 \, \text{m}^{-1}$ for the above figure.

Figure 7.24 shows the effective absorption ratio (μ) along the fiber for different coupling constant (γ_2). The quantity γ_2 is the power coupling from first cladding to core.

The results show that the coupling constants are the most important parameter to increase the effective pump power absorption coefficient. With all the other parameters the same, the effective absorption coefficient can be increased from 12% to 62% with a couple constant γ_2 from 0.1 to $0.8 \, \text{m}^{-1}$ for a 3 m long fiber. Apart from the cladding/core ratio, there are many other parameters that can change the coupling constant γ_2, such as the NA of the core, the shape of the first cladding, the launch angle of the pump power, the bending of the fiber, etc. The propagation loss of the pump light in the first cladding is not negligible. The loss in a fiber can be divided into two categories: material related loss and structure related loss. The material related losses include absorption loss and scattering loss, which are small for silica fibers. The structure related losses include bending loss, loss caused by cladding dimension, loss caused by dimension perturbation, etc. The propagation loss is another important parameter in determining the effective absorption ratio. When the propagation loss increases, more power is lost, and the effective pump absorption to core decreases. DCF amplifiers and lasers are being developed for various high-power applications such as space communications and industrial applications such as metal cutting and shaping. Nd- and Yb-doped fibers are more suitable for these applications.

References

1. S.G. Anikitchev, K.E. Lindsay and A. Starodoumov, Method for manufacturing a multimode fiber pump power combiner, U.S. Patent 7 272 956 (2007).
2. D.J. Digiovanni and A.J. Stentz, Tapered fiber bundles for coupling light and out of cladding-pumped fiber devices, U.S. Patent 5 864 644 (1999).
3. A.B. Grudinin *et al.*, Motion.lti-fibre arrangements for high power fibre lasers and amplifiers, U.S. Patent 6 826 335 (2004).
4. P. Valentin, V. F. Gapontsev and N. Platonov, Powerful fiber laser system, U.S. Patent 7 593 435 (2009).
5. D.J. Ripin and L. Goldberg, *Electron. Lett.* **31** (1995) 2204.
6. W. Dazheng, W. Yonggang, L. Suping and M. Xiaoyu, *Acta Opt. Sci.* **29** (2009) 974.
7. W.M. Sean, J.P. Koplow and A. Hansen, *Proceedings, 21st LEOS*, (2008) p. 870.
8. Z. Fan, W. Chun-can, N. Tigang, L. Chu, G. Rui and L. Yuchun, *Opt. Commun.* **282** (2009) 3325.
9. C. Jauregui, S. Böhme, G. Wenetiadis, J. Limpert and A. Tünnermann, *J. Opt. Soc.Am. B* **27** (2010) 1011.
10. Y. Jaouen, S. Bordais, E. Olmeda and J.Y. Allain, *Ann. Telecommun.* **58** (2003) 11.
11. J.J. Larsen and G. Vienne, *Opt. Lett.* **29** (2004) 436.
12. A. Kosterin, V. Temyanko, M. Fallahi and M. Mansuripur, *Appl. Opt.* **43** (2004) 3893.
13. A. Wetter, M. Faucher, M. Lovelady and F. Séguin, *Fiber lasers IV: technology, systems, and applications*, Vol. 6453, Proc. SPIE (2007).
14. F. Séguin, A. Wetter, L. Martineau, M. Faucher, C. Delisle and S. Caplette, *Fiber lasers III: technology, systems, and applications*, Vol. 6102, Proc. SPIE (2006).
15. H. Yu, D.A.V. Kliner and K.-H. Liao, *Proc. SPIE* **8237** (2012) 82370G.
16. Q. Xiao, P. Yan, J. He, Y. Wang, X. Zhang and M. Gong, *Laser Phys.* **21** (2011) 1415.
17. A. Salokatve, Optical fiber combiner and method of manufacturing thereof, U.S. Patent 0 154 881 (2009).
18. A. Tunnermann and H. Zellmar, In *Handbook of laser technology and applications*, Chapter 4.2, C. E. Webb & J. D. C. Jones (Eds.), Institute of Physics Publishing. 2004

19. Q. Xiao, H. Ren, X. Chen, P. Yan and M. Gong, *IEEE Photonics Technol. Lett.* **25** (2013) 2442.

20. P. Peterka, I. Kašík, V. Matějec, P. Honzátko and J. Sláníčka, *Proceedings, Optical Fiber Communications*, ME4 (2004).

21. L. Goldberg, Method and apparatus for side pumping an optical fiber, U.S. Patent 5 854 865 (1998).

22. T. Weber, W. Luthy, H.P. Weber, V. Neuman, H. Berthou and G. Kotrotsios, *Opt. Commun.* **115** (1995) 99.

23. J.P. Koplow, S.W. Moore and D.A. Kliner, *IEEE J. Quantum Electron.* **39** (2003) 529.

24. J.J. Larsen and G. Vienne, *Opt. Lett.* **29** (2004) 436.

25. L. Goldberg, B. Cole and E. Snitzer, *Electron. Lett.* **33** (1997) 2127.

26. C. Li, D. Shen, J. Song, N. S. Kim and K. Ueda, *CLEO, Pacific Rim* **ThV4** (1999) 805.

27. C.W. Huang, C.L. Chang, D.Y. Jheng, K.Y. Hsu, S.L. Huang and D.W. Huang, *IEEE Photonics J.* **4** (2012) 411.

28. Y. Kaneda, J. Zong, O. Romero, Z. Deng, B. Case, A. Chavez-Pirson, G. Paysnoe, J. Whitwham, P. Moran, P. Rohan, Z. Wang, S. Jiang, W. Eaton, M. Brutsch, P. Li and I. Song, *Proceedings, Optical Fiber Communication*, THD, p. 798 (2000).

29. J.P. Koplow, S.W. Moore and D.A.V. Kliner, *IEEE JQE* **39** (2003) 529.

30. T.Y. Fan, A. Sanchez-Rubio, J.N. Walpole, R.C. Williamson, I. Melngailis, J.R. Leger and W.C. Goltsos, Multiple-laser pump optical system, U.S. Patent 5 185 758 (1993).

31. T.Y. Fan, *Appl. Opt.* **30** (1991) 630.

32. F. Hakimi and H. Hakimi, *Conference on Lasers and Electro-Optics*, p. 116 (2001).

33. T. Aoyagi and K. Shigihara, U.S. Patent 5 170 458, (1992).

34. J.P. Koplow, L. Goldberg and D.A.V. Kliner, *IEEE Photonics Technol. Lett.* **10** (1998) 793.

35. L. Goldberg and J.P. Koplow, *Electron. Lett.* **34** (1998) 2027.

36. J.P. Koplow, D.A.V. Kliner and L. Goldberg, *Opt. Lett.* **25** (2000) 442.

37. H.M. Pask, J.L. Archambault, D.C. Hanna, L. Reekie, P. St. J. Russell, J.E. Townsend and A.C. Tropper, *Electron. Lett.* **30** (1994) 863.

38. M. Muendel, B. Engstrom, D. Kea, B. Laliberte, R. Minns, R. Robinson, B. Rockney, Y. Zhang, R. Collins, P. Gavrilovic and A. Rowley, *Conference on Lasers and Electro-Optics*, paper CPD30-2 (1997).

39. S.V. Chernikov, J.R. Taylor, N.S. Platonov, V.P. Gapontsev, P.J. Nacher, G. Tastevin, M. Leduc and M.J. Barlow, *Electron. Lett.* **33** (1997) 787.

40. R. Paschotta, D.C. Hanna, P. De Natale, G. Modugno, M. Inguscio and P. Laporta, *Opt. Commun.* **136** (1997) 243.

41. J.P. Koplow, L. Goldberg and D.A.V. Kliner, *IEEE Photonics Technol. Lett.* **10** (1998) 793.

42. C.-H. Liu, B. Ehlers, F. Doerfel, S. Heinemann, A. Carter, K. Tankala, J. Farroni and A. Galvanauskas, *Electron. Lett.* **40** (2004) 1000.

43. C.C. Ye, P.R. Morkel, E.R. Taylor and D.N. Payne, presented at *ECOC 93*, Montreux, September 1993.
44. J.L. Wagener, P.F. Wysocki, M.J. Shaw and D.J. DiGiovanni, *Opt. Lett.* **18** (1993) 2014.
45. J.T. Kringlebotn, J.L. Archambault, L. Reekie, J.E. Townsend, G.G. Vienne and D.N. Payne, *Electron. Lett.* **30** (1994) 972.
46. J.T. Kringlebotn, P.R. Morkel, L. Reekie, J.L. Archambault and D.N. Payne, *IEEE Photonics Technol. Lett.* **5** (1993) 1162.
47. Z.G. Lu, A. Lavigne, P. Lin and C.P. Grover, *Proceedings, Photonics North*, p. 180 (2004).
48. F. Di Pasquale and M. Federighi, *IEEE J. Quantum Electron.* **30** (1994) 450.
49. D.S. Knowles and H.P. Jenssen, Vol. 11, OSA Technical Digest Series (1993) p. 310.
50. T. Georges, E. Delevaque, M. Monerie, P. Lamouler and J.F. Bayon, *Optical amplifiers and their applications*, Vol. 17, Technical Digest, (1992) p. 71.
51. Q. Wang and N.K. Dutta, *Proceedings, ITCOM* **5246** (2003) 390.
52. O. Lumholt, T. Rasmussen and A. Bjarklev, *Electron. Lett.* **29** (1993) 495.
53. M. Karasek, *IEEE J. Quantum Electron.* **33** (1997) 1200.
54. T.Y. Fan, *IEEE J. Quantum Electron.* **28** (1992) 1400.
55. B. Majaron, *IEEE J. Quantum Electron.* **31** (1995) 400.
56. S. Bedo, *Opt. Commun.* **99** (1993) 331.

Chapter 8

Pump Laser

8.1. Introduction

Early work on rare earth-doped fiber amplifiers and fiber lasers were carried out using flashlamp or argon ion laser as pump sources. These sources were of high intensity to excite the rare earth ions to an excited state from which they cascaded down to the energy levels needed for laser action. These sources were utilized for the creation of much of the knowledge related to basic physics and demonstrations. However, they were not efficient i.e., the conversion efficiency from pump laser light to rare earth-doped laser light was low. With the advances and availability of semiconductor lasers, the pump light wavelength can be tailored for high efficiency. In addition, the semiconductor laser is small and allows a significant ease of operation. The pump lasers for various rare earth-doped systems are discussed in this Chapter. The principals among these are 808 nm pump for Nd-doped fiber, 980 nm, 1480 nm laser for Er-doped fiber and ~950 to 970 nm laser for Yb-doped fiber.

The concept of the laser dates back to 1958.[1] The successful demonstration of a solid state ruby laser and He–Ne gas laser was reported in 1960.[2,3] Laser action in the semiconductor was considered by many groups during that period.[4-6] The semiconductor injection laser was demonstrated in 1962.[7-10] The advantages of semiconductor lasers over other types of lasers, such as gas lasers, dye lasers, and solid-state lasers, lie in their considerably smaller size and lower cost and their unique ability to be modulated at gigahertz speeds simply by modulation of the injection current. These properties make the laser diode an ideal device as a source in several optoelectronic systems, especially optical fiber transmission systems. The semiconductor laser properties are discussed in several books.[14-17]

8.2. Materials, Epitaxial Growth and Operating Principle

The choice of materials for semiconductor lasers is principally determined by the requirement that the probability of radiative recombination be sufficiently high. This is usually satisfied for "direct gap" semiconductors. The various semiconductor material systems along with their range of emission wavelengths are shown in Fig. 8.1. Many of these material systems are ternary (three-element) and quaternary (four-element) crystalline alloys that can be grown lattice-matched over a binary substrate.

Many of these materials were first used to make semiconductor lasers.[7-10,14-17] The lines represent the range of band gaps that can be obtained by varying the composition (fraction of the constituting elements) of the material. The optical gain in amplifiers occurs at wavelengths close to the band gap. Thus a suitable set of materials must be chosen to get optical gain at the desired wavelength.

Another important criterion in selecting the semiconductor material for a specific heterostructure design is related to lattice matching i.e., the crystalline materials that form the heterostructure and the substrate must have very small lattice constant mismatch. The binary substrates that are commonly used are GaAs and InP. They can be grown in a single crystal form from a melt. The ternary or quaternary semiconductors are epitaxially grown over the binary substrate for semiconductor laser fabrication. In the epitaxial growth process the single crystal nature is preserved across the interface of the two materials. This leads to near absence of defect sites at the interface. The 808 nm pump laser for Nd-doped rare earth amplifier is fabricated using $Al_xGa_{1-x}As$ material grown on GaAs substrate. $Al_xGa_{1-x}As$ is a direct gap semiconductor which is lattice matched to GaAs. The development of epitaxial growth techniques has been of major significance for the development of semiconductor photonic devices such as lasers, amplifiers, and photodetectors.

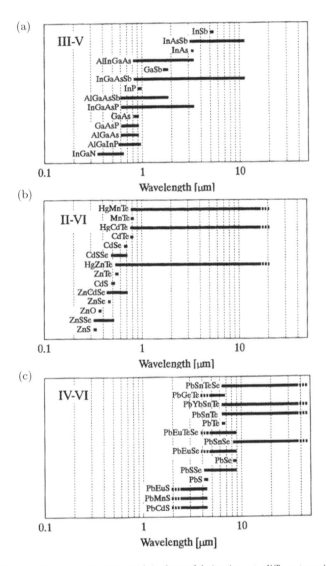

Fig. 8.1 Semiconductor materials used in laser fabrication at different regions of the spectrum. The three figures refer to compound semiconductors formed using group III and group V elements (III–V), group II and group VI elements (II–VI) and group IV and group VI elements (IV–VI) of the periodic table.[18] The quantum cascade lasers are fabricated using III–V semiconductors and they operate on intraband transitions in a quantum well.

The commonly used techniques for epitaxial growth are liquid phase epitaxy (LPE),[19] vapor-phase epitaxy (VPE),[20] molecular beam epitaxy (MBE),[21] metal organic chemical vapor deposition (MOCVD),[22] and chemical beam epitaxy.[23] Early work on lasers were carried out using the LPE growth technique. The MBE technique is very useful for the growth of very thin semiconductor layers and was first used to fabricate quantum well structures.[24] The MOCVD technique and its variants are generally used for commercial production of lasers, amplifier and photodetectors. These growth techniques are described in detail in Chapter 4 of Ref. 16. In addition to growth, processing techniques of semiconductor materials for laser or amplifier fabrication was developed. The processing techniques include current confinement, low resistance contacts and etching of the semiconductor material to form specific geometries.[25-30] The MOCVD technique and its variants are generally used for commercial production of lasers, amplifier and photodetectors.

8.2.1. *Metal Organic Chemical Vapor Deposition*

Metal organic chemical vapor deposition (MOCVD), also known as metal organic vapor phase epitaxy (MOVPE) is a technique that uses metal alkyls as sources from which epitaxial layers are formed.[31-43] The low pressure MOCVD technique where the gas pressure is ~ 0.1 atm was originally used for the growth of AlGaAs and InGaAsP semiconductors over GaAs and InP substrates respectively. MOCVD has proven to be a very versatile technique, it has been used to grow a wide variety of II–VI and III–V compound semiconductors.

Figure 8.2 shows the schematic of a low pressure MOCVD system. The quartz reaction chamber contains the InP substrate placed on a radio frequency (RF) heated ($\sim 600°C$) carbon susceptor. Group III alkyls ($Ga(C_2H_5)_3$ and $In(C_2H_5)_3$ and group V hydrides (AsH_3 and PH_3) are introduced into the reaction chamber. The gas flow near the substrate is laminar with velocities in the range of 1–15 cm/s for a pressure of ~ 0.1 atm. At the hot substrate surface, the metal alkyls and hydrides decompose, producing elemental In,Ga,As and P. The elemental species deposit on the surface forming an epitaxial

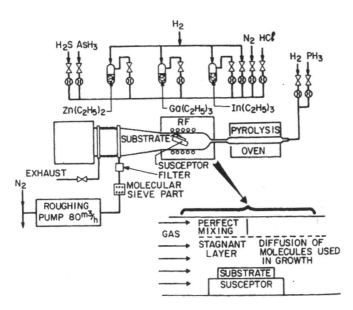

Fig. 8.2 Schematic illustration of a metal organic chemical vapor deposition (MOCVD) growth system.[37]

layer. The gas flow rates are controlled to produce InGaAsP layers of different compositions. $Zn(C_2H_5)_3$ and H_2S are used as sources for p-type (Zn-doped) and n-type (S-doped) doping respectively.

Although lattice matching is important for growth of high quality epitaxial layers, it is possible to make high quality semiconductor heterostructures with a small degree of lattice mismatch among them.[44–50] This lattice mismatch introduces a strain in the material, hence these are called strained layer heterostructures. The strain alters the band structure in a favorable way so as to produce higher gain than in the absence of strain. Typical values of tolerable strain ($\Delta a/a$ where a is the lattice constant of the substrate and Δa is the difference in lattice constant between the epitaxial layer and that of the substrate) are less than 1.5%. The larger the amount of strain, the thinner is the layer that can be grown free of dislocations on the substrate. Beyond a certain thickness, known as critical thickness, very large numbers of dislocations are generated. These dislocations reduce the luminescence property of the grown material.

The 980 nm pump laser for Er-doped rare earth is fabricated using $In_xGa_{1-x}As$ material grown on GaAs substrate. $In_xGa_{1-x}As$ is a direct gap semiconductor whose lattice mismatch with GaAs is $\sim 1.4\%$ for $x = 0.2$ i.e., $In_xGa_{1-x}As$ with $x = 0.2$ grown over GaAs emitting near 980 nm forms a strained layer suitable for stable and reliable laser operation.

In addition to growth, processing techniques of semiconductor materials for laser has been developed. The processing techniques include current confinement, low resistance contacts and etching of the semiconductor material to form specific geometries.[25-30]

8.2.2. *Operating Principle and Designs*

A schematic of a typical double heterostructure used for laser fabrication is shown in Fig. 8.3. It consists of a n-InP layer, undoped $In_{1-x}Ga_x P_yAs_{1-y}$ layer, p-InP layer and p-InGaAs layer grown over (100) oriented n-InP substrate. The undoped $In_{1-x}Ga_xP_yAs_{1-y}$ layer is the light emitting layer (active layer). It is lattice matched to InP for $x \sim 0.45\,y$. The band gap (E_g) of the $In_{1-x}Ga_xP_yAs_{1-y}$ material (lattice matched to InP) which determines the laser wavelength is given by[16]:

$$E_g(eV) = 1.35 - 0.72y + 0.12y^2.$$

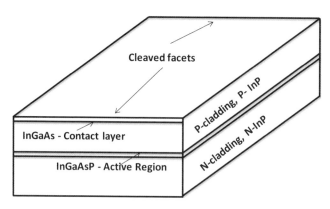

Fig. 8.3 Schematic of a semiconductor laser with no waveguide in the lateral (along the plane of p-n junction) direction. The cavity length is typically 200 to 400 μm for low power lasers. The laser facets ate cleaved. The side edges are generally saw cut.

For lasers emitting near 1.3 μm, y ~ 0.6. The double heterostructure material can be grown by LPE, GSMBE (gas source MBE) or MOCVD growth technique. The double heterostructure material can be processed to produce lasers in several ways. Perhaps the simplest is the broad area laser (Fig. 8.3) which involves putting contacts on the p and n-side and then cleaving.

The laser has a p-n junction which is forward biased during operation. The injected current produces gain in the active (gain) region. The majority carries are holes in the p-cladding layer and they are electrons in the n-cladding layers. The electrons and holes are injected into the gain region which is made of a lower band gap semiconductor than the cladding layers. The co-located electrons and holes recombine. This results in spontaneous emission of light and optical gain for light propagating in the gain region. It is a fortunate coincidence that semiconductor with lower band gap also has a higher index than semiconductors with higher band gap. The small index difference produces a waveguide for the propagating signal light. The signal is guided in this waveguide and it experiences amplification (gain) until it emerges from the output facet of the amplifier. Thus the double heterostructure material with n-type and p-type high band gap semiconductors around a low band gap semiconductor is instrumental in simultaneous confinement of the charge carriers (electrons and holes) and the optical signal. This is illustrated in Fig. 8.4. The electrons are located in the conduction band and holes are present in the valence band. In the gain region, the electrons and holes recombine to produce photons through both spontaneous and stimulated emission process. The optical gain of the input signal is due to the stimulated emission process. In the absence of current (electrons and holes), the semiconductor would absorb the incident photons. Certain minimum number densities of electrons (and holes) are needed to achieve net optical gain or amplification.

8.2.2.1. *Dielectric waveguide*

Low current operation of the laser requires that the optical signal remain confined in the vicinity of the gain region. In the double heterostructure this is accomplished by slightly higher index of the

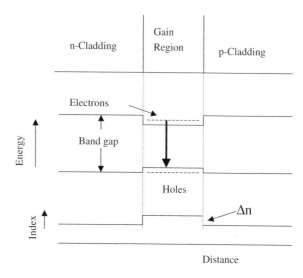

Fig. 8.4 Schematic illustration of confinement of the electrons and holes and also simultaneous confinement of optical mode in a double heterostructure.[16]

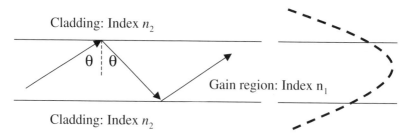

Fig. 8.5 Waveguiding in a double heterostructure. The gain region of index n_1 has cladding layers of index n_2 on both sides. The index $n_1 > n_2$. This figure shows the total internal reflection of a ray incident at an angle θ (with $\sin\theta > (n_2/n_1)$ propagating in the gain region. An alternate view is that a confined optical mode with intensity profile (shown dashed in the figure) propagates in the waveguide.[16]

gain material compared to that for the cladding materials. These three layers form a waveguide. The optical mode propagation in a three layer waveguide using the ray approach is shown in Fig. 8.5. The rays incident at an angle θ, with $\sin\theta > (n_2/n_1)$, undergoes total internal reflection at the interface of the cladding and active region.

Thus rays with angle of incidence larger than critical angle continue to propagate through the amplifier and gets amplified. Other

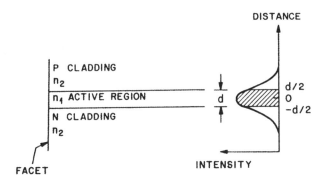

Fig. 8.6 The dielectric waveguide of the semiconductor amplifier. n_2 is the refractive index of the cladding layers and n_1 that of the active region. $n_1 > n_2$. The cladding layers are of a higher bandgap material than the active region. The intensity distribution of the fundamental mode is shown. The cross-hatched region represents the fraction of the mode Γ within the active region.

rays escape from the gain region. An alternative view is an optical mode with a certain profile determined by the thickness of the gain region and the indices can propagate through the amplifier without any diffraction loss. The intensity profile of a propagating mode is also sketched in Fig. 8.5.

Conceptually, stimulated emission in a semiconductor laser arises from electron-hole radiative recombination in the active region, and the light generated is confined and guided by a dielectric waveguide (Fig. 8.6). The active region has a slightly higher index than the p and n-type cladding layers, and the three layers form a dielectric waveguide. The energy distribution of the fundamental mode of the waveguide is also sketched in Fig. 8.6. A fraction of the optical mode is confined in the active region. Two types of fundamental transverse modes can propagate in the waveguide: The transverse electric (TE) and the transverse magnetic (TM) modes. The expression for the confinement factor (Γ), the fraction of mode in the active region, has been previously calculated.[16,17]

Figure 8.7 shows the calculated Γ as a function of active layer thickness for the TE and TM modes for the $\lambda = 1.3\,\mu m$ InGaAsP double heterostructure with p-InP and n-InP cladding layers. As the thickness of the active region increases, Γ approaches 1.

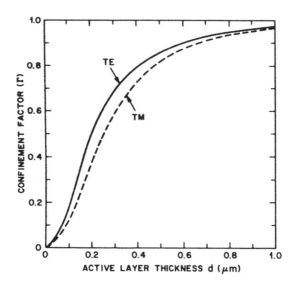

Fig. 8.7 Confinement factor of the fundamental TE and TM modes for a waveguide with InGaAsP ($\lambda = 1.3\,\mu$m) active layer and InP cladding layers as a function of the thickness of the active region.[16] The refractive indexes of the active and cladding region are 3.51 and 3.22, respectively.

For a three layer slab waveguide with cladding layer index n_2 and active layer index n_1, the confinement factor of the fundamental mode can be approximated by[16]:

$$\Gamma = D^2/(2 + D^2), \tag{8.1}$$

with $D = k_0 \, (n_1^2 - n_2^2)^{1/2} \, d$, where d is the thickness of the active region and $k_0 = 2\pi/\lambda_0$ where λ_0 is the wavelength in free space. The optical gain of a signal in the fundamental mode traveling through the amplifier is given by:

$$g_m = \Gamma g, \tag{8.2}$$

The mode gain (g_m) is proportional to the mode confinement factor Γ. Since the TE and TM modes have different confinement factors the optical gain for the TE and TM modes are different. Since Γ (TE) $> \Gamma$ (TM) (as shown in Fig. 8.7), and also the reflectivity of TE mode is larger than that for the TM mode,[16, 17] the semiconductor generally undergoes laser action in the TE mode.

8.2.2.2. *Condition for gain or laser action*

Sufficient numbers of electrons and holes must be excited in the semiconductor for stimulated emission or net optical gain.[15–19] A semiconductor with no injected carriers would absorb a photon whose energy is larger than the band gap. With increasing carrier injection this absorption decreases until there is no absorption (the material is transparent to the photon). At carrier densities higher than this amount the semiconductor will exhibit net optical gain. Consider the transition shown in Fig. 8.4 for a photon whose energy $h\nu = E = E_g + E_c + E_v$, where E_g is the band gap, E_c, E_v are energies of the electron and hole respectively. The photon can be absorbed creating an electron of energy E_c and hole of energy E_v. The stimulated emission rate is given by:

$$R_e = Bf_cf_v\rho(E), \qquad (8.3)$$

where B is the transition probability, $\rho(E)$ is the density of states of photons of energy E, $f_c(E_c)$ and $f_v(E_v)$ are the Fermi factors which is the probability that electron and hole states of energy E_c and E_v are occupied. The quantities $f_c(E_c)$ and $f_v(E_v)$ are given by:

$$f_c(E_c) = \frac{1}{1 + \exp[(E_c - E_{fc})/kT]}, \qquad (8.4)$$

$$f_v(E_v) = \frac{1}{1 + \exp[(E_v - E_{fv})/kT]}, \qquad (8.5)$$

where E_{fc}, E_{fv} are the quasi Fermi levels of the electrons and holes respectively. The stimulated emission process involves the recombination of an electron and hole pair and the absorption process creates an electron and hole pair. The absorption rate for photons of energy E is given by:

$$R_a = B(1 - f_c)(1 - f_v)\rho(E). \qquad (8.6)$$

The condition for net stimulated emission or gain is:

$$R_e > R_a, \qquad (8.7)$$

Using Eqs. (8.4) and (8.6) this becomes:

$$f_c + f_v > 1, \qquad (8.8)$$

Using Eqs. (8.4) and (8.5) for f_c and f_v the condition for gain at photon energy E becomes:

$$E_{fc} + E_{fv} > E - E_g, \tag{8.9}$$

The condition for zero net gain or zero absorption at photon energy is:

$$E_{fc} + E_{fv} = E - E_g, \tag{8.10}$$

Since the minimum value of E is E_g, the condition for gain at any energy is $E_{fc} + E_{fv} = 0$. This is often known as the condition for transparency.

For un-doped material at a temperature T the quasi-Fermi energy E_{fc} is related to the injected carrier (electron or hole) density n by[16]:

$$n = N_c \frac{2}{\sqrt{\pi}} \int \frac{d\varepsilon}{1 + \exp(\varepsilon - \varepsilon_{f_c})}, \tag{8.11}$$

with $N_c = 2(2\pi m_c \frac{kT}{h^2})^{3/2}$ and $\varepsilon_{f_c} = E_{f_c}/kT$,
where k is the Boltzmann constant, h is Planck's constant, T is the temperature, and m_c is the effective mass of the electrons in the conduction band. A similar equation holds for holes. Figure 8.8 shows the variation of the injected carrier density for transparency (n_t) as a function of temperature for undoped $\lambda = 1.3\,\mu$m InGaAsP. The parameter values used in the calculation are $m_c = 0.061\ m_0$, $m_{hh} = 0.45\ m_0$, $m_{lh} = 0.08\ m_0$, where m_0 m_{hh} m_{lh} are the free electrons,

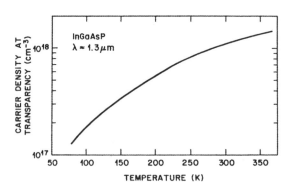

Fig. 8.8 The calculated injected carrier density for transparency as a function of temperature for undoped $\lambda = 1.3\,\mu$m InGaAsP.

heavy hole, and the light hole mass, respectively. Figure 8.8 shows that n_t, is considerably smaller at low temperatures. For optical gain the injected carrier density must be higher than n_t.

The optical gain (g) of a laser at a current density J has been calculated and measured.[16, 17] It is given by:

$$g = a(J - J_0), \tag{8.12}$$

where a is the gain constant and J_0 is the transparency current density.

The total cavity loss α_t is given by:

$$\alpha_t = \Gamma\alpha_a + (1 - \Gamma)\alpha_c + (1/L)\ln(1/R_1 R_2), \tag{8.13}$$

where α_a and α_c are the free carrier losses in the active and cladding region respectively, Γ is the mode confinement factor, L is the length of the optical cavity, and R_1, R_2 are the reflectivity of the two facets. At threshold, gain equals loss, hence it follows from (8.12) and (8.13) that the threshold current density (J_{th}) is given by:

$$J_{th} = \alpha/a + (1/La)\ln(1/R_1 R_2) + J_0, \tag{8.14}$$

with $\alpha = \Gamma\alpha_a + (1 - \Gamma)\alpha_c$.

Thus for a laser with high reflectivity facet coatings (R_1, $R_2 \sim 1$) and with low loss ($\alpha \sim 0$), $J_{th} \sim J_0$. For a quantum well (QW) laser (laser with a thin active region ~ 10 nm), $J_0 \sim 50\,\text{A/cm}^2$ and for a thick active region (~ 0.1 to $0.2\,\mu\text{m}$) laser, $J_0 \sim 700\,\text{A/cm}^2$, hence it is possible to get much lower threshold current using QW as the active region. The threshold current approximately given by $I_{th} = J_{th}\,LA$ where L is the length of the laser and A is the cross section of the active region. For a single mode laser, i.e., a laser operating in a single transverse mode, $A \sim 0.1$ to $0.2\,\mu\text{m}^2$ and L ~ 0.2 to 2 mm. For a laser with threshold current I_{th}, the power outputs (P_1 and P_2) from the facets with reflectivities R_1 and R_2 are given by:

$$P_1 = \eta(I - I_{th})(1/L)\ln(1/R_1)/\zeta$$
$$P_2 = \eta(I - I_{th})(1/L)\ln(1/R_2)/\zeta \tag{8.15}$$

with $\zeta = \alpha + (1/L)\ln(1/R_1 R_2)$.

The quantity η is the internal efficiency. In the absence of leakage current, $\eta \sim 0.8$ to 0.95. η is lower if they overlap between the optical mode and current distribution is low. Thus for higher power operation, i.e., more output power from one facet and less output power from the back facet, the laser is designed to have low front facet reflectivity (~3 to 5%) and high back facet reflectivity (~92 to 95%). These reflectivities are obtained using dielectric coatings on the facet of the laser.

The broad area lasers (Fig. 8.3) do not have transverse mode confinement or current confinement which leads to high threshold and nonlinearities in light vs. current characteristics. Several laser designs have been developed to address these problems. Among them are the gain guided laser, weakly index guided laser and buried heterostructure (strongly index guided) laser. A typical version of these laser structures is shown in Fig. 8.9. The gain guided structure uses a dielectric layer for current confinement. The current is injected

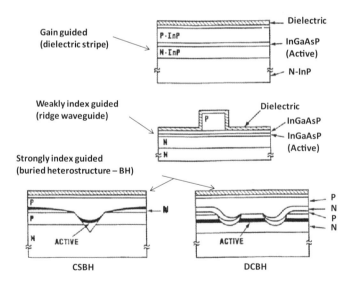

Fig. 8.9 Gain guided and index guided laser designs fabricated using the InGaAsP/InP material system. The layers labeled P and N are P-InP and N-InP layers. CSBH and DCBH are two buried heterostructure laser designs.[16]

in the opening in the dielectric (typically 6 to $12\,\mu$m wide), which produces gain in that region and hence the lasing mode is confined to that region. The weakly index guided structure has a ridge etched on the wafer, a dielectric layer surrounds the ridge. The current is injected in the region of the ridge, and the optical mode overlaps the dielectric (which has a low index) in the ridge. This results in weak index guiding. The buried heterostructure design shown in Fig. 8.9 has the active region surrounded (buried) by lower index layers. The large index difference ~0.3 ($\sim10\%$) between the active region and the surrounding regions lead to strong index guiding. Several strong index guided designs have been reported.[16]

8.3. 980 nm Laser

A single mode laser emitting near 980 nm is important as a pump laser for Er-doped single mode amplifier.[51-60] The light emitting region of a 980 nm laser is $In_xGa_{1-x}As$ with In mole fraction, $x \sim 0.2$. $In_xGa_{1-x}As$ has a slightly different lattice constant from GaAs. For $x \sim 0.2$, the lattice mismatch is $\sim1.4\%$. As stated earlier, thin epitaxial layers can be grown in the presence of a small lattice mismatch by a process called strained layer epitaxy. If the thickness of the grown layer exceeds a certain value (critical thickness), the grown layer has a lot of dislocations and is no longer suitable for device fabrication.[51] For a InGaAs/GaAs single quantum well, the critical well thickness (InGaAs layer thickness) is shown in Fig. 8.10 (dashed line). For thicknesses less than that shown by the dashed line, the grown material is free of dislocations.

Also shown in Fig. 8.10, solid lines corresponding to various emission wavelengths for a single quantum well laser. The figure illustrates that it is possible to fabricate laser emitting in the 900 nm to 1100 nm range using the $In_xGa_{1-x}As$/GaAs material.

8.3.1. *Single Mode 980 nm Laser*

For ~980 nm laser operation, thin layers of $In_{0.2}Ga_{0.8}As$ are grown on GaAs using either MOCVD or MBE growth technique. The lattice mismatch introduces a strain between the grown layer ($In_{0.2}Ga_{0.8}As$)

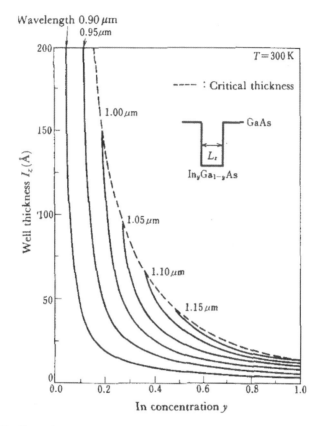

Fig. 8.10 In$_y$Ga$_{1-y}$As quantum well thickness vs. In composition for strained In$_y$ Ga$_{1-y}$As/GaAs single quantum well.[51]

and the substrate (GaAs). As a result such lasers are often called strained quantum well lasers. Typical design of a single mode 980 nm laser consists of one or two quantum wells of In$_{0.2}$Ga$_{0.8}$As surrounded by GaAs barrier layers. Exact well thickness needed for 980 nm laser operation is often determined experimentally. It is generally in the 7 to 10 nm range. For good transverse mode confinement often a graded index (GRIN) design is often used. The wafer is generally fabricated into a ridge waveguide type laser with a ridge width of ~4 μm for single transverse mode operation. Specific designs of active region for high power kink free operation or circular mode (i.e., nearly equal beam divergences along and normal to junction plane) has been

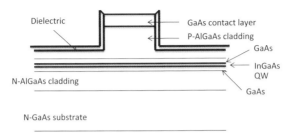

Fig. 8.11 A simple schematic of a ridge waveguide laser emitting near 980 nm. The device of Ref. 57 has graded index layers surrounding the active InGaAs quantum well (QW) region.

reported. The weak index guided ridge waveguide design allows a large area of the emitted light at the facet, thus, for a given output power the laser power density is lower at the facet compared to that of a strongly index guided buried heterostructure design. Lower optical power density at the facet reduces the probability of catastrophic mirror damage (COMD) at the facet. Various schemes have been developed to reduce/eliminate the COMD. The Schematic of a ridge waveguide laser is shown in Fig. 8.11.

This particular active region design provides high kink free output power. The output has an antireflection (AR ~4%) coating and the rear facet has a high reflection (HR ~93%) coating of dielectric materials. The Light vs. current characteristics of a 980 nm laser at different temperatures is shown in Fig. 8.12. Also shown is the voltage current (V–I) and slope (dP/dI–I) vs. current characteristics. The slope efficiency near room temperature is ~0.9 W/A. The far field patterns are shown in Fig. 8.13.

Reliability of the 980 nm pump laser has been extensively studied. The lasers are found to be reliable for communication system applications. Specialized facet coating in vacuum or impurity induced disordering has been used to reduce catastrophic mirror damage at high powers.

Another weakly index guided structure that operates to high power in a single transverse mode is the buried stripe design.[61-66] The design is shown in Fig. 8.14. The device was fabricated with two $In_{0.2}Ga_{0.8}As$ quantum wells. Both the current blocking layer (n-type

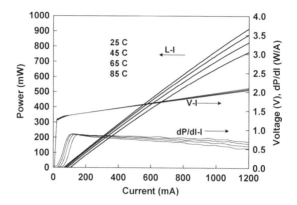

Fig. 8.12 Light vs. characteristics of a 980 nm laser.[58]

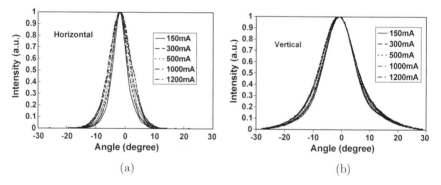

(a)   (b)

Fig. 8.13 The far field pattern along (horizontal) and normal (vertical) to the junction plane are shown. Single lobed pattern illustrates single transverse mode operation.[58]

shown) and the Si_3N_4 dielectric layer are effective in confining the current to the active region. The buried stripe width (W_b) is 2.2 μm. The CW light vs. characteristics of the laser at 25°C is shown in Fig. 8.15. The output facet is AR (antireflection) coated and the rear facet is HR (high reflection) coated. Also, shown is the derivative of $L-I$. It decreases with increasing current due to junction heating. Near threshold the differential quantum efficiency is $\sim$1 W/A. The laser operates kink-free to 500 mW. The far field pattern along the junction plane (horizontal) and normal to the junction plane (vertical) are measured. The traces are shown in Fig. 8.16. The full width at

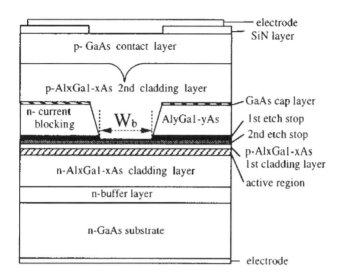

Fig. 8.14 Schematic of a weakly index guided buried stripe laser.[61]

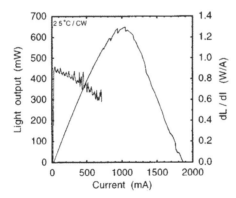

Fig. 8.15 CW light vs. current characteristics at a heat sink temperature of 25°C.[61]

half maximum (FWHM) of the far field along and normal to junction are 28° × 7° respectively. The FWHM along the junction broadens somewhat with increasing current probably due to current induced change in index. Figure 8.16 shows the laser operates in a single transverse mode at powers to ∼500 mW. A stable longitudinal mode is also observed to ∼500 mW.

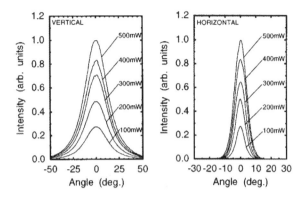

Fig. 8.16 Far field patterns normal to (vertical) and along (horizontal) the junction plane.[61]

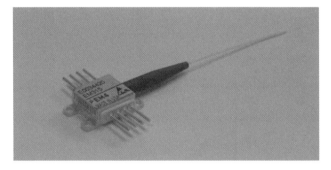

Fig. 8.17 Single mode pump laser package. The output is coupled to a single mode fiber.

An initial aging test on this structure has been carried out. The lasers are operated at 350 mW at 50°C. The data shows no degradation after 2000 h.[61] 980 nm lasers with InGaP cladding region have been fabricated.[64] These are known as Al-free lasers. Single mode lasers are typically packaged with a fiber coupled output (Fig. 8.17). The package has a thermoelectric cooler which keeps the laser at a certain temperature. The temperature control is important for fixed wavelength operation and for power stability.

8.3.2. *Multimode 970 nm Laser*

Lasers emitting near 960 to 970 nm are important as pump lasers for multimode large area Yb-doped fiber amplifier and also Er–Yb-doped

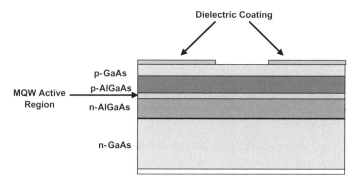

Fig. 8.18 Schematic of a 100 μm stripe laser. The current is injected through an opening in the dielectric.

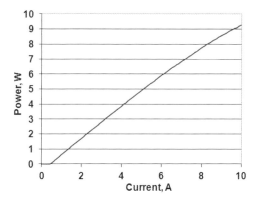

Fig. 8.19 CW Light vs. current characteristics of a 100 μm stripe laser at 25°C.

double clad fibers. These lasers are generally fabricated as $100\,\mu m$ wide stripe devices. A Schematic of the device cross section is shown in Fig. 8.18. The active region is InGaAs with In composition chosen to produce emission in the 960 to 970 nm wavelength range. The output facet is AR (anti-reflection) coated and the rear facet is HR (high-reflection) coated.

The light vs. current characteristics of a laser is shown in Fig. 8.19. The laser cavity length is 2 mm. The long cavity length is important for reducing thermal impedance. The lasers typically emit $\sim$9–10 W at 10 A. The lasers are similar to broad area lasers with an opening in the SiO_2 dielectric ($\sim$100 μm wide). The current is injected in the active region through this opening. This makes the mode area larger and hence lowers the power density at the facet which prevents high power induced facet degradation. For higher power operation, multiple openings (typically 50 to 100 μm wide) are present in the dielectric stripe. These openings are typically 50 to 100 μm apart. Lasers with 10 openings (10 stripes) emit in ten spots along the active region. The combined output power can be >100 W. These devices are also called laser arrays. These laser arrays have been stacked in two dimensions also and are known to produce nearly 1 kW in quasi-CW operation. These types of laser arrays have been used as a pump for Yb-doped lasers. Although the laser array does not produce a well collimated beam, the output from the Yb laser is well collimated. The conversion efficiency is also high (>70%). Thus the rare earth-doped lasers are also called brightness converters.

8.4. 1480 nm Laser

Lasers emitting near 1480 nm are important for Er-doped single mode amplifiers as a pump laser source. The laser must emit in a single transverse mode for high coupling efficiency to a single mode fiber. These lasers are fabricated using the InGaAsP/InP material system and have a strongly index guided buried heterostructure design.[67–76] A buried heterostructure design that has been used for 1480 nm pump laser fabrication is the capped mesa buried heterostructure (CMBH) design. The layer structure and scanning electron micrograph of a capped mesa (CMBH) buried heterostructure design along with the cross section are shown in Figs. 8.20 and 8.21 respectively. The current blocking layers in this structure consist of i-InP (Fe-doped InP), n-InP, i-InP and n-InP layers. These sets of blocking layers provide good current confinement, i.e., most of the current injected at the top contact goes through the active region instead of around it. An optimization of the thickness of these layers is needed for high output power.

The fabrication involves the following steps. An n-InP layer, an InGaAsP gain layer (active region), a p-InP layer, and a p-InGaAs layer are grown over a (100) oriented n-InP substrate using MOCVD

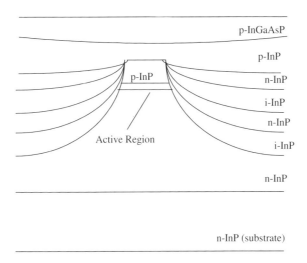

Fig. 8.20 The various layers of a buried heterostructure (BH) 1480 nm laser.

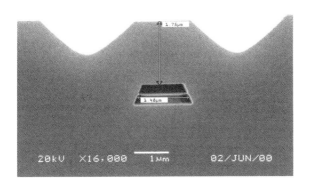

Fig. 8.21 Scanning electron photomicrograph of a buried heterostructure (BH) 1480 nm laser.

growth technique. The p-InGaAs layer is etched away. Then $\sim 1\,\mu m$ wide mesas are etched on the wafer using a SiO_2 mask and wet chemical etching. The current blocking layers consisting of i-InP, n-InP i-InP and n-InP layers are grown on the wafer using a second

MOCVD growth step with the SiO_2 (oxide) layer on top of the mesa in place.

The oxide layer is then removed and a third growth of p-InP cladding layer and p-InGaAs contact layer is carried out. The wafer is then processed using standard lithography, metal deposition and cleaving techniques to produce the chips. The chips are then antireflection (AR) coated ($\sim$4%) on the output facet and high reflection ($\sim$90%) coated on the other facet to produce high power 1480 nm pump lasers.

8.4.1. *Leakage Current*

For buried heterostructure devices the confinement of the injected current to the active region is achieved through reverse biased heterojunctions or forward biased InP homojunctions (which turn on at a voltage higher than that needed for laser emission). The difference between the total current I injected into the lasers and the current going through the active region (I_a) is the leakage current (I_l) i.e.,

$$I_l = I - I_a, \tag{8.16}$$

The magnitude of I_a and its variation with I depends on the carrier concentration of the current blocking layers, their thickness and also on the presence of any defects in the current confining junctions or in any of the layers. A large leakage current would lead to low optical power at high injected currents and is therefore not desirable.

For the analysis of leakage currents, a buried heterostructure design is represented by its electrical equivalent circuit. This circuit has several paths for the flow of current from p-contact to the n-contact; one of which is the active region, represented by a diode. For the purpose of illustration, one of the buried heterostructure designs of Fig. 8.9 along with its various electrical paths is shown in Fig. 8.22. The values of the resistors and the gain of the transistors determine these amount of leakage. These quantities are determined by the carrier concentration in the layers and their thickness. A detailed analysis of leakage in buried heterostructure designs is given in Ref. 76. The leakage path marked by I_l in the schematic of Fig. 8.22 shows the leakage path consisting of a resistor and a InP

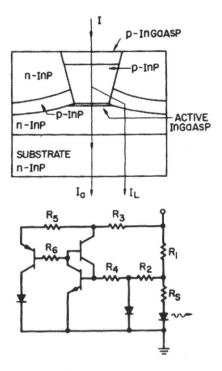

Fig. 8.22 Schematic cross section of a buried heterostructure design and its electrical equivalent circuit.[76]

homojunction diode. The electrical equivalent circuit of the active junction and this leakage path is shown in Fig. 8.22.

The low current turn-on voltage of the InP homojunction is higher than that of the laser active junction. However, at high current depending on the value of the resistors in each path the I–V curves associated with these two paths would cross and the homojunction leakage may exceed the current going through the active junction. This is also illustrated in Fig. 8.23. Thus the design of the current confinement layers with low leakage is important for the fabrication of pump lasers that operate at high power and hence high current.

8.4.2. Laser Design and Performance

In addition to low leakage current, a high differential quantum efficiency and low threshold current is important for high power

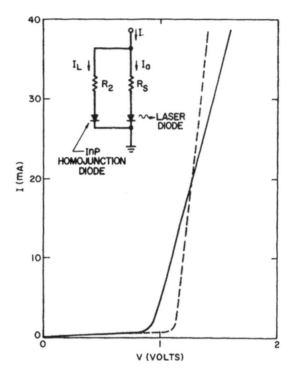

Fig. 8.23 Electrical equivalent circuit of an active heterojunction diode in parallel with a InP homojunction diode is shown in the inset. Representative I–V characteristics of the heterojunction diode path (solid curve) and that of the homojunction diode path (dashed curve).[76]

operation.[77–79] The optical losses in the active region determine these quantities. Thus it is important to optimize the active region design. The design used for a high power 1480 nm pump has a multiquantum well (MQW) active region with a graded index region (GRIN) for optical confinement. The scanning transmission electron micrograph (TEM) of a MQW active region is shown in Fig. 8.24.

The parameters that need to be optimized are doping of layers, number of wells, GRIN design and the optical cavity length. They are many trade-offs. For example, long cavity length reduces the thermal impedance but increases the threshold current and decreases quantum efficiency due to higher cavity optical loss. Similarly higher doping reduces resistance but increases optical loss. Increasing the

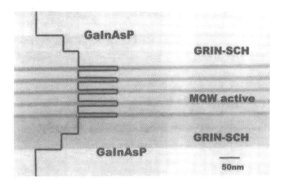

Fig. 8.24 Scanning transmission electron micrograph (TEM) of the active region of a 1480 nm pump laser.[77]

number of active layer wells increases the threshold current beyond a certain number of wells. An experimental investigation has been carried out using the active region band diagram shown in Fig. 8.25. The active layer is 40 Å thick InGaAs quantum wells with 130 Å thick InGaAsP ($\lambda \sim 1.15\,\mu$m, $E_g = 1.08$ eV) barriers. The width of the entire active region is 2000 Å. The wafers are grown by MOCVD and strongly index guided lasers are fabricated using the DCBH structure (Fig. 8.9). Lasers with 2, 3, 5, and 7 quantum wells are fabricated. The measured data on threshold current and inverse quantum efficiency as a function of cavity lengths is shown in Fig. 8.26. The quantity N_w is the number of wells in the active region.

The light vs. current characteristics of a 1800 μm long laser with five quantum wells at various temperatures is shown in Fig. 8.25. The laser emits more than 250 mW near room temperature.

Light vs. current characteristics of a laser with a GRIN heterostructure design is shown in Fig. 8.27. The data is for lasers with different cavity length. Also shown is the far field emission pattern. The laser emits in a single transverse mode. Longer lasers emit higher power before rollover due to lower thermal impedance. The aging data on 1480 nm lasers at high temperature and high power is shown in Fig. 8.28 in the automatic power control (APC) mode. The data show stable operation for 20,000 h at 60°C without a significant increase of drive current. The estimated mean time to

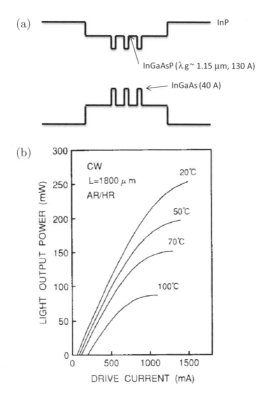

Fig. 8.25 (a): Band diagram of the MQW active region. (b): Light vs. current characteristics of a 1480 nm pump laser at various temperatures of the design shown in Fig. 8.24.[78]

failure (MTTF) using activation energy of 0.62 eV is 100 million h at 150 mW.

8.5. 808 nm Laser

Semiconductor laser emitting near 808 nm is important as a pump for Nd-doped rare earth material. Both single mode and multimode broad stripe 808 nm lasers are fabricated using the AlGaAs/GaAs material system.[80–86] The Al composition in the active region $Al_x Ga_{1-x} As$ is chosen so that the emission is near 808 nm. The band gap of $Al_x Ga_{1-x} As$ varies with the Al composition (x). The band gap E_g is given by $E_g(x) = 1.424 + 1.247\, x$ (eV). The layers are grown by MBE or MOCVD growth technique. The layers are: N-AlGaAs cladding layer, $Al_x Ga_{1-x} As$ active layer and P-AlGaAs cladding layer

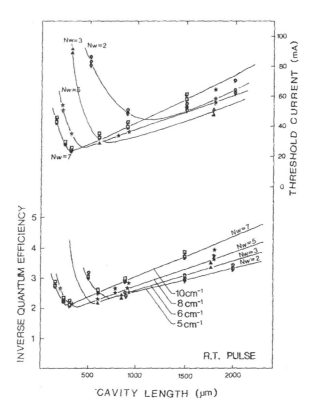

Fig. 8.26 Threshold current (room temperature, pulsed) and inverse quantum efficiency plotted as a function of cavity length of the design shown in Fig. 8.24.[78]

and P-GaAs contact layer. The grown wafer is fabricated into ridge waveguide lasers. The reliability of these types of lasers is generally limited by catastrophic facet degradation which occurs at high powers. A special facet coating process has been reported to lessen this problem. It involves the cleaving of the lasers in vacuum (to prevent facet oxidation) and applying a dielectric coating after cleaving. It is the same cleaving and coating process which lessens the degradation of lasers emitting near 980 nm.

8.5.1. *Single Mode 808 nm Laser*

For the single mode device described here, the active region is a single quantum well and is grown by MBE growth technique. The Light vs.

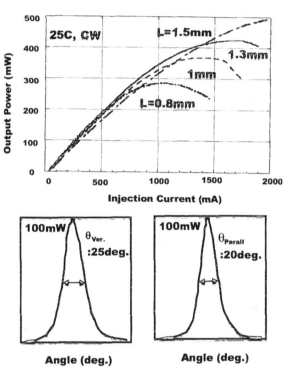

Fig. 8.27 (Top) Light vs. current characteristics for different cavity lengths. (Bottom) Far field pattern perpendicular and parallel to the junction plane.[77]

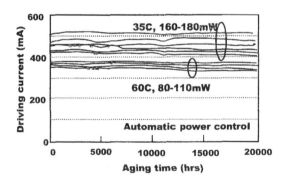

Fig. 8.28 Drive current as a function of operating time under the conditions shown.[77]

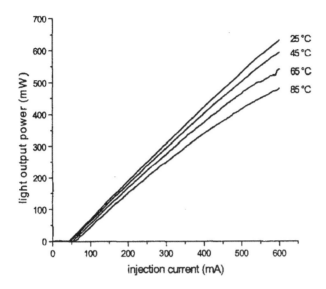

Fig. 8.29 Light vs. Current characteristics of a laser emitting near 808 nm.[84]

current characteristics at various temperatures is shown in Fig. 8.29. The laser has an antireflection coating at the emitting facet and high reflectivity coating at the rear facet. The device emits >800 mW at 25°C @ ~900 mA. The slope efficiency is ~1.1 W/A up to ~600 mA at 25°C. At higher current or higher temperature the slope efficiency decreases due to increase in junction temperature.

The single transverse mode nature of the emission is determined through a measurement of the far field characteristics. The far field pattern shown in Fig. 8.30 shows a full-width at half maximum normal to the junction plane and along the junction plane of 27° and 7° respectively.

The aging test results on 25 devices are shown in Fig. 8.31. The lasers are first operated at 300 mA (~300 mW for 1000 h followed by operation at 400 mA (~400 mW) for 1000 h. The results show stable operation.

8.5.2. *Multimode 808 nm Laser*

Multimode devices with 100 μm stripe width have been reported. They produce several W of output power and generally fail after

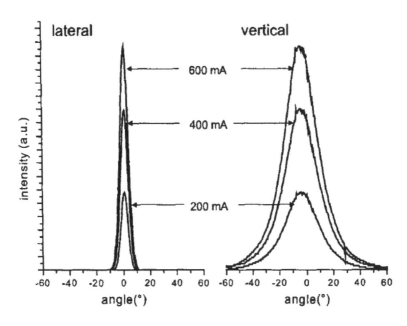

Fig. 8.30 Far field pattern along (lateral) and normal (vertical) to junction plane.[84]

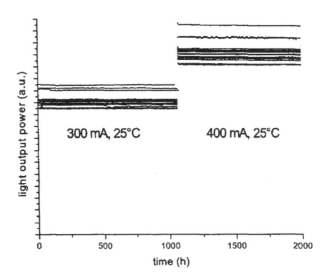

Fig. 8.31 Aging test results at high power.[84]

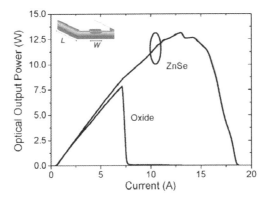

Fig. 8.32 CW light vs. characteristics of 808 nm stripe lasers tested to peak power.[86] Stripe width is 100 μm.

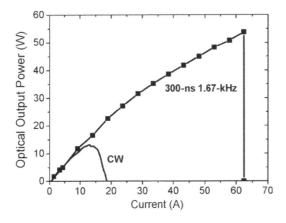

Fig. 8.33 Pulsed and CW light vs. characteristics of 100 μm stripe lasers tested to peak power.[86] The lasers have ZnZe coating on facets for passivation.

sometime due to catastrophic mirror damage (COMD). An example of light vs. current characteristics of a facet passivated device (ZnSe coated) and unpassivated device is shown in Fig. 8.32. The passivated device operates to peak power without sudden degradation and rolls over due to heating. The inset shows a schematic of the 100 μm stripe design.

The passivated device emits 55 W of peak power for short pulse operation (Fig. 8.33). Under short pulse operation the heating is reduced hence the thermal rollover of Fig. 8.32 does not take place.

Semiconductor lasers operating at high power have been fabricated at many wavelengths. They offer reliable turn-key pump sources for rare earth-doped amplifiers and lasers. Advances in cooling schemes described in Chapter 11 has resulted in >100 W of cw output power from rare earth-doped lasers using semiconductor laser pump sources.

References

1. A.L. Schawlow and C.H. Townes, *Phys. Rev.* **112** (1958) 1940.
2. T.H. Maiman, *Nature* **187** (1960) 493.
3. A. Javan, W.R. Bennett, Jr and D.R. Herriot, *Phys. Rev. Lett.* **6** (1961) 106.
4. N.G. Basov, O.N. Krokhin and Yu. M. Popov, *Sov. Phys. JETP* **13** (1961) 1320.
5. M.G.A. Bernard and G. Duraffourg. *Phys. Status Solidi.* **1** (1961) 699.
6. W.P. Dumke, *Phys. Rev.* **127** (1962) 1559.
7. R.N. Hall, G.E. Fenner, J.D. Kingley, T.J. Soltys and R.O. Carlson, *Phys. Rev. Lett.* **9** (1962) 366.
8. M.I. Nathan, W.P. Dumke, G. Burns, F.H. Dill, Jr and G. Lasher, *Appl. Phys. Lett.* **1** (1962) 63.
9. T.M. Quist, R.H. Rediker, R.J. Keyes, W.E. Krag, B. Lax, A.L. McWhorter and H.J. Ziegler, *Appl. Phys. Lett.* **1** (1962) 91.
10. N. Holonyak Jr and S.F. Bevacqua, *Appl. Phys. Lett.* **1** (1962) 82.
11. Zh.I. Alferov V.M. Andreev E.L. Portnoi and M.K. Trukan, *Sov. Phys. Semiconductors* **3** (1970) 1107.
12. I. Hayashi, M.B. Panish, P.W. Foy and S. Sumski, *Appl. Phys. Lett.* **17** (1970) 109.
13. H. Kroemer, *Proc. IEEE.* **51** (1963) 1782.
14. H. Kressel and J.K. Butler, *Semiconductor lasers and Heterojunction LEDs.* New York: Academic Press. 1977.
15. H.C. Casey, Jr and M.B. Panish, *Heterostructure Lasers.* New York: Academic Press (1978).
16. G.P. Agrawal and N.K. Dutta, *Semiconductor Lasers.* 2nd Edition. New York: Van Nostrand Reinhold. 1992.
17. L.A. Coldren and S.W. Corzine, *Diode Lasers and Photonic Integrated Circuits.* New York: John Wiley. 1995.
18. P.G. Eliseev, Chapter 2. In *Semiconductor Lasers II*, E. Kapon (Ed.) Academic Press (1998).
19. H. Nelson, *RCA Rev.* **24** (1963) 603.
20. W.F. Finch and EW. Mehal, *J. Electrochem Soc.* **111** (1964) 814.
21. A.Y. Cho, *J. Vac. Sci. Technol.* **8** (1971) 531.
22. R.D. Dupuis, *J. Crystal Growth* **55** (1981) 213.
23. W.T. Tsang, *Appl. Phys. Lett.* **45** (1984)1234.
24. R. Dingle, W. Wiegmann and C.H. Henry. *Phys. Rev. Lett.* **33** (1974) 827.

25. J.C. Dyment, *Appl. Phys. Lett.* **10** (1967) 84.

26. J.J. Hsieh, J.A. Rossi, and J.P. Donnelly. *Appl. Phys. Lett.* **28** (1976) 709.

27. Y. Suematsu, *Proc. IEEE.* **71** (1983) 692.

28. I.P. Kaminow, R.E. Nahory, M.A. Pollack, L.W. Stulz and I.C. Dewinter. *Electron. Lett.* **15** (1979) 763.

29. Y. Suematsu, K. Iga and K. Kishino. In *GaInAsP Alloy Semiconductors*, T.P. Pearsall (Ed.) New York: John Wiley & Sons. 1982.

30. R.J. Nelson and N.K. Dutta. In *Semiconductor and Semimetals*, W.T. Tsang (Ed.). New York: Academic Press. 1985.

31. H.M. Manasevit and W.I. Simpson. *J. Electrochem. Sac.* **116** (1969) 1725.

32. Y. Seki, K. Tanno, K. Iida and E. Ichiki. *J. Electrachem. Soc.* **122** (1975) 1108.

33. R.D. Dupuis, P.D. Dapkus, R.D. Yingling and L.A. Moudy. *Appl. Phys. Lett.* **31** (1978) 201.

34. R.D. Dupuis, *J. Cryst. Growth.* **55** (1981) 213.

35. P.D. Dapkus, *Annu. Rev. Mater. Sci.* **12** (1982) 243.

36. J.P. Hirtz, M. Razeghi, M. Bonnet and J.P. Duchemin, Chapter. 3. In *GaInAsP Alloy Semiconductors*, T.P. Pearsall (Ed.). New York: John Wiley & Sons, 1982; S. Hersee and J.P. Duchemin. *Annu. Rev. Mater. Sci.* **12** (1982) 65.

37. J.P. Hirtz, J.P. Larivain, J.P. Duchemin, T.P. Pearsall and M. Bonnet, *Electron. Lett.* **16** (1980) 415.

38. J.P. Hirtz, J.P. Larivain, D. Leguen, M. Razeghi and J.P. Duchemin, In *Gallium Arsenide and Related Compounds 1980*, Conference. series 1956, Institute of Phys. Bristol, (1981) pp. 29–35.

39. J.P. Hirtz, M. Razeghi, J.P. Larivain, S. Hersee and J.P. Duchemin, *Electron. Lett.* **17** (1981) 113.

40. M. Razeghi, S. Hersee, J.P. Hirtz, R. Blondeau, B. de Cremoux and I.P. Duchemin, *Electron. Lett.* **19** (1983) 336.

41. T. Fukui and Y. Horikoshi, *Jpn. J. Appl. Phys.* Part 1. **19** (1980) 395.

42. C.B. Cooper, R.R. Saxena and M.J. Ludowise, *Electron. Lett.* **16** (1980) 892.

43. J. Yoshino, T. lawnot and H. Kukimoto, *J. Cryst. Growth.* **55** (1981) 74.

44. T. Tanbun-Ek, R.A. Logan, H. Temkin, S.N.G. Chu, N.A. Olsson, A.M. Sergent and K.W. Wecht, *IEEE J. Quantum Electron.* QE-**26** (1990) 1323.

45. G.C. Osbourne, *J. Vac. Sci. Technol.* B-**1** (1983) 379.

46. W.T. Massalink, T. Henderson, J. Klem, R. Fischer, P. Pearah, H. Morkoc, M. Hafich, P.D. Wang and G.Y. Robinson, *Appl. Phys. Lett.* **45** (1984) 1309.

47. S.E. Fischer, D. Fekete, G.B. Feak and J.A. Ballantyne, *Appl. Phys. Lett.* **50** (1984) 714.

48. J.W. Matthews and A.E. Blakeslee, *J. Cryst. Growth.* **27** (1974) 118.

49. T. Tanbun-Ek, R.A. Logan, H. Temkin, S.N.G. Chu, N.A. Olsson, A.M. Sergent and K.W. Wecht. *IEEE J. Quantum Electron.* QE-**26** (1990) 1323.

50. P.R. Berger, K. Chang, P. Bhattacharya, J. Singh and K.K. Bajaj. *Appl. Phys. Lett.* **53** (1988) 684.

51. S. Uehara, Chapter 8. In *Optical Amplifiers and Their Applications*, S. Shimada and H. Ishio, (Eds.) John Wiley. 1994.

52. G.W. Yang, J.Y. Xu, Z.T. Xu, L H. Chen and Q.M. Wang, *J. Appl. Phys.* **83** (1998) 8.

53. G. Lin, S. Yen, C. Lee and D. Liu, *IEEE Photon. Technol. Lett.* **8** (1996) 1588.

54. M. C. Wu, Y.K. Chen, M. Hong, J.P. Mannaerts, M.A. Chin and A.M. Sergent, *Appl. Phys. Lett.* **59** (1991) 1046.

55. T. Temmyo and S. Sugo, *Electron. Lett.* **31** (1995) 642.

56. S.T. Yen and C.P. Lee, *IEEE J. Quantum Electron.* **32** (1996) 1588.

57. K. Shigihara, K. Kawasaki, Y. Yoshida, Si Yamamura, T. Yagi and E. Omura, *IEEE JQE.* **38** (2002) 1081.

58. G. Yang, G.M. Smith, M.K. Davis, A. Kussmaul, D.A.S. Loeber, M.H. Hu, H-K Nguyen, C.E. Zah and R. Bhat, *IEEE Photonic Tech. Letts.* **16** (2004) 981.

59. C.J. Chang-Hasnain, R. Bhat, H. Leblanc and M.A. Koza, *Electron. Lett.* **29** (1993) 1.

60. G. Hunziker and C. Harder, *Appl. Opt.* **34** (1995) 6118.

61. H. Horie, N. Arai, Y. Mitsuishi, N. Komuro, H. Kaneda, H. Gotoh, M. Usami and Y. Matsushima, *IEEE Photonic Tech. Lett.* **12** (2000) 1304.

62. A. Okubo, Y. Yamada, Y. Oeda, K. Igarashi, T. Fujimoto, Y. Yamada and K. Muro, *In Proceedings. Tech. Dig. Optical Fiber Commun. Conference.*, San Diego, CA, 1999, paper TuC3.

63. T. Hiramoto, M. Sagawa, T. Kikawa and S. Tsuji, *IEEE J. Select. Topics Quantum Electron.* **5** (1999) 817.

64. H. Horie, S. Nagao, K. Shimoyama and T. Fujimori, *Jpn. J. Appl. Phys.* **38** (1999) 5888.

65. M. Usami, N. Edagawa, Y. Matsushima, H. Horie, I. Sakamoto, T. Fujimori and H. Gotoh. *In Proceedings, Optical Fiber Commun.* San Diego, CA, 1999, paper PD-39.

66. H. Horie, H. Ohta, Y. Yamamoto, N. Arai, B. Kelly, T. Fujimori, H. Gotoh, M. Usami and Y. Matsushima, *Proc. SPIE,* **3945** (2000) 280.

67. M. Hirao, S. Tsuji, K. Mizuishi, A. Doi and M. Nakamura, *J. Opt. Commun.* **1** (1980) 10.

68. I. Mito, M. Kitamura, K. Kobayashi, S. Murata, M. Seki, Y. Odagiri, H. Nishimoto, M. Yamaguchi and K. Kobayashi, *J. Lightwave Technol.* LT-1 (1983) 195.

69. I. Mito, M. Kitamura, K. Kaede, Y. Odagiri, M. Seki, M. Sugimoto and K. Kobayashi, *Electron. Lett.* **18** (1982) 2.

70. R.J. Nelson, P.D. Wright, P.A. Barnes, R.L. Brown, T. Cella and R.G. Sobers, *Appl. Phys. Lett.* **36** (1980) 358.

71. H. Ishikawa, H. Imai, T. Tanahashi, Y. Nishitani, M. Takusagawa and K. Takahei, *Electron. Lett.* **17** (1981) 465.

72. N.K. Dutta, D.P. Wilt, P. Besomi, W.C. Dautremont-Smith, P.D. Wright and R.J. Nelson, *Appl. Phys. Lett.* **44** (1984) 483.

73. R.A. Logan, J.P. Van der Ziel and H. Tamkin, *Proc. SPIE Int. Soc. Opt. Eng.* **380** (1981) 181.

74. M. Oron, N. Tamari, H. Shtrikman and C.A. Burrus, *Appl. Phys. Lett.* **41** (1982) 609.

75. T. Murotani, E. Oomura, H. Higuchi, H. Namizaki and W. Susaki, *Electron. Lett.* 16 (1980) 566.

76. N.K. Dutta, D.P. Wilt and R.J. Nelson, *J. Lightwave Technol.* LT-**2** (1984) 201.

77. A. Kasukawa, Chapter 3. In *WDM Technologies: Active Optical Components*, A. K. Dutta, N. K. Dutta and M. Fujiwara (Eds.).

78. H. Asano, S. Takano, M. Kawaradani, M. Kitamura and I. Mito, *IEEE Photonic Tech. Letts.* **3** (1991) 415.

79. T. Tanbun-Ek, R.A. Logan, N.A. Olsson, H. Temkin, A.M. Sergent and K.W. Wecht, *Appl. Phys. Lett.* **57** (1990) 224.

80. J. Sebastian, G. Beister, F. Bugge, F. Buhrandt, G. Erbert, H.G. Hänsel, R. Hülsewede, A. Knauer, W. Pittroff, R. Staske, M. Schröder, H. Wenzel, M. Weyers, and G. Tränkle, *IEEE J. Sel. Topics Quantum Electron.* **7** (2001) 334.

81. J.N. Walpole, *Opt. Quantum Electron.* **28** (1996) 623.

82. G. Erbert, J. Fricke, R. Hülsewede, A. Knauer, W. Pittroff, P. Ressel, J. Sebastian, B. Sumpf, H. Wenzel and G. Tränkle, *Proc. SPIE*, **29** (2003) 4995.

83. F. Dittmar, B. Sumpf, J. Fricke, G. Erbert and G. Tränkle, *IEEE Photonic Tech. Lett.* **18** (2006) 601.

84. S. Pawlik, J. Muller, N. Lichtenstein, D Jaeggi and B. Schmidt, *In Proceedings. Optical Fiber Communication.* Paper ThP3. (2000).

85. Y. He, H. An, J. Cai, C. Galstad, S. Macomber and M. Kanskar, *Electron Letts.* **45** (2009) 3.

86. P. Crump, H. Wenzel, G. Erbert, P. Ressel, M. Zorn, F. Bugge, S. Einfeldt, R. Staske, U. Zeimer, A. Pietrzak and G. Tränkle, *IEEE Photonic Tech. Letts.* **20** (2006) 1378.

Chapter 9

Transmission System Application

9.1. Introduction

Erbium-doped fiber amplifier (EDFA) which operates in the telecommunication wavelength band (~1530 to 1560 nm) is an important device for both terrestrial and submarine optical communication systems and next generation all-optical networks.[1-20] The amplification factor or gain can be greater than 100 (>20 dB) in some of these applications. The amplifiers used are single mode amplifiers, i.e., the amplifier fiber has a single mode core doped with Er. For high power, an Er–Yb co-doped double clad amplifier with a doped single mode core is also used.

The amplifiers are deployed in terrestrial multichannel Wavelength division multiplexed (WDM) networks where the typical transmission distance prior to regeneration is ~40 km. In these systems the amplifier could be used as a post amplifier (i.e., after transmitter) or as a preamplifier (i.e., prior to the receiver). The first submarine application of optical amplification was for a link across the Atlantic Ocean. Since then, many long distance submarine links have been deployed. Instead of conventional regenerators, a chain of optical amplifiers spaced about 60 km for the entire link distance of ~6000 km (for Atlantic system) have been deployed. The link using optical amplifiers has the advantage that it can be upgraded to higher data rate simply by changing the transmitters and receivers which are located on the shores unlike a link using conventional regenerators where an entirely new system with new regenerators need to be deployed for higher capacity. Thus increasing the capacity for amplifier links is much easier. Amplifiers have also been used for short distance submarine links; such would be the case for population centers (cities) located along the shores or from mainland to an island. These amplifier based systems are often referred to as bit-rate flexible transmission system.

9.2. Long Distance Transmission

Various transmission system experiments for long distance transmission are described in this section. These are bit-rate flexible link, multiwavelength WDM links, and very long distance loop transmission experiments.

9.2.1. *Bit-Rate Flexible Link*

A typical optical transmitter and optical receiver schematic is shown in Fig. 9.1. The transmitter has a InGaAsP distributed feedback (DFB) laser (operating near 1550 nm) the output of which is modulated using a LiNbO$_3$ modulator. The modulator is driven by a 5 Gb/s or 10 Gb/s data. The output power of the modulator is

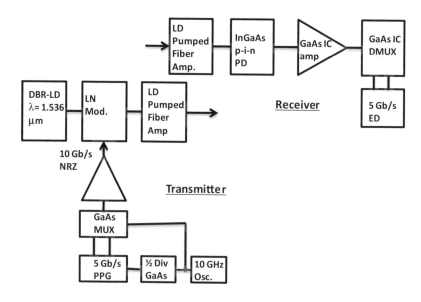

Fig. 9.1 Transmitter and receiver configurations.[19]

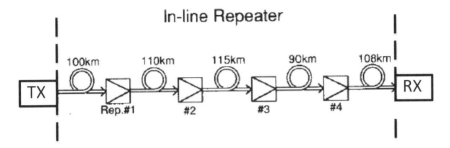

Fig. 9.2 Link Schematic.[19] The devices marked represent #1, 2, 3, 4 which are EDFAs. TX and RX are transmitters and receivers as shown in Fig. 9.1. The transmitter is followed by a EDFA post amplifier and the receiver has a EDFA preamplifier prior to photodiode.

amplified using an EDFA. The receiver has an EDFA preamplifier followed by a InGaAs photodiode and electronics.

A 500 km long bit-rate flexible link has been demonstrated using this transmitter and receiver configuration. The link has four EDFAs as shown in Fig. 9.2. The transmitter uses a distributed Bragg reflector (DBR) laser. The laser is modulated by a LiNbO$_3$ external modulator. The laser diode (LD) pumped fiber amplifier follows the modulator as a post amplifier. The modulator is driven by a 5 Gb/s Pulse pattern generator (PPG). The receiver has a preamplifier (EDFA) pumped by a LD. The error detector (ED) measures the error rate.

The distances between the EDFAs in the 500 km link are shown in Fig. 9.2. The input power for each EDFA in the link is ~ -15 dBm and the output power is ~ 0 to 5 dBm. Optical filters, 1 nm wide, are used to reduce the spontaneous emission noise at each amplifier. The number of EDFAs in the transmission link depends on the distance and data rate. At higher data rates the dispersion effects are larger. So, often dispersion compensating fibers (DCF) are used along with EDFA at each amplifier/repeater junction. The power level through a 505 km transmission link for 10 Gb/s experiment is shown in Fig. 9.3. There were 5 in-line EDFAs for this experiment. Note the EDFA amplifies the power back to ~ 0 dBm.

The bit error rate (BER) performance for 5 Gb/s and 10 Gb/s transmission is shown in Figs. 9.4 and 9.5 respectively. The receiver

Fiber Amplifiers and Fiber Lasers

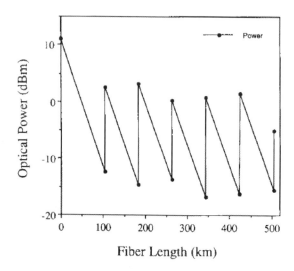

Fig. 9.3 Power levels at the 505 km amplifier chain for 10 Gb/s operation.[19]

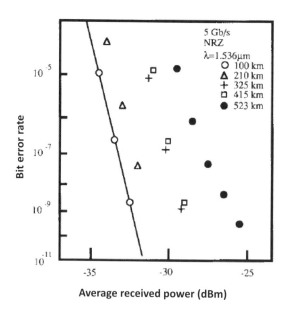

Fig. 9.4 (BER) measurement as a function of received power for 5 Gb/s transmission.[19]

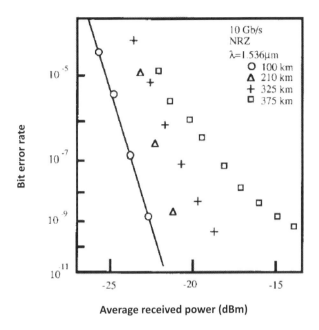

Fig. 9.5 BER measurement as a function of received power for 10 Gb/s transmission.[19]

sensitivity i.e., the received power needed for 10^{-9} BER increases with increasing transmission distance. The power penalty (increase in receiver sensitivity with distance) is larger for 10 Gb/s transmission than that for 5 Gb/s transmission. This is due to larger filter width needed for 10 Gb/s data. The results show that 505 km transmission at 10 Gb/s is feasible.

9.2.2. WDM Transmission Experiment

A WDM transmission experiment with 32 wavelength channels (100 GHz apart on the ITU grid) with each channel operating at 10 Gb/s over ∼500 km transmission distance has been carried out.[21] The system uses four booster amplifiers. Each booster amplifier has two EDFAs with a DCF — fiber with high negative dispersion. The booster amplifier gains are ∼30 dB. The schematic of the experiment is shown in Fig. 9.6. The fiber loss is 0.19 dB/km.

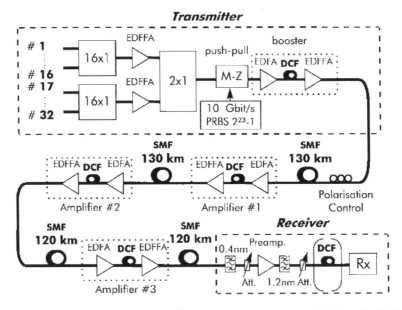

Fig. 9.6 Schematic of the experiment.[21] The experiment uses two EDFAs with DCF in between as single amplifier blocks. DCFs are needed for dispersion compensation of high data rate signals. The dispersion causes pulse broadening.

The optical spectrum at the transmitter and at the receiver after ~500 km transmission shows all 32 wavelengths with some variation in power. Error-free transmission (BER $<10^{-9}$) for all wavelength channels is observed. Figure 9.7 shows the receiver sensitivity i.e., received power for BER of 10^{-9} for the entire transmitted wavelength range. Adding an extra DCF reduces the BER sensitivity for longer wavelength channels.

9.2.3. *Loop Transmission Experiment*

To simulate very long distance transmission (many thousands of km), a loop experiment is done. In a loop experiment, the optical data circulates in a loop many times.[22–27] The loop (Fig. 9.8) typically has all the elements of a transmission experiment such as fibers and chain of amplifiers. Typical loop lengths are few tens of km to few hundreds of km. The transmitter, receiver and the error rate test equipment are outside the loop. The experiment starts with the transmitter switch

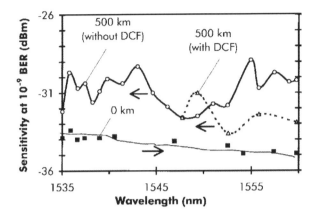

Fig. 9.7 Receiver sensitivity for 0 km (back to back) and after 500 km.[21] Bit rate is 10 Gb/s.

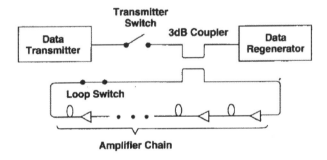

Fig. 9.8 Schematic of a loop transmission experiment.[27]

on to load the loop with data. The data is allowed to circulate in the loop for some specified number of revolutions. The number of revolutions corresponds to the total transmission distance. The delay per loop circulation is known from loop length ($\sim$4.9 ps/km of fiber). After a specific total transmission distance, the data is let out of the loop by a switch and the error rate is measured. Figure 9.9 shows the eye diagram and BER measurement after 9000 km of transmission at 5 Gb/s. The back-to-back BER (i.e., $\sim$0 km) is also shown in the figure. BER of less than 10^{-9} is obtained. Similar error free performance was obtained after 20,000 km of transmission.

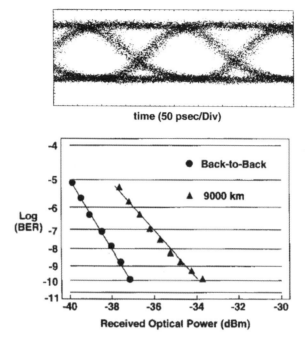

Fig. 9.9 (Top) Eye diagram after 9000 km of transmission at 5 Gb/s (Bottom) BER as a function of received power back to back (left) and after 9000 km (right.).[27]

9.2.4. *Distributed EDFA*

A class of EDFAs, known as distributed EDFA, has been investigated for long distance fiber transmission.[28–39] For distributed EDFA (DEDFA), the amplifier gain is present over the entire length of the transmission fiber. For this purpose the transmission fiber is lightly doped with Er and pumped along the entire length with multiple 1480 nm pump lasers. In the absence of Er, the absorption of 1480 nm pump is $\sim$0.3 dB/km. The gain of the DEDFA, depends on the number of 1480 nm pump sources used. Optical signal gains of $\sim$10 dB has been reported using multiple pump sources. Initial experiments using DEDFA has been for the demonstration of soliton propagation over long distances.

The following describes a NRZ experiment using DEDFA (Fig. 9.10). The pulses are generated using a mode locked external cavity laser. The pulse width is $\sim$8 ps (repetition rate 10 GHz)

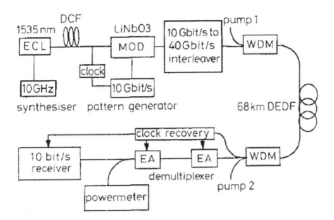

Fig. 9.10 Schematic of a DEDFA transmission experiment at 40 Gb/s over 68 km of DEDFA.[35]

with a time-bandwidth product off ~0.4. The NRZ data at 10 Gb/s is impressed using a LiNbO₃ modulator. For the 40 Gb/s experiment, the 10 Gb/s pulses are multiplexed to 40 Gb/s. The pulses are transmitted through 68 km of DEDFA pumped with 100 mW (total) of 1480 nm pump. The DEDFA net amplification is ~2 dB with −3 dBm input power. The DEDFA fiber is lightly doped with Er. The unpumped attenuation of the doped fiber is ~0.68 dB/km.

At the receiving end, the signal is demultiplexed to 10 Gb/s and the error-rate is measured using a BER detector. The demultipexer is based on electroabsorption modulator. The BER data is shown in Fig. 9.11.

9.3. Coherent Transmission

EDFA has been used in coherent transmission system experiments for achieving longer distance transmission.[40-49] Frequency shift keying (FSK) mode is used for the transmitter. The source is a DFB laser with the two sections (ME-DFB laser in Fig. 9.12). One of the sections is biased CW and the current in the other section is modulated so that the emission frequency of the signal varies with the modulation current. This generates a FSK signal. The receiver has a DFB single wavelength laser as a local oscillator (LO DFB

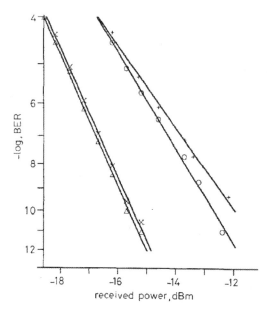

Fig. 9.11 Error-rate as a function of received power for various cases as indicated. The crosses and triangles are back-to-back and after transmission at 10 Gb/s. The circles and dots are back-to-back and after transmission at 40 Gb/s.[36]

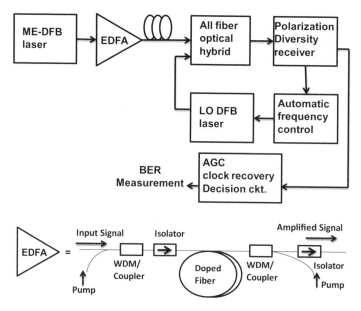

Fig. 9.12 Schematic of a coherent FSK transmission system.[44] The EDFA is shown at the bottom.

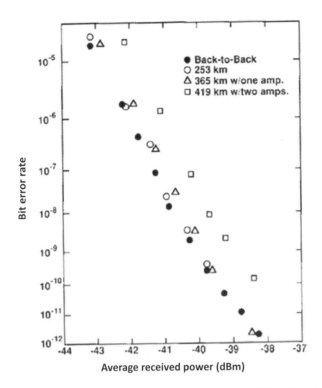

Fig. 9.13 FSK coherent system transmission results using EDFAs. The data rate is 1.7 Gb/s.[44]

laser). A polarization diversity scheme is used to increase the receiver sensitivity.

The EDFA is forward and backward pumped with laser diodes with output power of ~18 dBm each. The output of the EDFA is >15 dBm. Results of a transmission experiment at 1.7 Gb/s using the coherent FSK transmission format is shown in Fig. 9.13. EDFAs are added to increase the transmission distance. A 253 km transmission span was achieved (as a system) without EDFA. The span length increases to 365 km and 415 km using one and two EDFAs in the link respectively.

A CPFSK transmission system using ten EDFAs in a 1028 km transmission link has been reported. The system operates at 565 Mb/s. It uses a polarization diversity receiver similar to that used in the previous experiment. The input to the receiver goes to a polarization beam splitter. The polarization beam splitter (PBS) module splits the data input into four beams. Two sets of these go to balanced receivers and another beam from the local oscillator module is added to the PBS module for mixing at the photodiodes.

The schematic of the transmission system experiment is shown in Fig. 9.14 (a). It consists of 10 EDFAs (noted as REP1 to 10 in the figure). The single mode fiber links between each EDFA is $\sim$100 km.

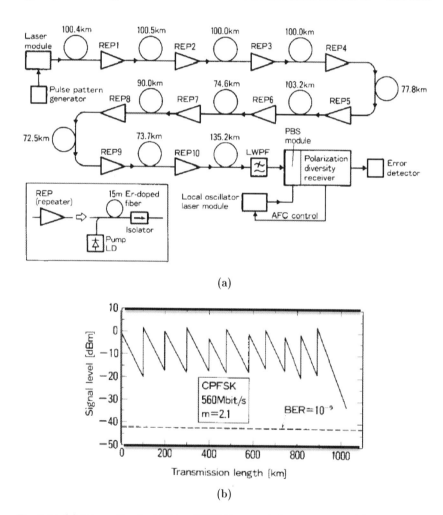

(a)

(b)

Fig. 9.14 (a) Schematic of a 1028 km CPFSK transmission experiment (b) Signal power levels through the link.[47]

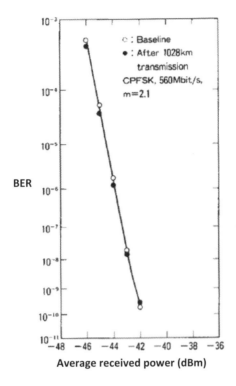

Fig. 9.15 BER data before and after 1028 km transmission.[47]

The EDFA has a 15 m long Er-doped fiber and is pumped by a laser diode. The EDFAs amplify the power level to ∼0 dBm after transmission through the previous ∼100 km link (attenuation ∼20 dB). This is shown in Fig. 9.14(b). The data signal from the link and a local oscillator (laser) signal are inputs to the polarization diversity receiver.

The error-rate measurement through the link is shown in Fig. 9.15. The results show that error-free transmission (BER $< 10^{-9}$) has been obtained.

9.4. Subscriber Transmission

So far only long haul high data rate transmission using optical amplifiers have been discussed. Amplifiers (EDFAs) have also been studied for subscriber transmission systems.[50–60] These systems transmit a wide range of information signals to the subscribers (home/office). The signals are low speed 64 kb/s voice signals, fax, data at few Mb/s to Gb/s, TV images, and broadband high quality images (HDTV signals). The conventional TV signals for amplitude modulated (AM) signals. In the US they are often called CATV systems, generally there are many channels (~40 to 120 channels) in a multi-channel AM CATV systems. These channels are spaced 6MHz apart. For example US Channel 3 transmits at ~50 MHz. The frequencies and bandwidth of these AM transmission channels are standardized (NTSC standard). Most of the other subscriber feeds, such as voice, data, satellite based transmission and HDTV are digital signals. A schematic of a subscriber information distribution system using optical fibers, EDFAs and coaxial cables are shown in Fig. 9.16. All of the information types are combined at a unit called the "Head end". At the Head end, the electrical signal is converted to an optical signal using a laser and transmitted to the subscribers using optical fibers and EDFAs. The low loss optical fibers and the EDFAs form

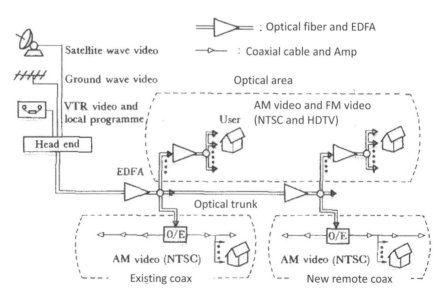

Fig. 9.16 Subscriber distribution system using optical fibers, EDFAs and coaxial cables.[58]

an optical trunk system from which the signal is further split up for transmission to different areas using optical splitter. This signal is transmitted and amplified using EDFAs before conversion to electrical signal using an optical to electrical (O/E) converter. The latter is essentially an optical detector and amplifier and other electronic circuits for splitting the incoming data to different types of signal. After the O/E conversion, the signal is transmitted to home using electronic amplifiers and co-axial cables. This is the original format for transmission first used with the advent of EDFAs. More recently, for Gb/s broadband transmission, HDTV transmission and CATV transmission this O/E converter is located at the subscriber site — this is often referred to as fiber to the home. Use of optical fibers and EDFAs allow much longer distance transmission of broadband signals without the need for amplification or regeneration. Of all the type of signals, the multichannel analog AM CATV systems is most sensitive to any nonlinearities in the EDFA or in the incoming signal. The nonlinearity causes intermixing among frequencies through the generation of second order and higher order products (frequencies).

The first experiment on multichannel AM CATV channel transmission using EDFA was reported in Ref. 54. A 19 AM television channels are combined and used to modulate a DFB laser (Fig. 9.17). The laser output is coupled to a single mode fiber and then goes though a EDFA pumped by a 1480 nm laser. Various optical isolators

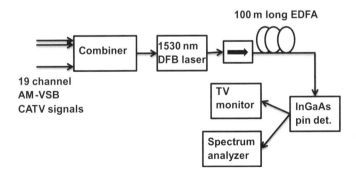

Fig. 9.17 Schematic of an experimental set up for 19 television channel transmission.[54] The EFDA is pumped by a 1480 nm color center laser.

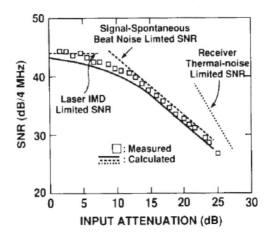

Fig. 9.18 SNR of a received TV channel vs. the input attenuation.[54]

are used to reduce reflection effects. The EDFA operated under saturated gain of 11.5 dB with an output power of 8 dBm.

In order to measure the performance with increasing optical loss, the attenuator in front of the photodiode is varied and the signal to noise ratio (SNR) is measured. The results are shown in Fig. 9.18. Also, shown is the calculated signal-spontaneous beat noise which is believed to have been the major source of noise in the system. Also, shown is the much smaller thermal noise. Adding many more channels introduces gain-tilt related nonlinear noise (CSO) discussed next.

This section discusses the change in this nonlinear mixing products (if any) due to EDFA.[61–68] The distortion introduced by a doped fiber amplifier for a transmitter with chirp arises due to the departure from flatness of the gain spectrum, different signal levels then experience different gains and the original waveform is distorted.[66] The composite second order distortion (CSO) is such a nonlinear effect, new frequencies of the form $f_i \pm f_j$ are generated due to the presence of the channels (frequencies) of the system, some of which lie within the transmission bandwidth and distort the signal. With up to ~100 channels, tens of second order intermodulation products are produced within each channel. For a modulated DFB laser the input to the amplifier has power and wavelength varying as:

$$P_i(t) = P_0 + mP_0 \sin \omega t, \qquad (9.1)$$

$$\lambda(t) = \lambda_0 - \Delta\lambda m \sin \omega t, \qquad (9.2)$$

where P_0 is the average input power, m is the optical modulation depth and $\omega = 2\pi f t$, f is the modulation frequency, λ_0 is the average signal wavelength and $\Delta\lambda$ is the variation in the wavelength of the input light. The amplifier gain is written as:

$$G = G_0 + \left(\frac{\partial G}{\partial \lambda}\right)_{\lambda_0} (\lambda(t) - \lambda_0), \qquad (9.3)$$

Here, G_0 is time invariant since the speed of the dynamics of the signal power and frequency variations are much faster than the doped fiber dynamics. $(\partial G/\partial \lambda)_{\lambda_0}$ is the slope of the gain curve at wavelength λ_0.

The amplified output power is:

$$P_{\text{out}}(t) = GP_i(t), \qquad (9.4)$$

Substituting for G and $P_i(t)$:

$$P_{\text{out}}(t) = \left[G_0 + \left(\frac{\partial G}{\partial \lambda}\right)_{\lambda_0} (\lambda(t) - \lambda_0)\right] [P_0 + mP_0 \sin \omega t]$$

$$= G_0 P_0 + mP_0 \left[G_0 - \Delta\lambda \left(\frac{\partial G}{\partial \lambda}\right)_{\lambda_0}\right] \sin \omega t$$

$$+ \frac{\Delta\lambda}{2} \left(\frac{\partial G}{\partial \lambda}\right)_{\lambda_0} P_0 m^2 (\cos 2\omega t), \qquad (9.5)$$

where the smaller terms have been eliminated and used $\cos(2\omega t) = 1 - 2\sin^2(\omega t)$. The presence of a term with frequency 2ω shows that when gain varies as a function of the wavelength and the source is chirped, second order overtones are produced due to the coupling between the signal and the optical amplifier.[67]

The experimental setup used for gain tilt measurement of the high power Erbium/Ytterbium co-doped double clad fiber amplifier (DCFA) is shown in Fig. 9.19. The wavelength of the input light from the tunable laser source can be varied from 1519 nm to 1564 nm.

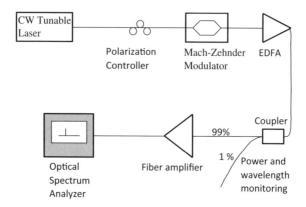

Fig. 9.19 Schematic of the experimental set up. The tunable laser is used to measure gain of the amplifier as a function of wavelength.

A Mach–Zehnder modulator is used to modulate the light from the laser. The modulated light output was pre-amplified and input to the amplifier (EDFA noted in figure) under test. ~1 watt of output power was obtained from the DCFA, which consisted of 5 m of cladding pumped Er/Yb co-doped fiber. A 1% coupler was used to monitor the power and wavelength of the light input to the fiber amplifier under test. The dependence of output power and gain on the input light wavelength has been discussed in previous chapters. The gain tilt, G_t is calculated using:

$$G_t = \frac{G(\lambda_2) - G(\lambda_1)}{\Delta\lambda}, \tag{9.6}$$

where $G(\lambda_1)$ and $G(\lambda_2)$ are the Er–Yb-doped fiber amplifier gain values at wavelengths of λ_1 and λ_2 respectively. The experimentally obtained gain difference under AC conditions, at a modulation frequency of 10 MHz, is nearly proportional to the wavelength difference $\Delta\lambda$. To maintain a high CNR the EYDFA is operated in the gain saturation region, as is the case for AM-SCM systems. The measured gain tilt varies with the wavelength of input light. The gain tilt values range from $-0.47\,\mathrm{dB/nm}$ to $0.5\,\mathrm{dB/nm}$ in the measured wavelength range of 1528 nm to 1564 nm. This large AC gain tilt causes CSO distortion. The CSO for an AM-SCM 60 channel transmission system is calculated from the gain tilt and laser chirp. The expression is given by[63]:

$$CSO = 20.\log\left\{\sqrt{n}.\frac{G_t(\lambda)}{G(\lambda)}.\frac{\lambda_{\text{chirp}}}{2\sqrt{N}}\right\}, \qquad (9.7)$$

where n is the number of generated frequency components, 40 in the experiment and N is the total number of channels, 60 in the experiment. λ_{chirp} is the laser light chirp due to modulation. For the system shown, $\lambda_{\text{chirp}} = 0.0012\,\text{nm}$ (wavelength chirp per channel), $n = 40$ and $N = 60$. The calculated values for the second order distortion (using the measured gain tilt values) are in the range of -45.5 dBc to -53 dBc. The variation is due to variation in gain tilt with input wavelength. The experimentally measured values of CSO with and without the double clad Er–Yb fiber amplifier are shown in Fig. 9.20. The CSO measurements show that the DCFA causes a penalty of 4–7 dB.

An electronic predistortion circuit for the laser for improving the CSO due to gain tilt has been developed.[69,70] The CSO can

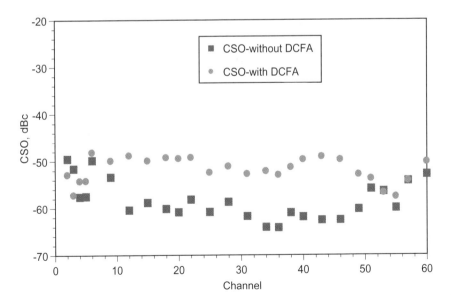

Fig. 9.20 Measured CSO for a AM subcarrier modulated transmission system with and without Er–Yb co-doped fiber amplifier.[68]

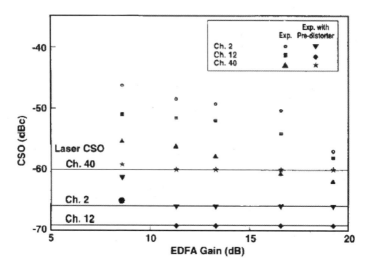

Fig. 9.21 Measured CSO with and without the predistortion circuit as a function of gain for channels 2, 12 and 40 respectively.[70]

be significantly reduced using the predistortion circuit. The results of CSO measurement at 1548 nm for an EDFA link are shown in Fig. 9.21. The data is shown for Channels 2, 12 and 40 respectively. The measured CSO is plotted as a function of amplifier gain.

9.5. Soliton Transmission

The demand for the ultra large capacity transmission systems i.e., with capacities approaching Tb/s continues to increase. For such systems, high-speed transmission with the bit rate of multiple 10 Gb/s is quite attractive, since it can reduce the number of WDM channels. Time division multiplexing and transmission using optical solitons is important for these systems. Solitons allow error-free ultra long distance transmission in dispersion managed systems.[71–77]

A schematic of an optical soliton transmission system experiment at 40 Gb/s is shown in Fig. 9.22. In this scheme, the cumulative chromatic dispersion is offset periodically by DCF with negative (normal) dispersion so that the total system dispersion is close to zero. The Gordon–Haus timing jitter is also reduced in this system with close to zero dispersion.[78] The experimental system uses a recirculating

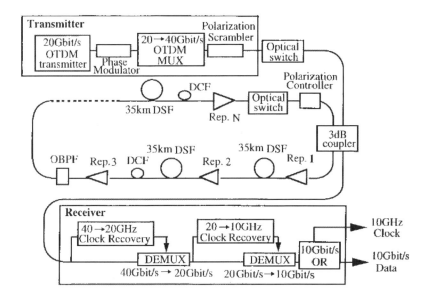

Fig. 9.22 Soliton transmission experiment at 40 Gb/s.[77]

loop (described previously) for ultra long distance transmission. The recirculating loop consists of several units. Each unit has a dispersion shifted fiber (DSF), a 980 nm laser pumped EDFA and a DCF. In addition it has a polarization controller and an optical band pass filter (OBPF). The latter reduces the spontaneous emission noise.

For the transmitter, a 20 Gb/s optical soliton data stream is produced by optically time division multiplexing (OTDM) of 10 Gb/s RZ (return to zero) data pulses. These data pulses are generated by a DFB laser, sinusoidally-driven electroabsorption (EA) modulators and two LiNbO$_3$ intensity modulators operated at 10 Gb/s with a pseudorandom binary sequence. The generated pulse width is about 9 ps. These pulses pass through a LiNbO$_3$ phase modulator driven by a 20 GHz clock. The phase condition is optimized by adjusting the delay between the optical data bits and the phase modulation signal using an electric phase shifter. This initial phase modulation is effective in improving the transmission performance. Then 40 Gb/s signal is generated by OTDM of 20 Gb/s signals.

In the receiver, the clock signal is recovered from the transmitted signals. The transmitted 40 Gb/s signals are demultiplxed in the optical domain using EA modulators in two stages; 40 Gb/s to 20 Gb/s followed by 20 Gb/s to 10 Gb/s. The BER for the demultiplexed 10 Gb/s signals is measured. The transmission measurements (i.e., BER data) are carried out for different dispersion maps. The dispersion map is varied by changing the signal wavelength which varied the average dispersion of DSF (D_{local}). The system average dispersion (D_{ave}) is changed with D_{local} and the dispersion is compensated by dispersion compensating fibers (DCFs). BER of less than 10^{-9} for all four 10 Gb/s demultiplexed channels are observed for ∼9000 km of transmission for D_{local} values of ∼0.3 ps/km–nm. The experiment showed that 40 Gb/s transmission over all long distances is feasible without active dispersion compensation.

System performance impairment due to soliton–soliton interaction was reduced by the polarization division multiplexing. By using the polarization division multiplexing and optimum dispersion map, 40 Gb/s single-channel transmission over 10,200 km was successfully demonstrated without any active inline transmission control.

References

1. K. Hagimoto and K. Aida, *J. Lightwave Technol.* **6** (1988) 1678.
2. A.H. Gnauck, J.E. Bowers and J.C. Campbell, *Electron. Lett.* **22** (1986) 600.
3. S.K. Korotky *et al.*, *J. Lightwave Technol.* LT-**5** (1987) 1505.
4. S. Fujita *et al.*, *Electron. Lett.* **25** (1989) 702.
5. Y. Yamamoto, *IEEE J.Quantum Elecrron.* QE-**16** (1980) 1073.
6. K. Hagimoto *et al.*, Presented at OFC1989, Paper pD-15.1989.
7. R.I. Mears, L. Reekie, I.M. Jauncey and D.N. Payne, *Electron. Lett.* **23** (1987) 1026.
8. E. Desurvire, J.R. Simpson and P.C. Becker, *Opt. Lett.* **12** (1987) 888.
9. K. Hagimoto *et al.*, *Electron. Lett.* **25** (1989) 662.
10. K. Hagimoto, Y. Miyagawa, A. Takada, K. Kawano and Y. Tohmori, Presented at ECOC1989, Paper TuA5-5, 1989.
11. K. Hagimoto *et al.*, Presented at IOOC'89, Paper 20PDA-6, 1989; also Trans. IEICE. E**73** (1990) 27.
12. H. Nishimoto *et al.*, Presented at IOOC1989, Paper 20PDA-8, 1989.
13. K. Aida, S. Nishi, Y. Sato, K. Hagimoto and K. Nakagawa, Presented at ECOC 1989, Paper PDA-7, 1989.
14. A. Righetti., presented at ECOC 1989, Paper PDA-10, 1989.
15. D. Bayart, P. Bousselet, F. Chiquet, C. Le Sergent, B. Clesca, V. Havard and J.-L. Beylat, Presented at OFC 1997, Dallas, TX, 1997, paper WL1.

16. A. Takada, *Trans. IEICE.* (1989) E72–21.
17. S. Artigaud, M.W. Chbat, P. Nouchi, F. Chiquet, D. Bayart, L. Hamon, A. Pitel, F. Goudeseune, P. Bousselet and J.-L. Beylat, Presented at OFC 1997, San Jose, CA, 1996, postdeadline paper PD27.
18. A.K. Srivastava, J.B. Judkins, Y. Sun, L. Garrett, J.L. Zyskind, J.W. Sulhoff, C. Wolf, R.M. Derosier, A.H. Gnauck, R.W. Tkach, J. Zhou, R.P. Espindola, A.M. Vengsarkar and A.R. Chraplyvy, Presented at OFC 1997, Dallas, TX,1997, postdeadline paper PD18.
19. K. Hagimoto, S. Nishi and K. Nakagawa, *J. Lightwave Tech.* **8** (1990) 1387.
20. N. Edagawa *et al.*, Presented at ECOC 1989, Paper PDA-8, 1989.
21. S. Bigo, A. Bertaina, M.W. Chbat, S. Gurib, J. Da Loura, J.-C. Jacquinot, J. Hervo, P. Bousselet, S. Borne, D. Bayart, L. Gasca and J.-L. Beylat, *IEEE Photonics Tech. Letts.* **10**, (1998) 1045.
22. T. Tanifuji and M. Ikeda, *Opt. Lett.* **16**(8) (1977).
23. P.R. Trischitta, P. Sannuti, and C. Chamzas, *IEEE Trans. Commun.* **36** (1988) 675.
24. L.F. Mollenauer and K. Smith, *Opt. Lett.* **13** (1988) 675.
25. D. Malyon, T. Widdowson, E.G. Bryant, S.F. Carter, J.V. Wright and W.A. Stallard, *Electron. Lett.* **27**(2) (1991).
26. N.S. Bergano. J. AsDell. C.R. Davidson, P.R. Trischitta, B.M. Nyman, and F.W. Kerfoot, *Electron. Lett.* **27** (1991) 21.
27. N.S. Bergano and C.R. Davidson, *J. Lightwave Tech.* **13** (1995) 879.
28. M. Nakazawa, *IEEE, J. Quantum Electron.* **26** (1990) 2103.
29. D.M. Spirit, *Electron. Lett.* **27** (1991) 222.
30. K. Kurukawa and M. Nakazawa, *IEEE J. Quantum Electron.* **28** (1992) 1922.
31. C. Lester, *Electron. Lett.* **31**. (1995) 219.
32. D.M. Spirit, G.E. Wickens, T. Widdowson, G.R. Walker, D.L. Williams and L.C. Blank, *Electron. Lett.* **28** (1992) 1218.
33. M. Nakazawa, Y. Kimura and K. Suzuki, *IEEE J. Quantum Electron.* **26** (1990) 2103.
34. F. Chiaraluce, E. Gambi and P. Pierleoni, *Opt. Commun.* **105** (1994) 47.
35. A. Altuncu, L. Noel, W.A. Pender, A.S. Siddiqui, T. Widdowson, A.D. Ellis, M.A. Newhouse, A.J. Antos. G. Kar and P.W. Chu, *Electron. Lett.* **32** (1996) 233.
36. C. Lester, K. Bertilsson, K. Rottwitt, P.A. Andrekson, M.A. Newhouse and A.J. Antos, *Electron. Lett.* **31** (1995) 219.
37. A. Altuncu, A.S. Siddiqui and A.D. Ellis, *Electron. Lett.* **33** (1997) 1558.
38. S. Wen, *Opt. Lett.* **19** (1994) 22.
39. H. Kawakami, T. Kataoka, Y. Miyamoto, K. Hagimoto and H. Toba, *J. Lightwave Tech.* **19** (2001) 1887.
40. G.R. Walker, N.G. Walker, R.C. Steele, M.J. Creaner and M.C. Brain, *J. Lightwave Tech.* **9** (1991) 182.
41. R.E. Wagner, In Proc. ECOC 1989. **2**, paper ThA21-1 (1989).
42. S. Yamazaki, T. Ono, H. Shimizu, M. Kitamura and K. Emura. In Proc. OFC 1990, paper PD12. (1990).

43. G.R. Walker, R.C. Steele and N.G. Walker, *J. Lightwave Technol.* **8** (1990) 1409.
44. Y.K. Park, J-M. P. Delavaux, T.W. Cline and C.F. Flores, *Proc. ICC.* 1205 (1991)
45. M.J. Creaner, *Electron. Lett.* **24** (1988) 1354.
46. M.J. Creaner, *Electron. Lett.*, **26** (1990) 442.
47. S. Ryu, S. Yamamoto, H. Taga, N. Edagawa, Y. Yoshida and H. Wakabayashi, *J. Lightwave Tech.* **9** (1991) 2551.
48. S. Ryu, N. Edagawa, Y. Yoshida and H. Wakabayashi, *IEEE Photon. Tech. Lett.* **2**, (1990) 428.
49. R. Welter, R.I. Laming, W.B. Sessa, R.S. Vodhanel, M.W. Maeda and R.E. Wagner, *Electron. Lett.* **25** (1989) 1335.
50. H. Shinohara, FTTH experiences in Japan, *JON*, **6** (2007) 616.
51. K-I. Suzuki, Y. Fukada, D, Nesset and R. Davey, *JON*. **6** (2007) 422.
52. Y. Fukada, K-I. Suzuki, H. Nakamura, N. Yoshimoto and M. Tsubokawa, ECOC Paper We.2.F.4. (2008).
53. K-I. Suzuki, Y. Fukada, N. Yoshimoto, K. Kumozaki and M. Tsubokawa, PON, OFC Paper OTuH1.(2009)
54. W.I. Way, M.M. Choy, A. Yi-Yan, M. Andrejco, M. Saifi and C. Lin, *IEEE Photon.Technol. Lett.* **1** (1989) 343.
55. C.R. Giles, E. Desurvire and J.R. Simpson, *Opt. Lett.* **14** (1989) 880.
56. A.A. Saleh, T.E. Darcie and R. Jopson, *Electron. Lett.* **25** (1989) 79.
57. S.Y. Huang, T.W. Cline, L.C. Upadhyayula, R.E. Tench and J. Lipson, Top. Meet. Broadband Analog Optoelectron. Devices and Systems, *Tech. Dig.* Monterey, CA, paper BAM7 (1990).
58. K. Kikushima, Chapter 10. In Optical Amplifiers and Their Applications. S. Shimada and H. Ishio (Eds) John Wiley. 1994.
59. W.I. Way, *IEEE J. Lightwave Tech.* **7** (1989) 1806.
60. K. Kikushima and E. Yoneda, *Trans. IEICE Jpn.* E **74** (1991) 2042.
61. S.L. Hansen, P. Thorsen, K. Dybdal and S.B. Andreasen, *IEEE Photon. Technol Lett.* **4** (1993) 409.
62. B. Clesca, P. Bousselet and L. Hamon, *IEEE Photon. Technol. Lett.*, 5(9) 1993.
63. K. Kikushima, AC and DC gain tilt of Erbium doped fiber amplifiers, *J. Lightwave Technol.* **12** (1994) 3.
64. F. Lai, C. Liu and J. Jou, *IEEE Photon. Technol. Lett.* **11** (1999) 545.
65. C.R. Giles, E. Desurvire and J.R. Simpson, *Opt. Lett.* **14** (1989) 880.
66. K. Kikushima and H. Yoshinaga, *IEEE Photon. Technol. Lett.* **3** (1991) 945.
67. P.C. Becker, N.A. Olsson and J.R. Simpson, *Erbium doped fiber amplifiers-Fundamentals and Technology*, Chapter.7. California: Academic Press 1999.
68. P. Dua, K. Lu, N.K. Dutta and J. Jaques, Chapter 11. In *Guided Wave Optical Components and Devices* B. P. Pal (Ed). Elsevier Academic Press. 2006.
69. C.Y. Kuo and E.E. Bergmann, *IEEE J. Lightwave Tech.* **10** (1992) 1751.
70. C.Y. Kuo and E.E. Bergmann, *IEEE Photon. Tech. Lett.* **3** (1991) 829.

71. M. Suzuki, N. Edagawa, H. Taga, H. Tanaka, S. Yamamoto and S. Akiba, *Electron. Lett.* **30** (1994) 1083.
72. F. Favre and D. LeGuen, *Electron. Lett.* **31** (1995) 991.
73. G. Aubin, E. Jeanney, T. Montalant, J. Moulu, F. Pirio, J.-B. Thomine and F. Devaux, *Electron. Lett.* **31** (1995) 1079.
74. J. King, I. Hardcastle, J. Harvey, P. Greene, B. Shaw, M. Jones, D. Forbes and M. Wright, *Electron. Lett.* **31** (1995) 1090.
75. M. Suzuki, I. Morita, N. Edagawa, S. Yamamoto, H. Taga and S. Akiba, *Electron. Lett.* **31** (1995) 2027.
76. G. Aubin, T. Montalant, J. Moulu, F. Pirio, J.-B. Thomine and F. Devaux, *Electron. Lett.* **32** (1996) 2188.
77. I. Morita, K. Tanaka, M. Suzuki and N. Edagawa, *IEEE J. Lightwave Tech.* **17** (1999) 2506.
78. J. Gordon and H. Haus, *Opt. Lett.* **11** (1986) 665.

Chapter 10

Nonlinear Effects

10.1. Introduction

Erbium-doped optical fiber amplifier is an important device for both terrestrial and submarine optical communication systems and next generation all-optical networks. A typical transmission fiber fabricated using silica exhibits optical nonlinearity. The silica glass has third order nonlinearity (Sec. 6.6). Er-doped amplifier is also generally made using silica as the host as discussed in Chapter 4. This third order nonlinearity in silica can result in various observables such as four wave mixing, self focusing, stimulated Raman scattering, stimulated Brillioun scattering, and supercontinuum generation. For transmission fibers stimulated Raman scattering and stimulated Brillioun scattering are also important nonlinear effects. These nonlinear effects in fibers (primarily transmission fibers) have been discussed in detail in several articles and books.[1-18] In this chapter many of these nonlinear effects are described with specific attention to doped fiber amplifiers. In WDM transmission systems, where data at multiple equally spaced wavelengths are transmitted, four wave mixing (FWM) process can result in intermixing of data through creation of new wavelengths, which coincides with an existing WDM wavelength channel. The transmission fiber provides very long interaction lengths with low dispersion near 1550 nm which allows creation of high intensity for the FWM signal.[1,17,18] Although the interaction lengths are smaller for Er-doped fibers, the FWM efficiency could be significant due to smaller cross section and high signal gain.

10.2. FWM

FWM is a nonlinear optical process in single mode silica fibers. When two signals propagate in the fiber with frequencies f_1 and f_2, a new set of optical waves at frequencies $2f_1 - f_2$ and $2f_2 - f_1$ are produced. These new set of frequencies are sometimes known as sidebands in analogy with electronics. These new frequencies co-propagate with the original signals and continue to grow at their expense. A set of three propagating waves (at frequencies f_i, f_j, f_k) also generate new optical frequencies (nine in this case) at frequencies $f_{ijk} = f_i + f_j - f_k$. where i, j, k, are 1, 2, 3 respectively. These are generally known as FWM products and are schematically shown in Fig. 10.1.[18] The appearance of these new waves would degrade the performance of a multichannel transmission system through crosstalk.

In a multichannel WDM transmission system, the channel spacing is fixed i.e., the frequency of the nth channel is given by $f_m = f_0 + m\Delta f$, where m is an integer. The quantity Δf is the channel spacing, its typical value is 50, 100 or 200 GHz and f_0 is $\sim 1.93 \times 10^5$ GHz (i.e., ~ 1550 nm wavelength). In addition to the value of the nonlinear coefficient, an important factor that determines the magnitude of the FWM signal is the phase matching factor. For the case where a FWM signal at frequency $f_3 = 2f_2 - f_1$ is generated from original signal frequencies f_1 and f_2, (neglecting optical loss)

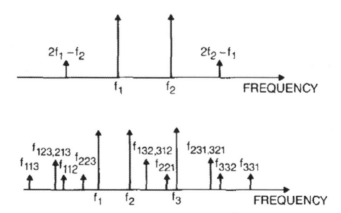

Fig. 10.1 Schematic of four wave mixing (FWM) processes.[18]

the phase matching factor (F) after traveling though a fiber of length L is (in a dimensionless form):

$$F = \sin^2(\Delta k L/2)/(\Delta k L/2)^2, \tag{10.1}$$

where $\Delta k = 2k_2 - k_1 - k_3 = 2\pi(2n_2 f_2 - n_1 f_1 - n_3 f_3)/c$, k_1, k_2, k_3 are the wavevectors of waves at frequencies f_1, f_2, f_3 and n_1, n_2, n_3 are the refractive indices at frequencies at frequencies f_1, f_2, f_3 respectively. Using $f_3 = 2f_2 - f_1$, the quantity $\Delta k = 2\pi(2(n_2 - n_3)f_2 - (n_1 - n_3)f_1)/c$, and for the case of a WDM system $(f_1 = f_0 + m_1\Delta f$, etc.) this reduces to:

$$\Delta k = (2n_2 - n_1 - n_3)f_0 + \{2(n_2 - n_3)m_2 - (n_1 - n_3)m_1\}\Delta f, \tag{10.2}$$

Thus the phase mismatch Δk depends on the dispersion and channel spacing (Δf). If the dispersion is ~ 0, $(n_1 \sim n_2 \sim n_3)$, then Δk is small and the quantity F will be near unity. For a fiber, the dispersion is non zero and hence $F < 1$, but it depends on channel spacing and length of fiber traversed, L. For the same dispersion, for larger channel spacing, the phase matching factor is smaller. The power generated at the end of a fiber of length L, for a FWM process which generates $f_{ijk} = f_i + f_j - f_k$. from three frequencies f_i, f_j, f_k is given by using notation of Ref. 19:

$$P_{ijk}(L) = (1024\pi^6/n^4\lambda^2 c^2)(DX_{1111})^2(P_i P_j P_k/A_{eff}^2)$$
$$\times |\{\exp(i\Delta\beta - \alpha)L - 1\}/(i\Delta\beta - \alpha)|^2, \tag{10.3}$$

where n is the refractive index of the core, λ is the wavelength, c is the velocity of light in free space, D is the degeneracy factor (3 for two input wavelengths i.e., $i = j$, 6 for three input wavelengths), χ is the nonlinear coefficient, P_i, P_j, P_k are the input powers at the three wavelengths, α is the optical loss which is assumed to be the same for all wavelengths, A_{eff} is the effective mode area, and $\Delta\beta$ is the propagation constant difference, (i.e., phase mismatch — same as Δk in Eq. (10.2)]:

$$\Delta\beta = \beta_{ijk} + \beta_k - \beta_i - \beta_j, \tag{10.4}$$

The quantity β is a function of optical frequency $\omega(= 2\pi f)$. $\beta(\omega)$ can be expanded in a Taylor series about ω_k up to third order (i.e.,

$(\omega - \omega_k)^3)$. The results are as follows[18]:

$$\beta(\omega) = \beta[\omega_k] + (\omega - \omega_k)[d\beta(\omega_k)/d\omega]$$
$$+ (1/2)(\omega - \omega_k)^2 \times \lceil d^2\beta(\omega_k)/d\omega^2 \rceil$$
$$+ (1/6)(\omega - \omega_k)^3 \lceil d^3\beta(\omega_k)/d\omega^3 \rceil$$
$$= \omega_k/v_p + (\omega - \omega_k)/v_g$$
$$+ (\omega - \omega_k)^2[\lambda_k^2 D_c(\lambda_k)/4\pi c]$$
$$+ (\omega - \omega_k)^3(\lambda_k^4/24\pi^2 c^2)[dD_c(\lambda_k)/d\lambda], \qquad (10.5)$$

with D_c (fiber chromatic dispersion) given by:

$$D_c = -(\omega_k^2/2\pi c)[d^2\beta(\omega_k)/d\omega^2],$$

It follows from Eq. (10.5), $\Delta\beta$ is proportional to dispersion and the derivative of the dispersion needs to be included when the wavelengths fall near the zero dispersion wavelength of optical fiber. The FWM efficiency (η) can be defined using the equation of $\Delta\beta$ as follows[19]:

$$\eta = P_{ijk}(L, \Delta\beta)/P_{ijk}(L, \Delta\beta = 0)$$
$$= [\alpha^2/\{\alpha^2 + (\Delta\beta)^2\}]$$
$$\times [1 + 4\exp(-\alpha L)\sin^2(\Delta\beta L)/\{1 - \exp(-\alpha L)\}^2], \quad (10.6)$$

The quantity η is the ratio of the nonlinear power at frequency f_{ijk} for a phase mismatch of β to the nonlinear power at frequency f_{ijk} for no phase mismatch ($\beta = 0$).

Two examples of the value of η as a function of channel separation is shown in Fig. 10.2 for two dispersion parameters.[18] For a conventional fiber ($D = 16$ ps/km-nm), the FWM process is efficient for channel spacing <20 GHz whereas for dispersion shifted fibers ($D = 1$ ps/km-nm), the FWM process is efficient for channel spacing to 50 GHz.

The result shows that dispersion is critical in reducing FWM. For zero dispersion FWM is highest. However, for pulses propagating along a fiber, dispersion causes pulse width broadening, and hence a fiber with high dispersion is not desirable. Dispersion shifted fibers with zero dispersion at 1550 nm has been developed to reduce pulse width broadening. These fibers produce large FWM which is not

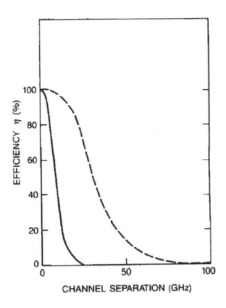

Fig. 10.2 FWM efficiency as a function of channel separation for two dispersion values. Both input wavelengths are near 1550 nm. The solid curve represents standard single-mode fiber with a dispersion of 16 ps/nm km. The dashed curve is for dispersion shifted fiber with dispersion of 1 ps/nm-km.[17]

desirable. A new class fibers with dispersion ∼1 to 2 ps/km-nm has been developed which reduces both FWM and limits pulse width broadening. Figure 10.3 shows the chromatic dispersion curves (i.e., dispersion as a function of wavelength) for standard fiber (zero dispersion at 1550 nm), dispersion shifted fiber (zero dispersion at 1550 nm), and a new class of fibers called Truewave fiber which have slight dispersion (∼positive or negative of 1 to 2 ps/km-nm).

The effect of low dispersion is illustrated in Fig. 10.4. Four CW optical signals each with a power of 3 dBm is injected into 25 km dispersion shifted fibers with zero dispersion around the injected wavelengths. There are $(N^3-N^2)/2 = 24$ FWM products generated after traveling through the fiber. The spectrum of the output light with all the FWM products is shown in Fig. 10.4a. Similar experiment was carried out with a fiber with an average dispersion of 2 ps/km-nm near the wavelengths of the injected signal. The fiber length is 50 km. The output spectrum is shown in Fig. 10.4b. Results

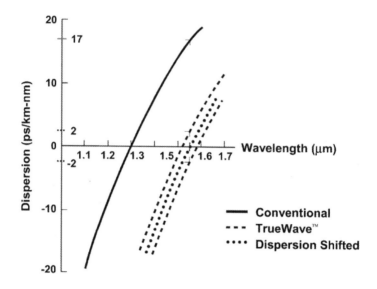

Fig. 10.3 Chromatic dispersion as a function of wavelength for three fiber types.[20]

show that a small amount of dispersion reduces FWM significantly. In the presence of FWM a crosstalk between different channels in a WDM system takes place. This crosstalk results in errors in the transmission system. Since dispersion causes pulse width broadening also, a management of dispersion is very important for optical fiber transmission over long distances.

FWM crosstalk in Er-doped fiber amplifiers (EDFA) has been measured.[21–26] Figure 10.5 shows the experimental set up for a particular experiment.[26] It involves injecting the output of 88 distributed feedback (DFB) lasers which emit in a single wavelength into a L-band EDFA. The laser wavelengths are in the 1572 to 1604 nm range. The wavelength spacing between the lasers is 50 GHz when all lasers are turned on and temperature adjusted. The wavelength spacing between the lasers can be made 100 GHz by turning only alternate lasers on.

The EDFA is pumped by 1480 nm pump laser. The optical gain for the multichannel system is shown in Fig. 10.6. The gain is in the 16 to 18 dB range. An optical spectrum analyzer is used to measure the powers of the generated FWM signals and the amplified signal.

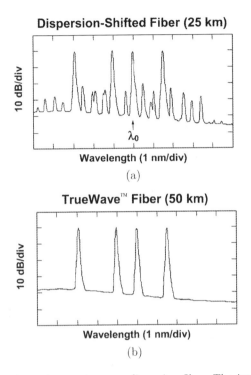

(a)

(b)

Fig. 10.4 (a) Output spectrum using zero dispersion fiber. The input power of each channel is 3 dBm. (b) Output spectrum using Truewave fiber with average dispersion of 2 ps/km-nm for the same input powers.[20]

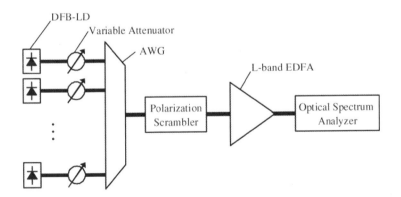

Fig. 10.5 Experimental set up for FWM measurement in a multichannel system.[26]

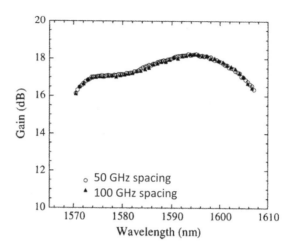

Fig. 10.6 Optical gain of EDFA for the multichannel system for 50 GHz spacing (88 inputs) and 100 GHz spacing (45 inputs).[26] The data for 50 Ghz and 100 Ghz spacing overlap.

The FWM signal was measured by turning off the laser source for the FWM signal channel. FWM crosstalk for each channel is estimated as the ratio of the FWM signal power to the output signal power at that channel and large number of four wave mixing products were produced. Figure 10.7 shows the FWM crosstalk for both 50 GHz and 100 GHz channel spacing. As expected (Fig. 10.2), the crosstalk is less for larger channel spacing.

10.3. Stimulated Raman Scattering

Stimulated Raman scattering (SRS) is a nonlinear process which takes place in optical fibers[13,27−36] The basis of the process is Raman scattering where a monochromatic wave propagating in the fiber generates a wave of different frequency. Typically the energy of the photons ($h\nu_p$) at the incident wavelength is larger than the energy of Raman process generated photon ($h\nu_s$) by an amount equal to the separation between two energy levels (δE) in the material i.e., $h\nu_p - h\nu_s = \delta E$. The photons at the lower energy are generated by both spontaneous and stimulated emission. In many materials, such as silica, δE represents the energy of the vibrational modes of Si and

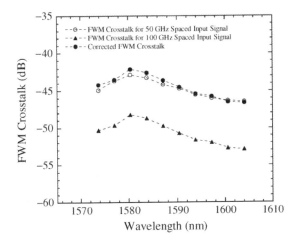

Fig. 10.7 FWM crosstalk for both 50 GHz and 100 GHz channel spacing. The corrected crosstalk for 50 GHz spacing takes into account a compensation factor which is related to number of combinations.[26]

O atoms. Typically a small fraction of the energy of the incident wave (also called pump wave with photon energy $h\nu_p$) gets converted to the lower photon energy ($h\nu_s$) wave. As in the case of a laser, the spontaneously generated photons cause stimulated emission of photons with same frequency and wavevector. This leads to amplification of spontaneously generated photons (by Raman scattering) and can cause laser action (Raman laser). This is discussed in detail in Chapter 13. Typically the Raman scattered photons in silica fibers are generated in a wide frequency range ($\sim$40 THz). So an injected signal within this Raman scattered wavelength range could be amplified by SRS if a sufficiently large amount of incident light (pump light) is present. If the generated wave is at a lower frequency than the pump it is called the Stokes wave and if it at a higher frequency than the pump it is called an antiStokes wave. If I_s is the intensity of the Stokes signal and I_p is the intensity of the pump, the growth of the Stokes signal due to SRS is given by the equation:

$$\frac{dI_s}{dz} = g_R I_P I_s, \tag{10.7}$$

where g_R is the Raman gain coefficient. The Raman spectrum in fused silica has been measured.[30] The data for a pump wavelength of 1 μm

Fiber Amplifiers and Fiber Lasers

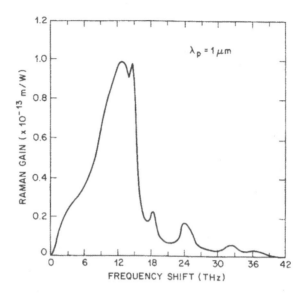

Fig. 10.8 Measured Raman gain for fused silica at a pump wavelength of 1 μm.[31]

is shown in Fig. 10.8. The Raman gain is $\sim 10^{-13}$ m/W for a frequency shift of ~ 13 THz. Thus for an input signal power of 1 W into a single mode fiber (cross section $\sim 50\,\mu\text{m}^2$, $I_p = 2 \times 10^{10}$ W/m^2), the Raman gain is $\sim 2 \times 10^{-3}$ m^{-1} i.e., for a 100 m long fiber, the single pass gain is ~ 0.2 which is large enough for Stokes wave (Raman) laser action. In the case of pure silica, the Stokes wave is downshifted from the pump by ~ 13.2 THz (440 cm^{-1}).

While propagating through the fiber, the intensity of both the pump and the Stokes wave decrease due to losses. Thus the propagation equations for the Stokes (I_s) and pump (I_p) intensity are written as:

$$\frac{dI_s}{dz} = g_R I_P I_s - \alpha_s I_s, \tag{10.8}$$

$$\frac{dI_p}{dz} = g_R I_P I_s - \alpha_p I_p, \tag{10.9}$$

where α_s and α_p are absorption coefficient of the Stokes and pump wave respectively, ω_s and ω_p are the angular frequencies of the Stokes and pump wave, and g_R is the Raman gain coefficient. Equations (10.8) and (10.9) shows that the Stokes intensity increases and pump intensity decreases due to SRS as the light propagates in the fiber. For the purpose of estimating the pump threshold (which is defined as threshold pump power needed at input so that pump power equals Stokes power at the output), the depletion of the pump due to SRS is neglected. Equation (10.9) is then easily solved which is then substituted in Eq. (10.8) to yield the following equation:

$$\frac{dI_s}{dz} = g_R I_o \exp(-\alpha_p z) I_s - \alpha_s I_s, \tag{10.10}$$

where I_0 is the incident pump input intensity at $z = 0$. Solving Eq. (10.10), it follows:

$$I_s(L) = I_s(0) \exp(g_R I_0 L_{\text{eff}} - \alpha_s L), \tag{10.11}$$

$$L_{\text{eff}} = \frac{1}{\alpha_p}[1 - \exp(-\alpha_p L)], \tag{10.12}$$

L_{eff} is the effective interaction length which is less than L due to pump absorption. Equation (10.11) requires a Stokes power at fiber input $(z = 0)$. In practice the Stokes intensity builds up from spontaneous Raman scattering throughout the length of the fiber. It has been shown[13] this is equivalent to injecting one photon per mode at the input. The Stokes power is then calculated using $I_s(0) = \hbar\omega$ at the input and integrating over all frequency components. Thus:

$$P_s(L) = \int_{-\infty}^{\infty} \hbar\omega \exp[g_R(\omega) I_0 L_{\text{eff}} - \alpha_s L] d\omega. \tag{10.13}$$

It is assumed that the fiber supports a single mode at each frequency component. $g_R(\omega)$ is the frequency response of the gain spectrum shown in Fig. 10.8. Since, the main contribution to the integral comes from a narrow region near the gain peak $(\omega = \omega_s)$, Eq. (10.13) can be approximated (using method of steepest descent) as:

$$P_s(L) = P_{s0} \exp[g_R(\omega_s) I_0 L_{\text{eff}} - \alpha_s L], \tag{10.14}$$

The effective input power at z = 0, is:

$$P_{s0} = \hbar\omega_s B_{\text{eff}}, \tag{10.15}$$

with:

$$B_{\text{eff}} = \left[\frac{2\pi}{g_R''(\omega_s) I_0 L_{\text{eff}}}\right]^{1/2} \quad \text{and} \quad g_R''(\omega_s) = \left[\frac{\partial^2 g_R}{\partial\omega^2}\right]_{\omega=\omega_s}, \tag{10.16}$$

B_{eff} can be interpreted as the effective bandwidth of the Stokes radiation although it depends on the pump intensity and fiber length. The Raman threshold is defined as the input power at which the Stokes power becomes equal to the pump power at the fiber i.e.,:

$$P_s(L) = P_p(L) = P_0 \exp(-\alpha_p L), \tag{10.17}$$

where $P_0 = I_0 A_{\text{eff}}$ where P_0 is the input pump power and A_{eff} is the effective area of propagating pump mode. Using $\alpha_s = \alpha_p$, the threshold condition becomes:

$$P_{s0} \exp(g_R P_0 L_{\text{eff}}/A_{\text{eff}}) = P_0, \tag{10.18}$$

Note that from Eq. (10.18) P_{s0} also depends on P_0. Thus this needs to be solved numerically for different gain spectrum. For a Lorentzian gain spectrum, the threshold power to a good approximation is given by:

$$g_R P_{oth} L_{\text{eff}}/A_{\text{eff}} \sim 16. \tag{10.19}$$

Raman threshold power is now estimated using Eq. (10.19). For long fibers ($\alpha_p L \gg 1$), $L_{\text{eff}} \sim 1/\alpha_p$. For wavelengths near 1550 nm, loss = 0.2 dB/km, hence, $L_{\text{eff}} \sim 20$ km. Since g_R inversely proportional to the pump wavelength, assuming $g_R = 7 \times 10^{-14}$ m/W near 1550 nm, the pump threshold power using Eq. (10.19) is ~0.6 W. Thus SRS is not important for typical single channel optical fiber transmission systems with input powers of ~3 mW. A numerical model of SRS taking into account pump depletion has been carried out.[30] The result for threshold power is similar to that stated earlier.

For high pump powers, the generated Stokes signal can become large enough to act as a pump and create a second order Stokes signal. In a single pass Raman generation experiment pump pulses (~150 ns long) from Nd-YAG lasers are used to generate Stokes pulses. The first Stokes is observed at a pump power of 70 W. Higher order Stokes signals appeared at higher pump powers. At ~1 kW pump power, five Stokes lines are observed.[37] This multiple SRS scattering process is much more easily feasible in an optical cavity and has been used to demonstrate cascaded Raman Lasers (see Chapter 13).

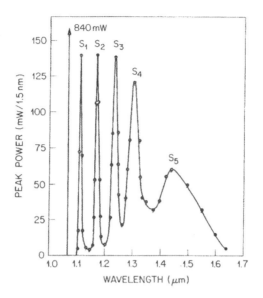

Fig. 10.9 SRS spectrum showing generation of five Stokes signals (S_1 to S_5). The line with the arrow is the residual input pump.[37]

10.4. Stimulated Brillouin Scattering

Stimulated Brillouin scattering (SBS) is a nonlinear process similar to SRS except it involves acoustic waves.[38–43] The pump frequency is downshifted to Stokes frequency by an acoustic wave frequency i.e.,:

$$\omega_s = \omega_p - \omega_A, \qquad (10.20)$$

$$\vec{k}_s = \vec{k}_p - \vec{k}_A, \qquad (10.21)$$

where ω_p and ω_s are the frequencies of the pump and Stokes signal and ω_A is the frequency of the acoustic wave. k_A, k_p and k_s are the wavevectors of the acoustic wave and pump and Stokes wave respectively. Since the magnitudes of $\boldsymbol{k}_p$ and $\boldsymbol{k}_s$ are nearly equal, it follows from Eq. (10.21):

$$\omega_A = |k_A|v_A = 2v_A|k_p|\sin\frac{\theta}{2}, \qquad (10.22)$$

where v_A is the velocity of the acoustic wave and θ is the angle between $\boldsymbol{k}_p$ and $\boldsymbol{k}_s$. Thus the frequency shift depends on the scattering angle. For forward scattering ($\theta = 0$), there is no frequency shift and for backward scattering ($\theta = \pi$), the frequency shift is maximum. The frequency shift in the backward direction is given by:

$$v_0 = \frac{\omega_A}{2\pi} = \frac{2nV_A}{\lambda_p}, \tag{10.23}$$

where $k_p = 2\pi/\lambda_p$, the pump wavelength is given by λ_p and n is the refractive index. For optical fibers, only forward and backward propagation directions are useful. For forward direction small Brillouin shifts ($\sim$10 to 1000 MHz) with low intensity have been observed due to guided nature of the optical and acoustic waves. The Brillouin scattering is primarily in the backward direction. Using $v_A = 6$ km/s and $n = 1.45$ for silica optical fibers in Eq. (10.23), the calculated $\nu = 11$ GHz at $\lambda_p \sim 1550$ nm.

Similar to the case of SRS, the SBS can be represented by a gain function. The width of the gain spectrum is small ($\sim$10 MHz), thus the gain can be assumed to be a Lorentzian with the spectral profile given by:

$$g(v) = \frac{(\Delta v/2)^2}{(v - v_0)^2 + (\Delta v/2)^2} g(v_0), \tag{10.24}$$

with:

$$g(v_0) = \frac{2\pi n^7 p^2}{c\lambda_p^2 \rho_0 v_A \Delta v}, \tag{10.25}$$

where p is the longitudinal elasto-optic coefficient and ρ_0 is the density of the material. Using the parameter values of fused silica, the SBS gain at 1550 nm is $g_b \sim 5 \times 10^{-11}$ m/W. This is about 500 times larger than the peak SRS gain coefficient shown in Fig. 10.8. Thus the SBS threshold in a single mode fiber is expected to be significantly smaller than the SRS threshold. Brillouin shift in single mode fibers have been measured using a heterodyne technique and an external cavity pump laser at 1525 nm with a narrow line width. The measured shift of 11.25 GHz is in good agreement with the result from Eq. (10.23). Brillouin gain measurements in optical fibers have been carried out.[44] The data is shown in Fig. 10.10.

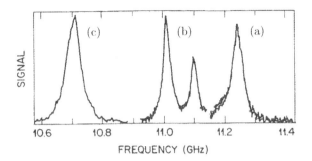

Fig. 10.10 Measured SBS gain spectrum for three fiber types.[44]

Similar to the SRS case, the pump and Stokes propagation equation for SBS is given by (note that Stokes power grows in the backward direction i.e., $-z$):

$$\frac{dI_s}{dz} = -g_b I_p I_s + \alpha I_s, \qquad (10.26)$$

$$\frac{dI_p}{dz} = -g_b I_p I_s - \alpha I_p, \qquad (10.27)$$

where it is assumed $\omega_p \sim \omega_s$ and $\alpha_p \sim \alpha_s$. As before, for the purpose of estimating threshold, the pump depletion due to SBS is neglected. The Stokes intensity then grows exponentially in the backward direction as follows:

$$I_s(0) = I_s(L) \exp(g_b P_0 L_{\text{eff}}/A_{\text{eff}} - \alpha L), \qquad (10.28)$$

with:

$$L_{\text{eff}} = \frac{1}{\alpha}[1 - \exp(-\alpha L)], \qquad (10.29)$$

Using a procedure as described earlier, the SBS threshold (P_0) is given by the relation[13]:

$$g_b P_{oth} L_{\text{eff}}/A_{\text{eff}} \sim 21, \qquad (10.30)$$

where g_b is the peak SBS gain. Using typical values for single mode fibers, $A_{\text{eff}} \sim 50\,\mu m^2$, $L_{\text{eff}} \sim 20$ km, and $g_b \sim 5 \times 10^{-11}\,m/W$, Eq. (10.29) yields a threshold power of ~ 1 mW. Due to its low threshold SBS is the dominant nonlinear process in optical fibers.

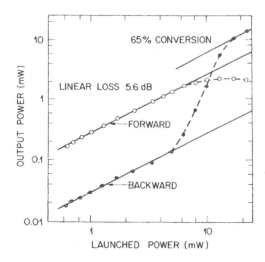

Fig. 10.11 Forward and backward powers as function of pump power. The fiber length is 13.6 km.[45]

Single pass SBS experiments have been reported. In one experiment a Nd-YAG laser emitting with a narrow linewidth ($\sim$1.6 MHz) near 1320 nm is used as a pump source.[45] The experiment used a 13.6 km long fiber with a loss of 0.41 dB/km. This resulted in L_{eff} of 7.7 km. The measured forward and backward power as a function of pump power is shown in Fig. 10.11. The figure shows that at a launched power of $\sim$5 mW, a substantial increase of backward power is observed due to SBS. At the same time, the transmitted power decreased due to pump conversion to SBS signal. A similar experiment has been reported using semiconductor distributed feedback laser with a linewidth of 10 MHz. The SBS threshold in the experiment was $\sim$9 mW.

10.5. Supercontinuum Generation

Broadband supercontinuum generation (SCG) schemes has gained significant interest due to its applications in optical coherence tomography, spectroscopy, and dense wavelength division multiplexing (DWDM) sources for high-capacity optical communication systems. In SC generation, extreme broadening of pulse spectrum can be

realized for sufficiently intense narrow-band incident pulses. The
primary mechanism of spectral broadening is considered as a combined action of self-phase modulation (SPM), cross-phase modulation
(XPM), SRS, FWM and the dispersive properties of the fiber. The
processes of the SCG are very sensitive to the dispersive and nonlinear properties of the optical fiber. However, for broad spectrum,
the control of the fiber dispersion is normally more important than
achieving the maximum possible nonlinearity per unit length. Therefore, there has been considerable research focusing on dispersion tailoring to maximize the bandwidth of the generated continuum. Many
schemes have been proposed by using dispersion-decreasing fiber,
dispersion-flattened fiber, dispersion-shifted fiber, tapered fiber and
photonic crystal fiber.[46-50] The mechanism of SCG has been analyzed
numerically.[51,52] The results showed that a dispersion-decreasing
fiber with a convex dispersion profile can generate a flat broadened
spectrum. The progress in the design of photonic crystal fiber (PCF)
enables the fabrication of fibers with two zero dispersion wavelengths
(ZDWs) and SCG in these fibers has been studied extensively.[53-58]
In Refs. 57–59, the authors investigated the possibility of obtaining the efficient mid-IR supercontinuum sources based on nonsilica
microstructured optical fibers (MOFs) technology. It showed that
small core MOFs with two ZDWs can have large efficiency for mid-IR
continuum generation using convenient pump wavelengths by phase-
matching across the upper (longer wavelength) ZDW. They found
that a seed wavelength approximately midway between the ZDWs
can produce the broadest spectrum. In Ref. 60, a ZBLAN fiber taper
with exponentially-decreasing core size was numerically modeled and
the coherent continuum could be generated. The authors showed that
the spectrum generated across the upper ZDW can be progressively
shifted with this non-uniform fiber taper design.

Although it is possible to enhance the SC broadening in optical
fibers with two ZDWs, the bandwidth of the spectrum is still limited in fibers with two ZDWs fibers if the longer wavelength ZDW
is fixed in wavelength. The reason is the power will transfer from
the soliton to the other wavelengths at frequencies determined by
the phase-matching condition (PMC),[60] so the spectrum cannot be

further extended to longer wavelength where the phase matching condition is not satisfied. Also Raman self-frequency shift of the soliton will be canceled by the spectral recoil effect,[61] which will stop the red shift of the soliton near the second ZDW. However, if the fiber taper has an increasing fiber core radius, the second ZDW can be shifted to longer wavelength and the phase matching condition will be continuously modified as well. The generated wavelengths can be guided towards longer wavelength eventually to generate a flat and broad spectrum.

10.5.1. *Theoretical Model*

SF57 (lead-silicate glass) is a material of choice for the fiber taper since the lead silicate glasses are promising materials for SCG. Although their material nonlinearity is lower than that for chalcogenide[61] and heavy metal oxide glass, they offer higher thermal and crystallization stability and less steep viscosity-temperature-curves, while exhibiting low softening temperatures[62-64] With microstructure fabrication technique, SF57 fibers with tight mode confinement and tailored dispersion have been demonstrated. Here for simplification, SF57 dispersion profile is simulated by using step-index waveguide model, the total dispersion in the fiber depends on both material and waveguide contributions. The wavelength dependent dispersion parameter is calculated by numerically solving the eigenvalue equation for the fundamental HE11 mode of step-index fiber. Figure 10.12 shows the calculated wavelength-dependent dispersion profile of SF57 fiber with 1.5 μm core radius. The similar dispersion profile can also be achieved in photonics crystal fiber.

The SCG can be numerically described by the generalized nonlinear Schrödinger equation (GNLS) under the slowly varying envelope approximation:

$$\frac{\partial A}{\partial z} + \frac{\alpha}{2}A + \sum_{m\geq 2}\frac{i^{m-1}}{m!}\beta_m\frac{\partial^m A}{\partial T^m}$$

$$= i\gamma\left(1 + \frac{i}{\omega_0}\frac{\partial}{\partial T}\right)\left(A\int_{-\infty}^{+\infty}R(T')|A(z, T - T')|^2 dT'\right),$$

$$(10.31)$$

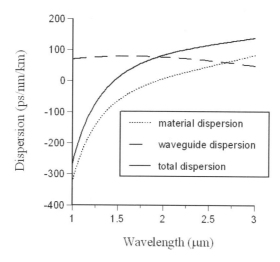

Fig. 10.12 Wavelength-dependent dispersion profile of SF57 fiber with $1.5\,\mu$m core radius.[60]

where $A(z, T)$ is the complex slowly varying amplitude of the light field in the reference frame moving with the group velocity of the input pulse and α is the fiber loss, γ is the effective nonlinearity parameter of the fiber that will be calculated by $\gamma = \frac{2\pi n_2}{\lambda A_{\text{eff}}}$, where n_2 is the nonlinear coefficient of the fiber, λ is the center wavelength of the pulse. β_m are the coefficients of Taylor series expansion of the propagation constant $\beta(\omega)$ about the carrier frequency ω_0, where $\beta = n(\omega)\omega/c$, $n(\omega)$ is the frequency dependent refractive index and c is the speed of light. Though $A(z, T)$ is the slowly varying amplitude, reasonably accurate simulation results can be obtained if sufficient number of higher order dispersive terms are included. The response function $R(T) = (1 - f_R)\delta(T) + f_R h_R(T)$ includes both the instantaneous electronic and non-instantaneous Raman responses, where the delta function represents the instantaneous electronic response, and $h_R(T)$ represents the delayed Raman response of the ions. In the simulations, $h_R(T)$ of the SF57 glass is described by means of an analytic form based on experimental measurements and $f_R = 0.1$.[65] A hyperbolic-secant input pulse with 100 fs full-width-at-half-maximum (FWHM) pulse width and 6 kW peak power at $1.55\,\mu$m is the input pulse. The pulse is launched into the SF57 fiber or fiber taper. The designed fiber taper has an increasing core radius r_{core} along the propagation length z with the relationship $r_{core}(z) = r_0(1 + z/z_0)^3$, where initial radius $r_0 = 0.7\,\mu m$ and $z_0 = 27.6\,cm$. This fiber taper has non-uniform structure which is similar to the one used in Ref. 59. However, in the design, the second ZDW is red shifted as taper radius increases and input pulse has much higher soliton number so that the soliton fission and compression can take place during propagation.

10.5.2. *Results and Discussion*

Figure 10.13 shows the wavelength dependent dispersion profile of SF57 fiber with different core radii. The second ZDW is formed for fibers with core radius smaller than $\sim 0.9\,\mu m$. With decreasing core radius, the second ZDW shifts to shorter wavelengths. The spectrum evolution in the fiber with $1.2\,\mu m$ core radius, which does not have the second ZDW is studied first. The seed wavelength is at $1.55\,\mu m$, which is close to the first ZDW at $\sim 1.38\,\mu m$. Now consider a dispersion profile with two ZDWs and a seed wavelength ($1.55\,\mu m$) near the middle of two ZDWs and a little closer to the first ZDW. The schematic of the SF57 fiber taper that is proposed earlier in Sec. 10.5.1 is shown in Fig. 10.14.

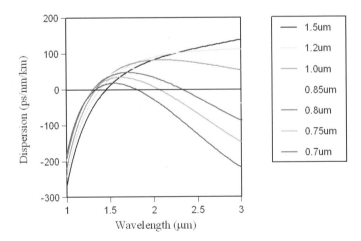

Fig. 10.13 Wavelength dependent dispersion profile of SF57 fiber with different core radii. Note the fibers with small core have two zero dispersion wavelengths (ZDW).[60]

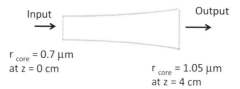

Fig. 10.14 A schematic of the SF57 fiber taper with nonlinear coefficient $n_2 = 4.1 *$ 10^{-19} m^{2}W^{-1} and $A_{\text{eff}} \sim 3.5\,\mu$m^2 at $1.55\,\mu$m at the input used.[60]

The results of the calculation for different z_0 values are shown in Fig. 10.15. The SC spectrum at the output of 4 cm SF57 fiber taper extends to $\sim$4.8 μm (for $z_0 = 27.6$ cm). The shifting of second ZDW along the fiber makes possible the generation of new dispersive waves (DWs) towards longer wavelength with continuously modified phase matching condition (PMC). Note that the spectrum looks less dense at wavelengths larger than $\sim$2 μm. This is because the energy of the solitons transfer to DWs and spreads out over a larger spectrum region, resulting in a broad and relatively uniform SC spectrum. The solitons also red shift to longer wavelength since the recoil effect is decreased when the second ZDW is shifting to longer wavelength. The cross-phase-modulation (XPM) between the solitons and generated DWs contribute to the flatness of the SC spectrum. Figure 10.15 shows the output spectra for various fiber taper structures with different tapering rates. The generated continuum spectrum is sensitive to the dispersion properties along the SF57 fiber taper, which is determined by the geometry of the taper. This suggests the possibility of carefully tailoring the dispersion profile to achieve a desired output spectrum based on the application requirements.

SC generation from 0.8–4.5 μm has been obtained by using 4.5 m ZBLAN fluoride fiber joined with a $\sim$1 m of silica single mode fiber.[64] In Ref. 65 a broad bandwidth, mid-IR SC generation using an 8 mm length of highly nonlinear telluride microstructured PCF has been demonstrated. It is pumped with 100 fs pulses of energy 1.9 nJ at 1550 nm. The resulting bandwidth is from 789 to 4870 nm which covers over 4000 nm spectrum range. The experimental data is shown in Fig. 10.16. For the tellurite PCF and pump pulses ($\beta_2 =$ 80 ps^2km^{-1}, $P_0 = 7954$ W, $\gamma = 596$ km^{-1}W^{-1}, $T_{\text{FWHM}} = 110\,fs$)

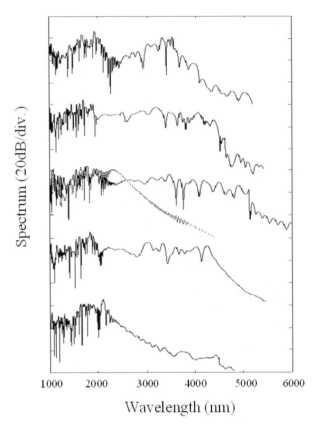

Fig. 10.15 Output spectra for SF57 fiber taper with various tapering rates with (a) $z_0 = 80$ cm (b) $z_0 = 29$ cm (c) $z_0 = 27.6$ cm (d) $z_0 = 21$ cm (e) $z_0 = 12$ cm. a–e are labeled top to bottom. The output spectrum, a uniform SF57 fiber is shown with the dotted line near the spectrum labeled (c)).[60]

the nonlinear length is calculated to be 0.21 mm, the dispersion length is 38 mm.[65] The soliton number found in the tellurite fiber is $N = 14$ indicating that higher order soliton dynamics affect the spectral characteristics of the supercontinuum radiation generated in this fiber.[65] For the tapered fiber described here a spectrum of width ($\sim$4000 nm, shown in Fig. 10.15(c)) is predicted with $\sim$1/3 input pulse energy ($\sim$0.64 nJ) than that for the tellurite fiber. For some applications, it is important to understand the coherence properties of the generated SC. To study the coherence properties of the generated SC, the complex degree of first-order coherence function

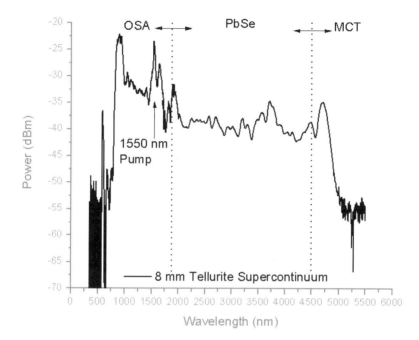

Fig. 10.16 Spectrum of SC generated in an 8 mm long tellurite microstructured fiber.[65] The different detector types are noted on top. OSA: optical spectrum analyzer, PbSe detector, MCT: mercury cadmium telluride.

introduced by Dudley and Coen[66,67] is used:

$$g_{12}(\lambda) = \frac{\langle E_1^*(\lambda)E_2(\lambda)\rangle}{[\langle|E_1(\lambda)|^2\rangle\langle|E_2(\lambda)|^2\rangle]^{1/2}}, \qquad (10.32)$$

where the angle brackets denote averaging over the independently generated SC pairs $[E_1(\lambda), E_2(\lambda)]$. The spectral coherence degree of the SC pulses is quantitatively measured by the modulus of g_{12}, which can be approximated as[66,67]:

$$|g_{12}(\lambda)| = \frac{1}{N^2 - N}\frac{N^2|\langle E(\lambda)\rangle|^2 - N\langle|E(\lambda)|^2\rangle}{\langle|E(\lambda)|^2\rangle}, \qquad (10.33)$$

where N is the total number of SC realizations. It is useful to introduce the overall degree of coherence across the SC spectrum as[66,67]:

$$\langle|g_{12}|\rangle = \frac{\int|g_{12}(\lambda)||E(\lambda)|^2 d\lambda}{\int|E(\lambda)|^2 d\lambda}. \qquad (10.34)$$

Both $|g_{12}(\lambda)|$ and $\langle|g_{12}|\rangle$ lie in the interval $[0, 1]$, a value close to 1 indicates more coherence. The degree of coherence of SC generated in the fiber is simulated by adding quantum noise seeds in the input field, and numerically solving the nonlinear Schrodinger equation applying the split-step Fourier method (SSFM).[60,68] The random noise in every temporal discrete bin of the input field is modeled as a stochastic variation with the standard deviation equal to the square root of the number of photons in that bin. The calculated spectrum and degree of coherence $|g_{12}(\lambda)|$ as a function of wavelength is shown in Fig. 10.17. A high degree of coherence is obtained for peak powers and pulse widths within a certain range.[68]

Nonlinear processes in single mode fibers and fiber amplifiers are important for the generation of Raman lasers and coherent supercontinuum generation. These types of sources provide new laser wavelengths for applications in spectroscopy, tomography and sensors.

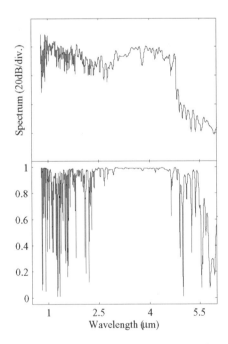

Fig. 10.17 Calculated spectrum (top) and degree of coherence (bottom) for 200 fs pulses at 6 kW peak power.[68]

References

1. G.P. Agrawal, Nonlinear Fiber Optics. 4th Edition. New York: Academic Press. 2007.
2. M.W. Maeda, W.B. Sessa, W.I. Way, A. Yi-yan, L. Curtis, R. Spicer and R.I. Laming, *J. Lightwave Technol.* **8** (1990) 1402.
3. N. Shibata, R. Braun and R. Waarts, *IEEE J. Quantum Electron.* **23** (1987) 1205.
4. R.G. Waarts and R.P. Brau, *Electron. Lett.* **22** (1986) 873.
5. F. Forgnieri, W.T. Robert, A.R. Chraplyvy and D. Marcuse, Tech. Deg. IOOC-OFC 1993, Paper FC4, 1993.
6. P.A. Andrekson, N.A. Olsson, J.R. Simpson, T. Tanban-EK, R.A. Logan and M. Haner, *Electron. Lett.* **27** (1991) 922.
7. A.H. Gnauck, R.M. Jopson and R.M. Derosier, *IEEE Photon. Technol. Lett.* **5** (1993) 663.
8. K.O. Hill, D.C. Johnson, B.S. Kawasaki and I.R. Macdonald, *J. Appl. Phys.* **49** (1978) 5098.
9. K. Inoue and H. Toba, *IEEE Photon. Technol. Lett.* **4** (1992) 69.
10. R. Hui and A. Mecozzi, *Appl. Phys. Lett.* **60** (1992) 2454.
11. B.P. Pal (Ed), Guided Wave Optical Components and Devices. Elsevier Academic Press. 2006.
12. S. Shimoda and H. Ishio (Ed). Optical amplifiers and their applications. John Wiley and Sons. 1994.
13. R.G. Smith, *Appl. Opt.* **11** (1972) 2489.
14. R.H. Stolen, Chapter 10. In *Optical Fiber Telecommunications*, S.E. Miller and A.G. Chynoweth (Eds). New York: Academic. 1979.
15. R.H. Stolen and J.E. Bjorkholm, *IEEE J. Quantum Electron.* QE-**18**, (1982) 1062.
16. N. Bloembergen, The stimulated Raman effect, *Am. J. Phys.* **35** (1967) 989.
17. W. Kaiser and M. Maier, Stimulated Rayleigh, Brillouin and Raman spectroscopy. In *Laser Handbook*, F.T. Arecchi and E.O. Schulz- Dubois (Eds). Amsterdam: North-Holland, pp. 1077.
18. A.R. Chraplyvy, *IEEE J. Lightwave Tech.* **8** (1990) 1548.
19. N. Shibata, R.P. Braun and R.G. Waarts, *IEEE JQE.* QE-**23** (1987) 1205.
20. A.H. Gnauck R.W. Tkach, A.R. Chraplyvy and T. Li, *IEEE J. Lightwave Tech.* **26** (2008) 1032.
21. S. Radic, G. Pendock, A. Srivastava, P. Wysocki and A. Chraplyvy. In *Proceedings. ECOC* 1999.
22. K. Song and M. Premaratne, *IEEE Photon. Technol. Lett.* **12** (2000) 1630.
23. M. Vasilyev, S. Tsuda, S. Burtsev, Y. Lui, G.G. Luther and R.S. Mozdy. In *Proceedings. ECOC.* 2000.
24. S. Radic, G. Pendock, A. Srivastava, P. Wysocki and A. Chraplyvy, *J. Lightwave. Technol.* **19** (2001) 636.
25. Y. Liu, S. Burtsev, S. Tsuda, S.P. Hegarty, R.S. Mozdy, M. Hempstead, G.G. Luther and R.G. Smart, *Electron. Lett.* **35** (1999) 2130.
26. H. Ono and M. Yamada, *IEEE J. Lightwave Tech.* **26** (2008) 2175.

27. R.G. Smith, *Appl. Opt.* **11** (1972) 2489.
28. R. Shuker and R.W. Gammon, *Phys. Rev. Lett.* **25** (1970) 222.
29. R.H. Stolen and E.P. Ippen, *Appl. Phys. Lett.* **22** (1973) 276.
30. J. Auyeung and A. Yariv, *IEEE J. Quantum Electron.* QE-**14** (1978) 347.
31. R.H. Stolen, *Proc. IEEE* **68** (1980) 1232.
32. Y. Ohmori, Y. Sasaki, M. Kawachi and T. Edahiro, *Electron. Lett.* **17** (1981) 593.
33. M. Ikeda, *Opt. Commun.* **37** (1981) 388.
34. R.H. Stolen, C. Lee and R.K. Jain, *J. Opt. Soc. Amer.* **1** (1984) 652.
35. A.R. Chraplyvy and P.S. Henry, *Electon. Lett.* **19** (1983) 641.
36. A.R. Chraplyvy, *Electron. Lett.* **20** (1984) 58.
37. L.G. Cohen and C. Lin, *IEEE J. Quantum Electron.* QE-**14** (1978) 855.
38. E.P. Ippen and R.H. Stolen, *Appl. Phys. Lett.* **21** (1972) 539.
39. D. Heiman, D.S. Hamilton and R.W. Hellwarth, *Phys. Rev. B* **19** (1979) 6583.
40. Y. Aoki and K. Tajima. In *Tech. Dig., Con6 Lasers and Electrooptics,* paper Tu 5. (Baltimore, Md). 1987.
41. E. Lichtman and A.A. Friesem, *Opt. Comm.* **64** (1987) 544.
42. C.L. Tang, *J. Appl. Phys.* **37** (1966) 2945.
43. E. Lichtman, R.G. Waarts, and A.A. Friesem, *J. Lightwave Technol.* **7** (1989) 171.
44. R.W. Tkach, A.R. Chraplyvy and R.M. Derosier, *Electron Lett.* **22** (1986) 1011.
45. D. Cotter, *Electron Lett.* **18** (1982) 492.
46. G. Genty, M. Lehtonen, H. Ludvigsen and M. Kaivola, *Opt. Express.* **12** (2004) 3471.
47. T.A. Birks, W.J. Wadsworth and P. St. J. Russell, *Opt. Lett.* **25** (2000) 1415.
48. T. Hori, J. Takayanagi, N. Nishizawa and T. Goto, *Opt. Express* **12** (2004) 3317.
49. C. Kakkar and K. Thyagarajan, *Opt. Express.* **14** (2006) 10292.
50. T. Okuno, M. Onishi, T. Kashiwada, S. Ishikawa and M. Nishimura, *IEEE J. Sel. Top. Quantum. Electron.* **5** (1999) 1385.
51. K. Mori, H. Takara, S. Kawanishi, M. Saruwatari and T. Morioka, *Electron. Lett.* **33** (1997) 1806.
52. K. Mori, H. Takara and S. Kawanishi, *J. Opt. Soc. Am. B.* **18** (2001) 1780.
53. T. Schreiber, T.V. Andersen, D. Schimpf, J. Limpert and A. Tunnermann, *Opt. Express* **13** (2005) 9556.
54. M.H. Frosz, P. Falk and O. Bang, *Opt. Express* **13** (2005) 6181.
55. A. Mussot, M. Beaugeois, M. Bouazaoui and T. Sylvestre, *Opt. Express.* **15** (2007) 11553.
56. J.H.V. Price, T.M. Monro, H. Ebendorff-Heidepriem, F. Poletti, P. Horak, V. Finazzi, J.Y.Y. Leong, P. Petropoulos, J.C. Flanagan, G. Brambilla, X. Feng and D.J. Richardson, *IEEE J. Quantum Electron.* **13** (2007) 738.
57. Zhigang Chen, Antoinette J. Taylor and Anatoly Efimov, *Opt. Express.* **17** (2009) 5852.

58. V. Skryabin, F. Luan, J.C. Knight and P. St. J. Russell, *Science* **301** (2003) 1705.

59. P. Petropoulos, T.M. Monro, H. Ebendorff-Heidepriem, K. Frampton, R.C. Moore, and D.J. Richardson, *Opt. Express.* **11** (2003) 3568.

60. Z. Chen, S. Ma and N.K. Dutta, *Opt. Commun.* **283** (2010) 3076.

61. S. Fujino, H. Ijiri, F. Shimizu and K. Morinaga, *J. Jpn. Inst. Met.* **62** (1998) 106.

62. J.Y.Y. Leong, P. Petropoulos, J.H.V. Price, H. Ebendorff-Heidepriem, S. Asimakis, R.C. Moore, K.E. Frampton, V. Finazzi, X. Feng, T.M. Monro and D.J. Richardson, *J. Lightwave. Technol* **24** (2006) 183.

63. V.L. Kalashnikov, E. Sorokin and I.T. Sorokina, *Appl. Phys. B.* **87** (2007) 37.

64. C. Xia, M. Kumar, O.P. Kulkarni, M.N. Islam, F.L. Terry Jr., M.J. Freeman, M. Poulain and G. Mazé, *Opt. Lett.* **31** (2006) 2553.

65. P. Domachuk, N.A. Wolchover, M. Cronin-Golomb, A. Wang, A.K. George, C.M.B. Cordeiro, J.C. Knight and F.G. Omenetto, *Opt. Express.* **16** (2008) 7161.

66. J.M. Dudley and S. Coen, *Opt. Lett.* **27** (2002) 1180.

67. J.M. Dudley and S. Coen, *IEEE J. Sel. Top. Quantum Electron.* **8** (2002) 651.

68. H. Hu, W. Li and N. K. Dutta, *Fiber and Integrated Optics.* **32** (2013) 209.

Chapter 11

Planar Waveguide Amplifiers and Lasers

11.1. Introduction

Rare earth-doped optical fiber amplifier and lasers are important devices for both terrestrial and submarine optical communication systems, for sensor systems, and as laser sources at various wavelengths for various applications including high power applications. Optical fiber amplifiers are typically 10 to 30 m in length. The core and cladding of the fiber form a waveguide through which the light travels and undergoes amplification. The core is typically doped with the rare earth dopant. The length of a planar waveguide amplifier (PWA) is typically limited to tens of centimeters both due to fabrication limitation and higher optical attenuation in planar waveguides. In order to achieve high gain in $\sim$10 cm long planar waveguides, the rare earth concentration is typically two orders of magnitude higher than that for fibers. This may introduce nonradiative mechanisms in some rare earths such as Er due to upconversion.

PWAs have been fabricated in many glass materials by several methods.[1-8] These include modifications of refractive index at the surface by ion exchange,[9] ion implantation,[11] or ion diffusion.[12] Also, a waveguide can be formed by growth or deposition of one material on top of another of a different refractive index.[13,14] Usually, the waveguides formed by these techniques are in the form of a planar thin film which may be patterned into an array of channel waveguides using photolithographic techniques. The optical confinement of the pump light in the waveguide results in low threshold for net gain or laser action for rare earth-doped planar waveguide devices. However,

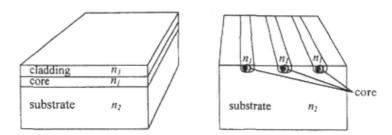

Fig. 11.1 Schematic of typical planar and channel waveguide structures.[8] The left figure shows a planar waveguide and to the right is channel waveguide. The core index $n_1 > n_2$: cladding index.

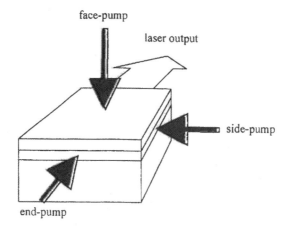

Fig. 11.2 Schematics of pump laser coupling into the waveguide.[8]

key to achieving low threshold operation is low optical loss in the material. The schematics of typical planar and channel waveguide structures are shown in Fig. 11.1.

Efficient coupling of high-power diode pump sources is important for low pump threshold. Methods such as optical fiber-based coupler for single mode waveguides, specialized lens optics, and diode beam shapers, have been used for efficient coupling. In general, the pump light can be coupled from the end faces of the waveguide, from the side or from the surface. This is shown schematically in Fig. 11.2.

Typically, a planar waveguide has a symmetric core and cladding region with the high-index core region being rare earth-doped

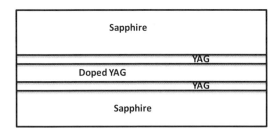

Fig. 11.3 Schematic of a double-clad waveguide. Both of these planar structures can be processed into channel waveguides. The undoped YAG regions have higher index than the sapphire.

bounded by the low-index cladding regions. Similar to the case for fibers, a double-cladded waveguide can be fabricated for the planar waveguide geometry (Fig. 11.3). In the latter case, the inner core is doped with rare earth, the outer layers (Fig. 11.3) are not doped with rare earth and has nearly the same index as the inner core. The entire region is bounded by lower index cladding layers. Figure 11.3 shows Nd-doped YAG (Yttrium–Aluminum–Garnet) double clad structure on a sapphire substrate.

Diode lasers are suitable for end pumping because the laser mode is laterally spread like the waveguide allowing good overlapping between the gain region in the waveguide and the diode laser mode. A typical configuration for end pumping of waveguide lasers is shown in Fig. 11.4(a). Also the asymmetric lasing and pump beam profile in the waveguide is shown. Dichroic mirrors with high transmission at pump wavelength and high reflectivity at laser wavelength are often used before the waveguide end. For double clad structures required for high-power laser fabrication, diode bars (which emit many W's of power) are used for pumping. The diode bar can be placed next to the waveguide with or without a lens and the light captured within the high numerical aperture of the double core waveguide gets coupled into the waveguide and serves as pump beam [Fig. 11.4(b)].

11.2. Er-doped Planar Waveguide

As mentioned earlier, in order to achieve significant gains in ~ 10 cm long waveguides, the concentration of rare earth dopant (e.g., Er)

Fiber Amplifiers and Fiber Lasers

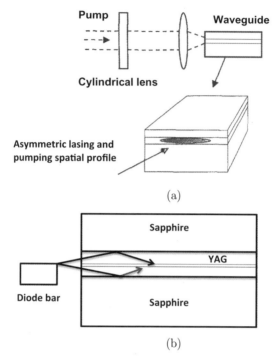

(a)

(b)

Fig. 11.4 (a) Schematic of end pumping a planar waveguide using a diode laser. Also shown is the pump laser mode in the waveguide. (b) Schematic of a double core waveguide pumping using a diode bar.[8, 15]

in planar waveguides needs to be two orders of magnitude greater than that for optical fibers. At higher concentration, the average spacing between Er ions decreases. At close spacings, the Er ions lose the exited energy by a nonradiative process known as up-conversion. Consider two Er ions both in their upper energy levels, in the up-conversion process, one electron (in one Er ion) decays nonradiatively to the ground state, transferring its energy to the other Er ion, which gets excited to a higher energy level. The clustering of Er ions in silica glass doped to high Er concentrations accentuates this nonradiative decay mechanism. Up-conversion is less pronounced in other glass types (e.g., soda lime glass due to its cage-like structure) where the atoms in the glass surround each Er ion and prevent clustering. These types of glasses have been used in the study of PWAs.

Er-doped silica based nearly single-mode waveguide has been reported by several authors. One of the early reports is by Shuto *et al.*[19] They reported a waveguide which has an Er-doped phosphosilicate glass core formed by plasma enhanced chemical vapor deposition (PECVD). The doped core has silica glass cladding layer formed by flame hydrolysis deposition (FHD) on a Si substrate. The core layer is deposited on the FHD grown bottom cladding layer at a substrate temperature of 400°C using PECVD growth technique using SiH and N_2O gases. P-alkoxide and Er-chelate are used as sources for P and Er doping. The doping densities (of P and Er) are controlled (using mass flow controllers) by transporting the vapor of the heated sources into the reaction region using N_2 carrier gas. The core is annealed after deposition. The lateral size of the core regions are etched using reactive ion etching (RIE) and then the core layer is embedded in the cladding region grown by FHD process. Thus, the Er forms a buried waveguide region. The refractive index of the core is ~1.6% higher than that of the surrounding cladding regions. The Er concentration in the core is 0.48%.

Prior to amplification studies, the propagation loss of the waveguide is measured. The absorption spectrum is shown in Fig. 11.5.

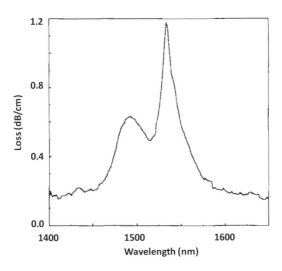

Fig. 11.5 Absorption loss as a function of wavelength.[19]

Fiber Amplifiers and Fiber Lasers

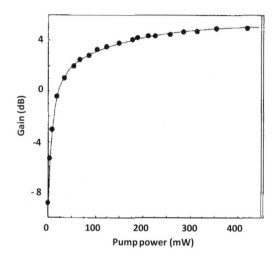

Fig. 11.6 Net gain at 1.53 μm as a function of input pump power at 0.98 μm.[19]

The optical loss at 1.53 μm is ~1.1 dB/cm. The waveguide is 7.5 cm long and has a spot size of 8×11 μm^2 at 1.55 μm. Pump laser light at a wavelength of 0.98 μm is coupled into the waveguide. The output signal at 1.53 μm is measured as a function of pump power. The optical gain is determined from the ratio of the output to input signal power. The data are shown in Fig. 11.6.

Using an S-shaped waveguide and a similar fabrication process as described earlier, a gain of ~10 dB has been reported at a pump power of 100 mW, and gain as high as 16 dB has been reported at a pump power of ~210 mW.[20]

Soda lime glass has been used as a core for Er doping.[21] For high gain at low pump power, optimizing Er concentration is important in addition to waveguide dimensions and index difference between the core and the cladding region. Although high Er concentration provides high gain, it also increases the up-conversion rate.[22-24] For the experiment of Ref. 21, an Er concentration of 0.7×10^{20} cm^{-3} is used. Er-doped films are deposited by RF sputtering from a soda lime glass target (doped with Er) on a silica lower cladding layer. This layer is 15 μm thick and is deposited on silicon substrate by thermal oxidation. Ion milling is used to produce 3 to 9 μm wide

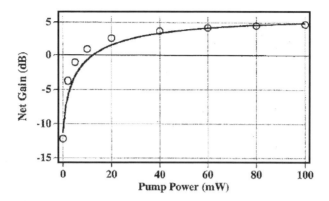

Fig. 11.7 Measured optical gain as a function of pump power.[21] Pump wavelength is 0.98 μm.

waveguides on the deposited Er-doped film. The etching induced side wall roughness is removed by reflowing the surface of the waveguides at a high temperature above the glass transition temperature. This results in a smooth surface. The refractive index difference between the core and lower cladding layer is 3%. An index matched oil is used as the upper cladding. The end faces of the Er-doped waveguides (6 cm long) is polished to optimize the fiber coupling.

The optical gain of the amplifier is measured as a function of pump power. The experimental data on small signal gain with an input power of −42 dBm at 1.53 μm is shown in Fig. 11.7. The low threshold (∼10 mW) for net gain is due to low scattering loss, tightly confined mode and low glass absorption loss.[21]

11.2.1. *Optical Gain and Gain Saturation*

Amplifier performance characteristics such as gain spectrum, gain saturation power, and noise figure discussed earlier (for fiber amplifiers) has been studied for Er-doped PWAs. As expected, these amplifiers can be pumped with 1480 nm pump lasers in addition to 980 nm pump lasers.[25–28] The small signal gain spectrum of a PWA for various pump powers is shown in Fig. 11.8.[28] The PWA is 14 cm long and has aluminosilicate guide layers. The amplifier is pumped using a 1470 nm pump laser. The gain spectrum is measured using the input

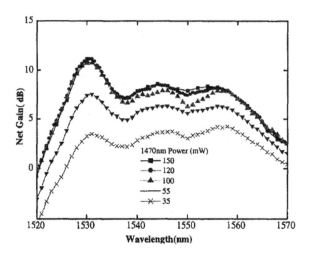

Fig. 11.8 Gain spectrum for various pump powers for an Er-doped PWA. The pump laser wavelength is 1470 nm. The gain is reasonably flat at low pump powers.[28]

signal from a tunable (grating tuned) external cavity laser. The input laser wavelength can be tuned from 1520 to 1570 nm range. The measured gain is reasonably flat for low pump powers suggesting that the PWA is suitable for multiwavelength WDM transmission.

The noise figure of the amplifier is measured for various input signal wavelengths and input signal powers. The data are shown in Fig. 11.9. The noise figure is obtained using the amplified spontaneous emission (ASE) spectrum of the amplifier.

Similar to fiber amplifiers, the PWA gain saturates with increasing signal power. The saturation of gain in amplifier is demonstrated by plotting the net gain as a function of output power. The data for an Er-doped PWA pumped using a 980 nm laser is shown in Fig. 11.10.

11.3. Nd-doped Planar Waveguide

Single-mode Nd-doped waveguide amplifiers and lasers on glass have been investigated.[29–36] In an early experimental study, Nd-doped buried channel waveguides were used.[37] The waveguides are formed by a field assisted ion migration process in the phosphate glass substrate (HOYA glass doped with Nd, 3.3% — by weight). The

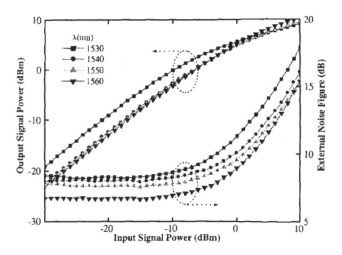

Fig. 11.9 Output signal power and noise figure as a function of input signal power. The pump laser is at 1480 nm.[28]

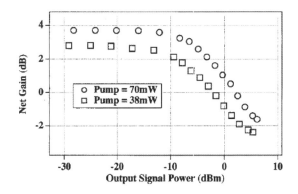

Fig. 11.10 Gain is plotted as a function of output signal power of an Er-doped PWA. The pump laser is at 980 nm.[21]

waveguides are buried with sodium-silver ion exchange in a molten salt (20%NaNO+ 80% CsNO). The waveguides are ∼1 cm long and the ends of the waveguides are polished. The multimode waveguides have elliptical cross sections with long and short axis of 33 and 17 μm, respectively.

For amplification measurement, pump light from an Ar laser (514 nm) or an 808 nm diode laser is coupled to the waveguide using a

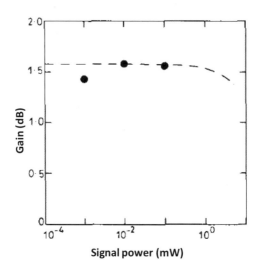

Fig. 11.11 Optical gain over a function of pump power for a Nd glass waveguide amplifier using 808 nm pump (figure adopted from Ref. 94).[37, 94]

single-mode optical fiber. The signal light $(\sim 10\,\mu W)$ is coupled using a dichroic mirror coupler to the same waveguide. The measured gain as a function of optical power is shown in Fig. 11.11.

Single-mode Nd-doped waveguide lasers fabricated on a Si substrate have been reported.[38–41] To fabricate the doped waveguide, $SiCl_4$ and PCl_3 are hydrolyzed (FHD) using an oxy-hydrogen burner to form a low-density soot on a Si substrate with a 10 μm thick SiO_2 layer (thermally grown). The soot is fused and immersed in an alcohol solution of NdCl. After drying, the porous structure is fused to form the Nd-doped SiO_2–P_2O_5 glass. Ridge waveguides are formed on the glass using standard photolithography and RIE. Flame hydrolysis technique is then used to form a cladding layer of SiO_2–P_2O_5–B_2O_3. The cladding layer is index matched to buffer layer and is $\sim 20\,\mu$m thick. The schematic of the fabrication process is shown in Fig. 11.12.

In one experiment, the waveguide dimensions are 12 μm × 8 μm and the Nd doping density is 0.38 wt.%. The index difference between core and cladding is 0.87% and the waveguide device length is 5.7 cm. The laser cavity is formed by using dielectric-coated mirror in close proximity to the waveguide ends using index matching

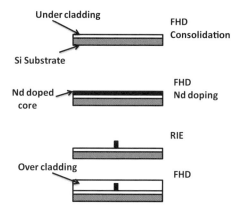

Fig. 11.12 Schematic of the fabrication process.[41, 94] The process starts at the top (figure adopted from Ref. 94).

liquids. The input mirror has a reflectivity of 99.9% at the laser wavelength (∼1060 nm) and transmission of 90% at the pump wavelength (804 nm). The output mirror has a reflectivity of 95% at the laser wavelength and transmission of 95% at the pump wavelength. The laser output as a function of pump power is shown in Fig. 11.13. The threshold power is ∼20 mW.

The schematic of another waveguide laser design is shown in Fig. 11.14. For this laser, the Nd-doped core has a Nd doping level of 0.2 wt.% and a thickness of 6 μm. The index difference between the core and cladding is 0.5%. The waveguide length is 4 cm and the widths varied in the 6–30 μm range. Dielectric mirrors are deposited on the ends of the waveguide cavity. The input mirror had high reflectivity ($R = 99.9\%$) at the lasing wavelength and high transmittance (>95%) in the pump wavelength range of 730–820 nm. The reflectivity of the output mirror is 95% at the lasing wavelength with a transmittance of >95% at the pump wavelength. The lasing spectrum and the output power as a function of pump power for a Nd-doped waveguide laser of Fig. 11.14 is shown in Fig. 11.15. The threshold power is ∼26 mW.

The threshold pump power is found to vary with the pump wavelength. The measured data points for various pump wavelengths are shown in Fig. 11.16. The pump wavelength is varied using a tunable

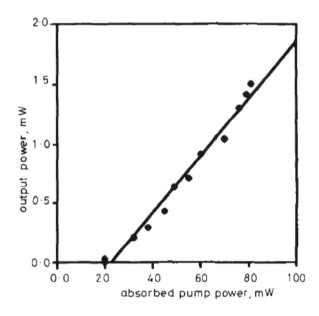

Fig. 11.13 Laser output power as a function of absorbed pump power.[42]

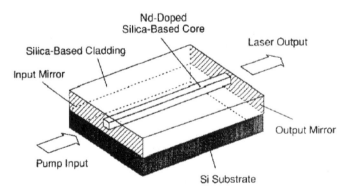

Fig. 11.14 Schematic of the Nd-doped waveguide laser.[41]

Ti–sapphire pump laser. The solid lines are the calculated results for two pump bands. The minimum laser threshold power is obtained at a pump wavelength of 805 nm. Nd-doped glass has been used in high-power applications using a double-core waveguide geometry. This is discussed in detail in Sec. 11.6.

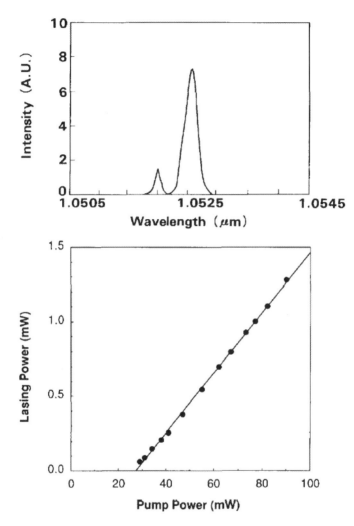

Fig. 11.15 Lasing spectra (top) and laser output power as a function of pump power (bottom). The waveguide width is 8 μm.[41]

11.4. Er–Yb Co-doped Planar Waveguide

Similar to the case of Er-doped fiber amplifiers, Er–Yb co-doped waveguide amplifiers have been investigated.[43−50] These have the potential of reducing the effect of up-conversion which is a nonradiative process at high Er densities. In Er–Yb co-doped amplifiers,

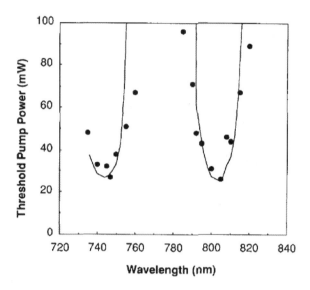

Fig. 11.16 Measured data on laser threshold as a function of pump wavelength. Solid lines are the calculated results using the known gain spectrum.[41]

energy transfer from excited Yb to upper Er level results in gain for the Er transition (Sec. 7.4).

The Er–Yb co-doped glasses containing ZnO are prepared by standard melting technique. The oxides used in the melt are SiO_2, Na_2O (14.2 mol.%), ZnO, Al_2O_3, Er_2O_3, and Yb_2O_3. The samples prepared had 0.6 at.% of Er but differing amounts of Yb in the 0 to 1.2 at.% range.[47] Although typically Al_2O_3 is used to enhance the solubility of Er, ZnO is used in this case. The glass components are melted in a crucible at 1470°C. Mechanical stirring and quenching at 520°C is used to produce the bulk glass which is cut into $40 \times 20 \times 2$ mm pieces for waveguide fabrication. Waveguide boundaries are formed by standard contact lithography. The widths of the waveguides varies from 2 to 6 μm. Waveguides are formed by the ion exchange process using K to Na or Ag to Na ion exchange. The process of ion exchange with K ions was performed in a melt of potassium nitrate at 400°C for various times, depending on the exact Yb concentration in the glass substrate. The Ag ion exchange is performed in eutectic $NaNO_3$–KNO_3 melt with additional 3.6 wt.% of silver nitrate at 280°C. The experimental setup used for measurements in shown in

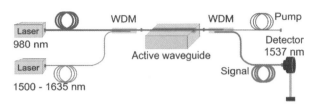

Fig. 11.17 Schematic of the experimental setup used for Er–Yb co-doped ion exchanged planar waveguide measurements.[47]

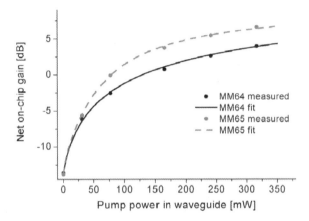

Fig. 11.18 Net gain as a function of pump power for two cases (i) Er-doped glass (ii) Er–Yb co-doped glass with equal amounts of Er and Yb.[47]

Fig. 11.17. The pump laser (970 nm) and the signal (used for gain spectrum measurement) is coupled into the waveguide using a WDM multiplexer.

The intensity profiles of the guided modes and the waveguide scattering losses are experimentally determined. The mode field profiles at the signal and pump wavelengths are obtained by near-field IR imaging. In potassium and silver ion exchanged waveguides, the mode dimensions are found to be 11×14 and $3.5 \times 5\ \mu\text{m}$ at 1550 nm, respectively. In the Er emission band, the K and Ag ion exchanged channel waveguide losses are estimated to be 0.18 and 0.8 dB/cm, respectively.

The net on chip gain as a function of pump power for K ion exchanged waveguide is shown in Fig. 11.18. The data are shown for

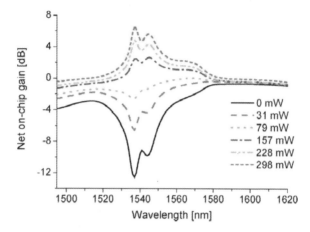

Fig. 11.19 Spectral dependence of gain/absorption at various pump powers for the Er–Yb co-doped glass. Er, Yb concentrations at 0.6 and 1.2 at.%, respectively.[47]

two cases (i) Er-doped glass only MM64, (ii) Er–Yb co-doped glass with equal amounts (both 0.6 at.%) of Er and Yb MM65. Optical gain at various input wavelengths is measured by using a tunable input laser. The spectral dependence of gain for several pump powers for K ion exchanged waveguide is shown in Fig. 11.19. An up-conversion coefficient for Er of $1 \times 10^{-24}\,\mathrm{m^{-3}\,s^{-1}}$ is determined from the data on different Yb concentration and from known model parameters.

11.5. Yb-doped Planar Waveguide

Yb-doped waveguide amplifiers have been investigated.[51–55] They generally have much higher gain due to high solubility and lack of nonradiative up-conversion process such as that present in Er. High optical gain has been reported in Yb-doped microstructured $KGd_xLu_yYb_{1-x-y}(WO_4)_2$ channel waveguides.[51] Yb-doped $KY(WO_4)_2$ layers were grown by liquid-phase epitaxy onto an undoped, (010)-oriented, polished, 1-cm²-sized $KY(WO_4)_2$ substrates in a $K_2W_2O_7$ solvent at temperatures of 920–923°C.[52] Co-doping the layers with appropriate percentages of optically inert Gd^{3+} and Lu^{3+} ions enables the growth of lattice-matched layers.[53] The replacement of a fraction of Lu^{3+} by Yb^{3+} ions of similar ionic radius resulted in up to 47.5 at.% Yb^{3+}-doped KGd_xLu_y $Yb_{1-x-y}(WO_4)_2$ layers. The index difference between the Yb doped layer and substrate is $\sim 2 \times 10^{-2}$. The samples were between 180 and 320 μm long and the Yb-doped layer surface is polished down to 2.2–3.5 μm thickness. The ridge waveguides were fabricated using Ar beam etching. This produced ~ 1.4 μm deep ridges about 6 μm wide. Undoped $KY(WO_4)_2$ is then grown over the sample burying the ridges.

The gain of the sample is measured using pump light from a Ti–sapphire laser emitting near 932 nm. The signal light is at 980 nm. The measured gain for different at.% of Yb is shown in Fig. 11.20. The measured maximum gain is ~ 900 dB/cm at 60 mW of pump power.

The spectral dependence of gain is measured using a tunable laser for signal input. The measured data and results of a model are shown in Fig. 11.21. The line with arrows indicates a 55 nm band for which the optical gain exceeds 150 dB/cm.

The above result illustrates that high gain can be obtained in Yb-doped planar waveguides. This suggests the possibility of high

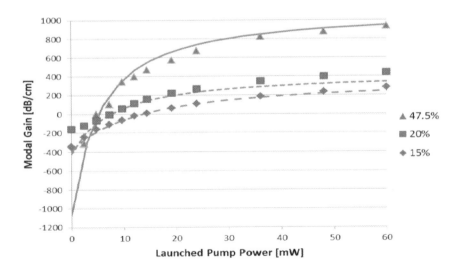

Fig. 11.20 Measured small signal modal gain as a function of pump power for different at.% of Yb. Signal wavelength is at 980 nm.[51]

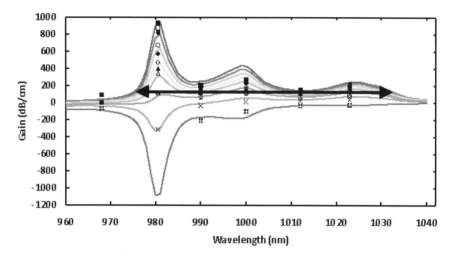

Fig. 11.21 The modal gain for different launched powers: solid lines are calculated results, the points indicate experimental data. The line with arrows indicate a 55 nm band for which the optical gain exceeds 150 dB/cm.[51]

power laser emission in Yb doped waveguide with appropriate thermal management and pump input geometry.

11.6. High-Power Waveguide Lasers

For high-power planar waveguide lasers, highest powers have been obtained using array of diode bars in a side pumping geometry (Fig. 11.2). This allows maximum coupling of pump light from diodes which have asymmetric beam profile. Nd or Yb or Tm are generally used as rare earth dopants for these high-power lasers or amplifiers.[56–61] In addition to high pump power another requirement is heat dissipation, i.e., a large fraction of the amount of pump power that is not converted to laser light gets absorbed and generates heat and this heat must be removed. Thus, mounting configurations with active cooling have produced high output powers.

The planar waveguides for high-power applications have a cladding pumped geometry (Fig. 11.3). The calculated mode profile in the double clad Nd-doped YAG structure is shown in Fig. 11.22. The figure also shows the various indices. The YAG is bounded by low-index sapphire on both sides. For end pumping, light from a

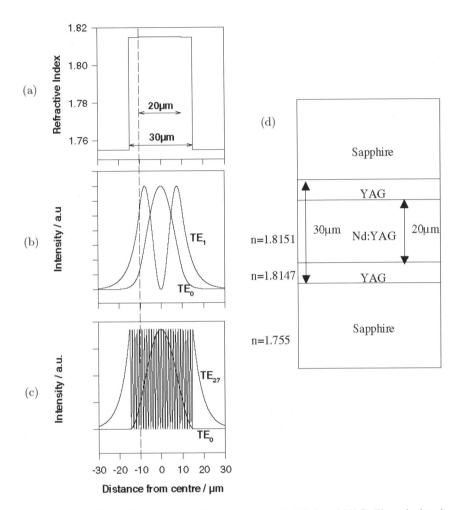

Fig. 11.22 Double clad planar waveguide structure with Nd-doped YAG. The calculated mode profiles are also shown. Similar structures have been made using Yb- and Tm-doped YAG.[56]

807 nm diode is coupled using suitable lenses to the Nd-doped waveguide. The Nd doping level is 1 at.%. Sapphire has a lower index than YAG, thus the light bounces at that interface and propagates along the waveguide much like a double clad fiber. The output mirror reflectivities are optimized for the particular Nd transition. It is ∼78% for the 1064 nm transition. The measured results (including that for the

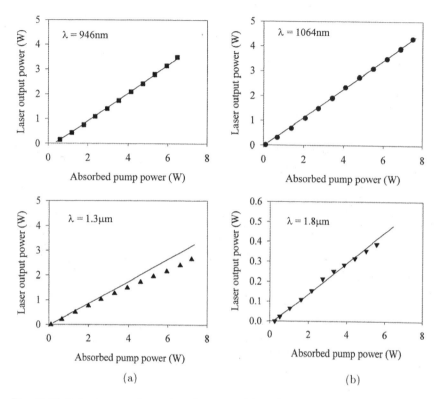

Fig. 11.23 Output power for various laser transitions (as noted in Table 11.6.1) as a function of absorbed pump power.[62]

most intense 1064 nm transition) are shown in Fig. 11.23. The results for other transitions are summarized in Table 11.1.

For higher power, side pumping and cooling is important.[63–66] The schematic diagram of a side pumped cladding pumped waveguide laser is shown in Fig. 11.23. Two 20 W diode bars pump the waveguide from each side. The waveguides are 1cm long and 5 mm wide. The pump light propagates along the short dimension. The Nd doping level is 1 at.%. The schematic of the layers in the planar waveguide is shown in the inset. Sapphire has a lower index than YAG, thus the light propagates along the waveguide much like a double clad fiber.

Double clad planar waveguide designs as shown in Fig. 11.24 have been made using Nd, Yb, and Tm doping. The doping levels are

Table 11.1 Summary of observations on four laser transitions in Nd-YAG.[62]

	$^4F_{3/2} \rightarrow {}^4I_{9/2}$	$^4F_{3/2} \rightarrow {}^4I_{11/2}$	$^4F_{3/2} \rightarrow {}^4I_{13/2}$	$^4F_{3/2} \rightarrow {}^4I_{15/2}$
Wavelength (μm)	0.946	1.064	1.318/1.338	1.833
Maximum output power (W)	3.5	4.3	2.7	0.4[a]
Slope efficiency η_s w.r.t. absorbed power (%)	57	58	36	7

[a]Laser power accounts for output from both ends of the cavity.

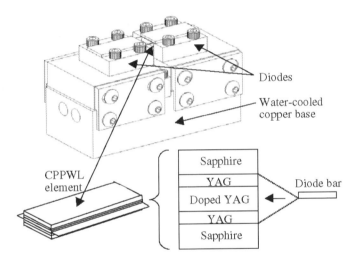

Fig. 11.24 Schematic of a diode bar pumped high-power planar waveguide laser. There are two diode bars located about 10μm from the waveguide. The entire arrangement is mounted on a water cooled Cu heat sink.[56, 63]

10 at.% for Yb and Tm and 1 at.% for Nd (as described previously). The waveguides have inner cladding widths of 18 and 30 μm, and core widths of 8 and 20 μm, for Yb- and Tm-doped structures, respectively. The reflectivity of output mirrors are 70% and 90%, respectively. The CW laser power as a function of pump power for Yb- and Tm-doped YAG is shown in Fig. 11.25. The Yb-doped laser emits near 1.03 μm and the Tm-doped lasers emits near 2.02 μm. Maximum output powers of 12.4 and 15.0 W are obtained for the Yb:YAG and Tm:YAG waveguide lasers. Higher powers have been

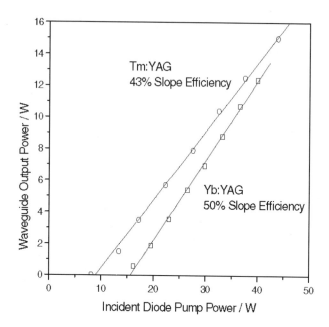

Fig. 11.25 CW laser power as a function of pump power.[56]

reported, for example, ~1.08 kW of output power has been obtained using two composite Yb–YAG rods pumped by 3.93 kW of diode laser power.[65]

Cooling is very important for high-power operation.[66] Using a water cooling arrangement, 150 W of quasi CW operation has been obtained using 430 W of pump power from 10 diode laser bars.[64] The active region of the laser has a planar Nd-doped YAG double clad waveguide laser similar to that described previously. For maximum output power, optimization of the output coupler transmission is important. For water cooled Nd-doped laser, the output power for different pump powers is shown in Fig. 11.26 as a function of output mirror transmission.

11.7. Supercontinuum Generation

As mentioned in Sec. 10.5, supercontinuum generation (SCG) is the spectral broadening of narrow-band incident pulses by the

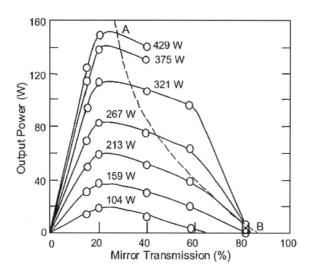

Fig. 11.26 Power output from a plane mirror multimode resonator with Nd-doped planar waveguide active region as a function of output mirror transmission. The various curves are for different pump powers as noted. Using an unstable resonator similar power levels have been demonstrated.[64]

propagation through nonlinear media. The physical mechanism of supercontinuum (SC) is demonstrated to be a combination of linear and nonlinear processes including self-phase modulation (SPM), cross-phase modulation (XPM), stimulated Raman scattering (SRS), four-wave mixing (FWM), soliton fission and dispersive wave (DW) (Cherenkov) radiation.[67-71] Various types of glasses such as lead silicate, fluoride[75] and chalcogenide glass[76-80] have been introduced as the core material, which benefit from higher nonlinearity and transparency than conventional silica fiber.[72-83] For example, photonic crystal fibers (PCFs) using lead silicate SF57 glass have been fabricated and a nonlinear parameter of $\gamma = 1860\,\mathrm{W}^{-1}\mathrm{km}^{-1}$ was obtained, approximately 2000 times that of a standard single-mode fiber.[72,73]

SC generation in planar waveguides has gained much interest recently. Fedotova *et al.*[83] simulated SCG in Air–TaFD5–SiO$_2$ and Air–SiO$_2$–Ag planar rib waveguides and predicted output spectra spanning up to two octaves. In Ref. 84, SC generated in silicon-on-insulator waveguides was numerically studied. It turned out that

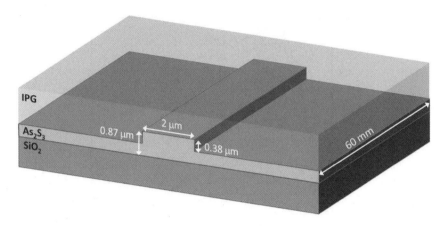

Fig. 11.27 Schematic of the planar waveguide used for SC generation. The waveguide cross section is $2\,\mu m \times 0.87\,\mu m$.[85]

the spectrum only extended over 400 nm, limited by two-photon absorption and free-carrier effects. In Ref. 85, dispersion-engineered highly nonlinear chalcogenide planar waveguides were experimentally demonstrated to have SC with a bandwidth of 750 nm. The schematic of the waveguide is shown in Fig. 11.27. A $0.87\,\mu m$ layer of As_2S_3 is deposited by thermal evaporation onto a thermally oxidized silicon substrate. The $2\,\mu m$ wide waveguides are defined using photolithography and created using RIE with CHF_3 gas. The waveguide chip is then coated in a protective coating layer of inorganic polymer glass (IPG). The waveguides are 6 cm long and the optical loss (α) of the waveguide is $\sim 0.6\,dB/cm$.

The nonlinear parameter of the material is $10\,W^{-1}m^{-1}$, and the dispersion is 29 ps/km-nm. A mode-locked fiber laser operating at a repetition rate of 10 MHz with $\sim 610\,fs$ wide pulses at 1550 nm is used as the input pulsed source. The maximum peak power is $\sim 136\,kW$. The input pulses could be coupled into TE and TM mode of the waveguide using a polarization controller. The measured SC spectrum for various peak powers for TM-coupled power is shown in Fig. 11.28. TE-coupled powers produced considerably less broadened spectrum.

A study of tapered planar rib waveguide which allows dispersion management for SCG is now discussed. The Air–SF57–SiO_2 rib

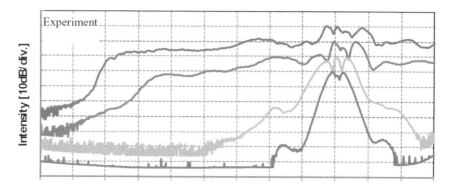

Fig. 11.28 SC spectrum for different coupled powers. The peak powers are 68, 46, 29 and 18 W from top to bottom curves, respectively. High peak produces broader spectrum. The wavelength range in the figure is from 1100 to 1700 nm (50 nm/div.).

waveguide continuously increases its etch depth along the propagation distance, which shifts the second zero dispersion wavelength (ZDW) (see Sec. 10.5). By launching hyperbolic secant pulses at $1.55\,\mu$m into this waveguide, SC with 30 dB bandwidth of $\sim$1 to $\sim$4.6 μm is obtained, limited by the multiphonon absorption edge of the material.

A numerical study of SCG in an Air–SF57–SiO$_2$ planar rib waveguide is now described. The waveguide schematic (with a rib width W, outer slab thickness d and etch depth h) is shown in Fig. 11.29. Scott SF57 is a commercially available lead–silicate glass mainly composed of SiO$_2$ and PbO, with a Pb cationic content of 40–50%.[86] The linear refractive index of SF57 at 1.55 μm is $n = 1.8$,[87] which results in an index contrast of 17.6% to the SiO$_2$ substrate, allowing for tight modal confinement. The nonlinear refractive index of SF57 measured at 1.06 μm is $n_2 = 4.1 \times 10^{-19}$ m^2/W, much higher than that of pure silica glass (2.7×10^{-20} m^2/W at 1.06 μm).[88] The material loss of SF57 glass is 1.6 dB/m at 1.55 μm.[88] The transmission window of SF57 glass is limited by the multiphonon absorption edge to $\sim$5 μm.

The wavelength-dependent dispersion profile of the rib waveguide for various h values (etch depth) is shown in Fig. 11.28. W and d are set to be 4 and 0.5 μm, respectively. The computation is done by a full-vector finite difference mode solver for the fundamental TM mode. Since the waveguide dispersion depends strongly on

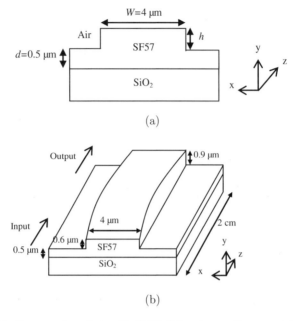

(a)

(b)

Fig. 11.29 (a) Cross section of the Air–SF57–SiO₂ planar rib waveguide with the rib width W, outer slab thickness d and etch depth h, respectively (b) Schematic of a tapered waveguide.

the geometrical design, the total dispersion characteristic, which is the combined effect of material and waveguide dispersion, can be controlled by varying the etch depth, as shown in Fig. 11.30. Note that for small h ($<0.83\,\mu$m), a second ZDW exists, and it shifts to shorter wavelengths while h is decreasing. For comparison, the material dispersion of SF57 bulk glass is also plotted, which has one ZDW at 1.97 μm.

Based on the dispersion property, a tapered waveguide illustrated in Fig. 11.29(b) has been designed. The waveguide is 2 cm long, with $W = 4\,\mu$m and $d = 0.5\,\mu$m. The etch depth h continuously increases from 0.6 to 0.9 μm along the propagation distance z by the following relationship:

$$h = h_0 \left[1 + \left(\frac{z}{z_0} \right)^{\frac{1}{3}} \right], \qquad (11.1)$$

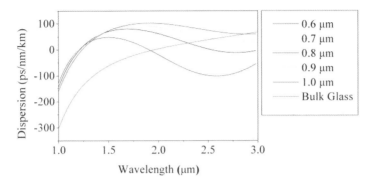

Fig. 11.30 Dispersion profile of SF57 rib waveguide with varying etch depths h. The rib width W and outer slab thickness d are 4 and 0.5 μm, respectively.

where $h_0 = 0.6 \, \mu$m and $z_0 = 16$ cm. Hyperbolic secant pulses centered at 1.55 μm are launched into the designed waveguide for SCG. The optical field of the input pulse takes the form $P^{1/2}\text{sech}(T/T_0)$, where P denotes the peak power and the full width at half maximum (FWHM) is $1.763T_0$. The pulse evolution is numerically simulated by the generalized nonlinear Schrödinger equation (GNLSE) with slowly-varying envelope approximation[89]:

$$\frac{\partial A}{\partial z} + \frac{\alpha}{2}A + \sum_{k \geq 2} \frac{i^{k-1}}{k!} \beta_k \frac{\partial^k A}{\partial T^k}$$

$$= i\gamma \left(1 + \frac{i}{\omega_0}\frac{\partial}{\partial T}\right) \left(A \int_{-\infty}^{+\infty} R(T')|A(z, T - T')|^2 dT'\right),$$

(11.2)

where $A(z,t)$ is the pulse envelope and $T = t - z/v_g$ is the retarded time frame moving at the pulse group velocity v_g. α is the linear propagation loss and β_k denote the Taylor-series expansion coefficients of the propagation constant $\beta(\omega)$ around the center frequency ω_0. γ is the nonlinear parameter defined as $\gamma(\omega_0) = n_2(\omega_0)\omega_0/(cA_{\text{eff}})$, where $A_{\text{eff}} = (\iint |E|^2 dxdy)^2/(\iint |E|^4 dxdy)$ is the effective mode area. The nonlinear response function $R(T) = (1 - f_R)\delta(T) + f_R h_R(T)$ includes both the instantaneous electronic response and the delayed Raman contribution, indicated by the delta function and $h_R(T)$, respectively. For SF57, f_R is 0.1 and the Raman response function can be expressed as[89–91]:

$$h_R(t) = \frac{\tau_1^2 + \tau_2^2}{\tau_1 \tau_2^2} \exp\left(-\frac{t}{\tau_2}\right) \sin\left(\frac{t}{\tau_1}\right) \qquad (11.3)$$

in which $\tau_1 = 5.5\,\text{fs}$ and $\tau_2 = 32\,\text{fs}$. The left side of Eq. (11.2) models the linear propagation effects, while the right side models the nonlinear effects. Equation (11.2) is numerically solved by the split-step Fourier method (SSFM).[91] The spectral coherence property of SC is studied by calculating the modulus of the complex degree of first-order coherence function introduced by Dudley and Coen[92,93]:

$$|g_{12}(\lambda)| = \left| \frac{\langle E_1^*(\lambda) E_2(\lambda) \rangle}{[\langle |E_1(\lambda)|^2 \rangle \langle |E_2(\lambda)|^2 \rangle]^{1/2}} \right|, \qquad (11.4)$$

where $E = A(z,t) \exp(-i\omega_0 t)$ is the electric field and the angle brackets represent averaging over the independently generated SC pairs $[E_1(\lambda), E_2(\lambda)]$.

11.7.1. *Results and Discussions*

First consider uniform waveguide structure with constant etch depth. For this case, the output SC spans from $0.9\,\mu\text{m}$ out to $2.5\,\mu\text{m}$. In this situation, the spectral components on the long-wavelength side are mainly formed by soliton-self-frequency shift (SSFS), while the emission of DWs is responsible for the short-wavelength components.

Figure 11.31(a) shows the spectrum evolution of the incident pulse $[P = 5\,\text{kW}$, FWHM $= 100\,\text{fs})$ traveling in the tapered waveguide (with etch depth given by Eq. (11.1)] if no optical loss is included in the simulation. The effective mode area A_{eff} at the input is equal to $3.2\,\mu\text{m}^2$, yielding a nonlinear parameter γ of $0.52/\text{W/m}$ at $1.55\,\mu\text{m}$, about 500 times that of a conventional single-mode fiber. The generated spectrum has a 30 dB bandwidth from ~ 1 to $\sim 6\,\mu\text{m}$. Since the continuum extends over the multiphonon edge, the loss should be considered. The spectrum including loss is shown in Fig. 11.31(b). It can be seen that the output spectrum reaches $\sim 4.6\,\mu\text{m}$, which is considerably larger than that of uniform waveguides.

The waveguide is carefully designed so the center wavelength of the incident pulse is within the anomalous dispersion regime. As a

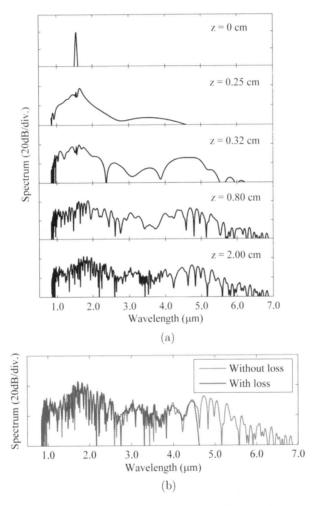

Fig. 11.31 (a) Spectrum evolution along the propagation distance for the tapered SF57 rib waveguide without loss. (b) Effect of loss on the output continuum.

result, the input pulses undergo soliton fission and DW emission across the upper ZDW, as described before. For the tapered waveguide with an increasing value of h, the 2nd ZDW shifts along the propagation distance, leading to a continuous modification of the phase-matched wavelength for DW emission. This allows the DW to be produced toward longer wavelengths and this significantly broadens the SC at the output. Clearly, different tapered structures other

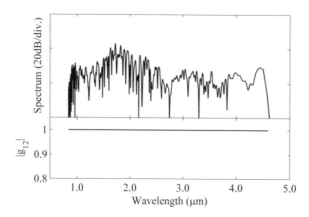

Fig. 11.32 Output spectrum generated from the tapered waveguide and the coherence degree $|g_{12}(\lambda)|$.

than that described by Eq. (11.1) may be used, but the tapering rate should be optimized to ensure efficient energy transfer from solitons to DWs.

The spectral coherence, $|g_{12}(\lambda)|$ defined by Eq. (11.4) has been calculated. Calculation is done by simulating an ensemble of 50 SC spectra with random quantum noise (including loss). Figure 11.32 shows the degree of coherence of the output spectrum shown in Fig. 11.31(b). The generated SC possesses excellent coherence with $|g_{12}|$ equal to 1 over the entire spectral range. The results show that this planar waveguide may be important as an on-chip broadband SC source for many applications.

Planar waveguides, as lasers, amplifiers, or as a broadband source, promise scalable geometries, low cost fabrication, and, the potential for integrated optical chip solutions.

References

1. J. Shmulovich, Y.H. Wong, G. Nykolak, P.C. Becker, R. Adar, A.J. Bruce, D.J. Muehlner, G. Adams and M. Fishteyn, *OSA Optical Amplifier Meet.* Optical Society of America, *paper*, PD18-1 (1993).
2. T. Kitagawa, K. Hattori, K. Shuto, M. Yasu, M. Kobayashi and M. Horiguchi, in *Optical amplifiers and their applications*, Vol. 17, Technical Digest Series. Optical Society of America, paper PD-1, (1992).

3. T. Kitagawa, K. Hattori, M. Shimizu, Y. Ohmori, M. Kobayashi and M. Horiguchi, *Electron Lett.* **28** (1992) 1818.
4. K. Shuto, K. Hattori, T. Kitagawa and M. Horiguchiin, *Proceedings, Nineteenth European Conference On Optical Communications*, Vol. 53 (1993).
5. T. Feuchter, E.K. Mwarania, J. Wang, L. Reekie and J.S. Wilkinson, *IEEE Photonics Technol. Lett.* **4** (1992) 542.
6. P. Becker, R. Brinkmann, M. Dinand, W. Sohler and H. Suche, *Appl. Phys. Lett.* **61** (1992) 1257.
7. G.N. van den Hoven, E. Snoeks, A. Polman, C. van Dam, J.W.M. van Uffelen and M.K. Smit, *Proceedings, Seventh European Conference on Integrat. Opt,* pp. 229 (1995).
8. D.P. Shepherd, Chapter B4.6, In *Handbook of laser technology and applications*, C. Webb & J. Jones (Eds.) Institute of Physics. 2004.
9. R.V. Ramaswamy and R. Srivastava, *IEEE J. Lightwave Technol.* **6** (1988) 984.
10. P.J. Chandler, L. Zhang and P.D. Townsend, *Nucl. Instrum. Methods* **B59** (1991) 1223.
11. R.V. Schmidt and I.P. Kaminow, *Appl. Phys. Lett.* **25** (1974) 458.
12. M. Svalgaard, C.V. Poulsen, A. Bjaerklev and O. Paulsen, *Electron Lett.* **30** (1994) 1401.
13. C.T.A. Brown, C.L. Bonner, T.J. Warburton, D.P. Shepherd, A.C. Tropper and D.C. Hanna, *Appl. Phys. Lett.* **71** (1997) 1139.
14. M. Kawachi, *Opt. Quantum Electron.* **22** (1990) 391.
15. J.I. Mackenzie and D.P. Shepherd, *Opt. Lett.* **27** (2002) 2161.
16. T. Kitagawa, K. Hattori, K. Shuto, M. Yasu, M. Kobayashi and M. Horiguchi, *Electron. Lett.* **28** (1992) 1818.
17. J. Shmulovich, Y.H. Wong, G. Nykolak, P.C. Becker, R. Adar and A.J. Bruce, *Electron. Lett.* **28** (1992) 1181.
18. T. Feuchter, E.K. Mwarania, I. Wang, L. Reekie and J.S. Wilkinson, *IEEE Photonics Technol. Lett.* **4** (1992) 542.
19. K. Shuto, K. Hattori, T. Kitagawa, Y. Ohmori and M. Horiguchi, *Electron. Lett.* **29** (1993) 139.
20. K. Hattori, T. Kitagawa, M. Oguma, M. Wada, J. Temmyo and M. Horiguchi, *Electron. Lett.* **29** (1993) 357.
21. R.N. Ghosh, J. Shmulovich, C.F. Kane, M.R.X. de Barros, G. Nykolak, A.J. Bruce and P.C. Becker, *IEEE Photonics Technol. Lett.* **8** (1996) 518.
22. G. Nykolak, P.C. Becker, J. Shmulovich, Y.H. Wong, D.J. DiGiovanni and A.J. Bruce, *IEEE Photonics Technol. Lett.* **5** (1993) 1014.
23. O. Lumholt, A. Bjarklev, T. Rasmussen and C. Lester, *IEEE J. Lightwave Technol.* **13** (1995) 275.
24. E. Snoeks, P.G. Kik and A. Polman, *Opt. Mater.* **5** (1996) 159.
25. J.-M.P. Delavaux, S. Granlund, O. Mizuhara, L.D. Tzeng, D. Barbier, M. Rattay, F. Saint Andre and A. Kevorkian, *IEEE Photonics Technol. Lett.* **9** (1997) 2.
26. J. Shmulovich, Technical Digest, OFC99, paper PD42 (1999).

27. E. Desurvire, *Erbium-Doped fiber amplifiers, principles and applications*, New York: Wiley. 1994.
28. J.-M.P. Delavaux, C. McIntosh, J. Shmulovich, A.J. Bruce, R.K. Pattnaik and B.R. Wirstiuk, Technical Digest, OFC 2000, paper WA2-1 (2000).
29. M. Saruwatari and T. Izawa, *Appl. Phys. Lett.* **24** (1974) 603.
30. Y. Hibino, T. Kitagawa, M. Shimizu, F. Hanawa and A. Sugita, *IEEE Photonics Technol. Lett.* **1** (1989) 349.
31. H. Aoki, O. Maruyama and Y. Asahara, *IEEE Photonics Technol. Lett.* **2** (1990) 459.
32. N.A. Sanford, K.J. Malone and D.R. Larson, *Opt. Lett.* **15** (1990) 366.
33. E.K. Mwarania, L. Reekie, J. Wang and J.S. Wilkinson, *Electron. Lett.* **26** (1990) 1317.
34. N. Takato, K. Jinguji, M. Yasu, H. Toba and M. Kawachi, *IEEE J. Lightwave Technol.* **6** (1988) 1003.
35. M.J.F. Digonnet and C.J. Gaeta, *Appl. Opt.* **24** (1985) 333.
36. Y. Hibino, T. Kitagawa, M. Shimizu, A. Sugita and Y. Ohmori, *Proceedings of the Integrated Photon. Res.*, Hilton Head, SC, paper TuJ2 (1990).
37. H. Ioki, E. Ishikawa and Y. Asahara, *Electron Lett.* **27** (1991) 2352.
38. G.R.J. Robertson and P.E. Jessop, *Appl. Opt.* **30** (1991) 276.
39. R. Tumnunelli, F. Halumi and J. Haavisto, *Opt. Lett.* **16** (1991) 1098.
40. K. Hattori and T. Kitagawa, *IEEE Photonics Technol. Lett.* **4** (1992) 973.
41. T. Kitagawa, K. Hattori, Y. Hibino and Y. Ohmori, *IEEE J. Lightwave Technol.* **12** (1994) 436.
42. J.R. Bonar, J.A. Bebbington, J.S. Aitchison, G.D. Maxwell and B.J. Ainslie, *Electron. Lett.* **30** (1994) 229.
43. F. Ondracek, *Opt. Mater.* (2007), DOI:10.1016/j.optmat.2006.12.004.
44. J. Jágerská, F. Ondráček, L. Salavcová, M. Míka, J. Spirková, and J. Ctyroký, *13th European Conference on Integrated Optics ECIO 2007*, 2007, Paper ThG14 (2007).
45. F. Ondráček, M. Skalský and J. Ctyroký, *Proc. SPIE* **6180** (2006) 414.
46. M.P. Hehlen, N.J. Cockroft and T.R. Gosnell, *Phys. Rev. B* **56** (1997) 9302.
47. F. Ondráček, J. Jágerská, L. Salavcová, M. Míka, J. Špirková and J.C. Tyroký, *IEEE JQE* **QE-44** (2008) 536.
48. F.D. Patel, S. DiCarolis, P.I. Lum, S. Venkatesh and J.N. Miller, *IEEE Photonics Technol. Lett.* **16** (2004) 2607.
49. D.L. Veasey, D.S. Funk, P.M. Peters, N.A. Sanford, G.E. Obarski, N. Fontaine, M. Young, A.P. Peskin, W.C. Liu, S.N. Houde-Walter and J.S. Hayden, *J. Non-Cryst. Solids* **263&264** (2000) 369.
50. F. Di Pasquale and M. Federighi, *IEEE J. Quantum Electron.* **30** (1994) 2127.
51. D. Geskus, S. Aravazhi, E.H. Bernhardi, L. Agazzi, S.M. García-Blanco and M. Pollnau, CLEO Technical Digest, paper CMA1.6 (2012).
52. Y.E. Romanyuk, C.N. Borca, M. Pollnau, S. Rivier, V. Petrov and U. Griebner, *Opt. Lett.* **31** (2006) 53.
53. F. Gardillou, Y.E. Romanyuk, C.N. Borca, R.P. Salathé and M. Pollnau, *Opt. Lett.* **32** (2007) 488.

54. D. Geskus, S. Aravazhi, C. Grivas, K. Wörhoff and M. Pollnau, *Opt. Express* **18** (2010) 8853.
55. F. Auzel, G. Baldacchini, L. Laversenne and G. Boulon, *Opt. Mater.* **24** (2003) 103.
56. D.P. Shepherd, S.J. Hettrick, C. Li, J.I. Mackenzie, R.J. Beach, S.C. Mitchell and H.E. Meissner, *J. Phys. D:Appl. Phys.* **34** (2001) 2424.
57. J.J. Chang, E.P. Dragon, C.A. Ebbers, L.I. Bass and C.W. Cochran, In *OSA TOPS on advanced solid-state lasers*, W.R. Bosenberg & M.M. Fejer (Eds.), Vol. 19, Washington, DC: Optical Society of America. 1998, p. 300.
58. D.P. Shepherd, C.L. Bonner, C.T.A. Brown, W.A. Clarkson, A.C. Tropper, D.C. Hanna and H.E. Meissner, *Opt. Commun.* **160** (1999) 47.
59. C.L. Bonner, T. Bhutta, D.P. Shepherd and A.C. Tropper, *IEEE J. Quantum Electron.* **36** (2000) 236.
60. T. Tamanuki, T. Sasaki and M. Kitamura, *Opt. Quantum Electron.* **28** (1996) 513.
61. J.D. Minelly, L.A. Zenteno, M.J. Dejneka, W.J. Miller, D.V. Kuksenkov, M.K. Davis, S.G. Crigler and M.E. Bardo, *Tech. Dig. Optical Fiber Communications Conference,* paper PD2-1 (2000).
62. J.I. Mackenzie, C. Li and D.P. Shepherd, *IEEE JQE* **QE-39** (2003) 493.
63. R.J. Beach, S.C. Mitchell, H.E. Meissner, O.R. Meissner, W.F. Krupke, J.M. McMahon and W.J. Bennett, *Opt. Lett.* **26** (2001) 881.
64. J.R. Lee, H.J. Baker, G.J. Friel, G.J. Hilton and D.R. Hall, *Opt. Lett.* **27** (2002) 524.
65. E.C. Honea, R.J. Beach, S.C. Mitchell, J.A. Skidmore, M.A. Emanuel, S.B. Sutton and S.A. Payne, *Opt. Lett.* **25** (2000) 805.
66. R.J. Beach, M.A. Emanuel, B.L. Freitas, J.A. Skidmore, N.W. Carlson, W.J. Bennett and R.W. Solarz, *Proc. SPIE* **2383** (1995) 283.
67. J.M. Dudley, G. Genty and S. Coen, *Rev. Mod. Phys.* **78** (2006) 1135.
68. J.M. Dudley and J.R. Talor, *Supercontinuum generation in optical fibers* New York: Cambridge University Press. 2010.
69. S. Coen, A.H.L. Chau, R. Leonhardt, J.D. Harvey, J.C. Knight, W.J. Wadsworth and P.S.J. Russell, *J. Opt. Soc. Am. B* **19** (2002) 753.
70. W.J. Wadsworth, A. Ortigosa-Blanch, J.C. Knight, T.A. Birks, T.P.M. Man and P.S.J. Russell, *J. Opt. Soc. Am. B* **19** (2002) 2148.
71. T. Yamamoto, H. Kubota, S. Kawanishi, M. Tanaka and S. Yamaguchi, *Opt. Express* **11** (2003) 1537.
72. J.Y.Y. Leong, P. Petropoulos, J.H.V. Price, H. Ebendorff-Heidepriem, S. Asimakis, R.C. Moore, K.E. Frampton, V. Finazzi, X. Feng, T.M. Monro and D.J. Richardson, *J. Lightwave Technol.* **24** (2006) 183.
73. Z. Chen, S. Ma and N.K. Dutta, *Opt. Commun.* **283** (2010) 3076.
74. J.H.V. Price, X. Feng, A.M. Heidt, G. Brambilla, P. Horak, F. Poletti, G. Ponzo, P. Petropoulos, M. Petrovich, J. Shi, M. Ibsen, W.H. Loh, H.N. Rutt and D.J. Richardson, *Opt. Fiber Technol.* **18** (2012) 327.
75. Z. Chen, A.J. Taylor and A. Efimov, *Opt. Express* **17** (2009) 5852.
76. D.I. Yeom, E.C. Mägi, M.R. Lamont, M.A. Roelens, L. Fu and B.J. Eggleton, *Opt. Lett.* **33** (2008) 660.

77. J. Hu, C.R. Menyuk, L.B. Shaw, J.S. Sanghera and I.D. Aggarwal, *Opt. Express* **18** (2010) 6722.

78. N. Granzow, S.P. Stark, M.A. Schmidt, A.S. Tverjanovich, L. Wondraczek and P.S.J. Russell, *Opt. Express* **19** (2011) 21003.

79. R.R. Gattass, L. Brandon Shaw, V.Q. Nguyen, P.C. Pureza, I.D. Aggarwal and J.S. Sanghera, *Opt. Fiber Technol.* **18** (2012) 345.

80. A. Marandi, C.W. Rudy, V.G. Plotnichenko, E.M. Dianov, K.L. Vodopyanov and R.L. Byer, *Opt. Express* **20** (2012) 24218.

81. A.V. Husakou and J. Herrmann, *Appl. Phys. B* **77** (2003) 227–234.

82. K.M. Hilligsøe, T. Andersen, H. Paulsen, C. Nielsen, K. Mølmer, S. Keiding, R. Kristiansen, K. Hansen and J. Larsen, *Opt. Express* **12** (2004) 1045.

83. O. Fedotova, A. Husakou and J. Herrmann, *Opt. Express* **14** (2006) 1512.

84. L. Yin, Q. Lin and G.P. Agrawal, *Opt. Lett.* **32** (2007) 391.

85. M.R. Lamont, B. Luther-Davies, D.Y. Choi, S. Madden and B.J. Eggleton, *Opt. Express* **16** (2008) 14938.

86. G. Genty, M. Surakka, J. Turunen and A.T. Friberg, *Opt. Lett.* **35** (2010) 3057.

87. V. Diez-Blanco, J. Siegel and J. Solis, *Appl. Surf. Sci.* (2006) 4523.

88. Schott Glass Catalogue (2003).

89. G.P. Agrawal, *Nonlinear fiber optics*, 4th Edn. Burlington, MA: Academic Press. 2007.

90. W. Bolaños, J.J. Carvajal, X. Mateos, G.S. Murugan, A. Subramanian, J.S. Wilkinson, E. Cantelar, G. Lifante, M. Aguiló and F. Díaz, *Opt. Mater.* **34** (2011) 475.

91. V.L. Kalashnikov, E. Sorokin and I.T. Sorokina, *Appl. Phys. B* **87** (2007) 37.

92. J.M. Dudley and S. Coen, *Opt. Lett.* **27** (2002) 1180.

93. J.M. Dudley and S. Coen, *IEEE J. Sel. Top. Quantum Electron.* **8** (2002) 651.

94. H. Hu, W. Li and N.K. Dutta, *Applied Optics.* **52** (2013) 7336.

Chapter 12

Fiber Laser

12.1. Introduction

Rare earth-doped fibers when pumped by a laser of suitable wavelength produce large gain. Thus it is reasonable to assume that lasers emitting at wavelengths corresponding to transitions at these rare earth dopants can be produced by providing suitable feedback. Many types of rare earth-doped optical fiber amplifier have been used as a gain medium for fiber laser research and its application in transmission and sensor systems. Erbium (Er), Nd, Yb, Tm-doped glass fiber have been used as gain medium for laser action near 1550, 1060, 940, 1000 and 2000 nm respectively. For higher power lasers near 1550 nm Er–Yb co-doped fiber is generally used as a gain medium. The feedback for these laser systems are generally provided using fiber Bragg gratings, although in some studies conventional mirrors or even the reflection from a cleaved fiber end (reflectivity $\sim$4%) has been used to provide feedback. Another class of lasers that has been used has a ring cavity design. This design has been found to be very suitable for tunable lasers and for mode locked short pulse generation.

12.2. Fiber Laser Designs

Various designs of fiber lasers have been reported.[1–10] They all rely on a rare earth-doped fiber gain medium with feedback provided by Bragg gratings or mirrors. A typical schematic is shown in Fig. 12.1a. The grating on the left has high reflectivity at fiber laser wavelength and high transmission at pump wavelength. For fiber amplifiers the gain region is generally long $\sim$1 to 20 m in length. This makes the

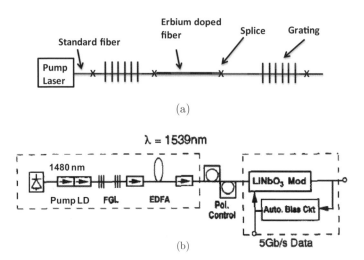

(a)

(b)

Fig. 12.1 (a) Schematic of a Er-doped fiber laser with FBGs. (b) Schematic of the laser with Er-doped amplifier (EDFA) and LiNbO₃ modulator for 5 Gb/s data generation at the output. Note the presence of various isolators (shown by arrow) to reduce reflections.[8] The amplifier fiber length is 2 cm.

laser operate in multiple longitudinal modes. In order to reduce the spectral width of the emission, e.g., single longitudinal mode emission, a short cavity length is desirable.

12.2.1. *Er-Doped Fiber Laser*

An Er-doped fiber laser that emits in a stable single mode has been reported.[8] In this design, the gain length is reduced by high doping, ∼600 ppm vs. a typical value of ∼10 to 30 ppm for a typical Er-doped amplifier. The Ge-doped core is co-doped with Al to reduce concentration quenching effects. The core diameter of the fiber is ∼2.6 μm. The Er-doped fiber is spliced to two fiber Bragg gratings (FBGs). FBGs are refractive index gratings generated in the fiber by optical interference of two light (UV) beams (Sec. 13.2). They can have very high reflectivity at a specific wavelength. The output coupler grating and the rear reflector have a reflectivity of 98% and >99% respectively.

Er-doped fiber lasers of the type shown in Fig. 12.1 has been pumped using both 1480 and 980 nm pump lasers.[8,9] The laser

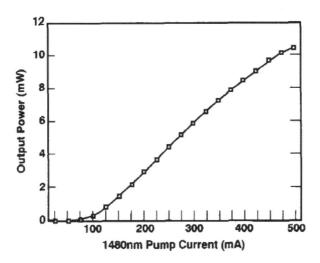

Fig. 12.2 Laser output as a function of 1480 nm pump laser current.[8]

output as a function of pump power for the laser design of Fig. 12.1a is shown in Fig. 12.2. The laser emits near 1539 nm. The amplifier fiber length is 2 cm.

An amplifier fiber has been added as shown in Fig. 12.1(b) for data transmission experiment. This also improved the low frequency stability of the fiber laser by reducing possibly reflection effects.[8] The laser emits near 1539 nm. A bit-error rate (BER) measurement at 5 Gb/s using this laser has been reported. Essentially stable error free performance (BER $<10^{-15}$) has been observed.[8] The reflection peak of FBGs can be tuned by changing the temperature of the FBG. Thus the laser design of Fig. 12.1 can be tuned somewhat (few A) by tuning the FBGs.

Er-doped fiber lasers have been extensively studied. A ring laser geometry with or without fiber Bragg gratings and with and without semiconductor optical amplifier (SOA) in the cavity has been studied for various investigations such as multiwavelength operation, tunable operation and low noise (stable) operation. These are discussed in Secs. 12.3 and 12.4. In addition, they have been extensively studied for generation of short pulses principally by mode locking. This is discussed in Chapter 14.

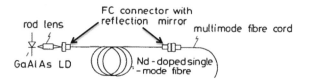

Fig. 12.3 Schematic of a single mode Nd-doped fiber laser experiment.

12.2.2. *Nd-Doped Fiber Laser*

Nd-doped rod lasers have been extensively studied for high power operation and have been a laser source for many years in the laboratory. Slab lasers have also been studied for high power application. With the advent of silica optical fibers and their ability to be doped with Nd without any deleterious effects, both single mode, multimode and cladding pumped fiber lasers have been studied.[11–21] These are also generally pumped by semiconductor diode lasers.

The schematic of an experimental set up for Nd-doped single mode fiber laser is shown in Fig. 12.3. The glass compositions of the core and cladding are Nd-doped SiO_2 and fluorine-doped SiO_2. The core diameter is $\sim 7\,\mu$m and the index difference between core and cladding is $\sim 0.32\%$. The Nd concentration is 150 ppm and the fiber length is ~ 10 m. The pump laser wavelength is $0.83\,\mu$m. The dielectric mirrors are deposited on the fiber end faces. The input mirror had a high reflectivity ($R = 99.9\%$) at the lasing wavelength and high transmission ($T = 99\%$) at the pump wavelength. The output mirror had $R = 89\%$ at lasing wavelength and $T = 92\%$ at the pump wavelength. The Nd laser output as a function of absorbed pump power is shown in Fig. 12.4.

The Nd-doped fiber has the highest gain near 1060 nm. However, it also exhibits gain near 940 and 1300 nm on different transitions. Using wavelength selective feedback, Nd-doped fiber can be made to operate as a laser near any of these wavelengths while suppressing lasing near 1060/1090 nm transition.

A cladding pumped geometry (also known as double clad fiber geometry) allows coupling of large amount of pump light hence high output power. Since the core of the fiber is doped with Nd (or any rare earth for a cladding pumped geometry) a single transverse mode

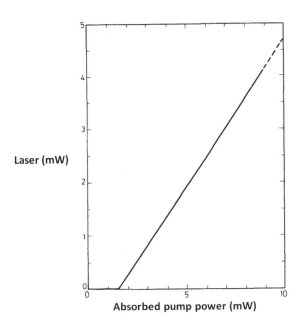

Fig. 12.4 Nd laser light at 1.06 μm vs. pump light injected into the fiber.[15]

laser emission is generally observed. Results of a cladding pumped Nd-doped fiber experiment in a multicomponent glass are discussed in the following. The multicomponent glass results in output at both 1060 and 1090 nm simultaneously. By incorporating significant amounts of both Al_2O_3 and GeO_2 into the Nd-doped silica glass core during fabrication, the dopant ions are subsequently situated at sites relating to either Al-rich regions or Ge-rich regions of the germano-aluminosilicate glass. This allows near independent laser oscillation on the transition at the two separate sites. The Nd-doped double clad fiber has a core diameter of 5.5 μm, and a Nd density of 6000 ppm. The pump cladding diameter is 250 μm. Nd-doped fiber length is ∼35 m which allowed 92% of the pump to be absorbed by the core. A broadband dichroic mirror is used at the pump input end of the fiber and the cleaved fiber served as a reflector (Fresnel reflection) at the output end. The pump laser is a diode laser emitting near 805 nm. The output power both at 1060 nm and 1090 nm as a function of pump power is shown in Fig. 12.5.[21] Total laser power of

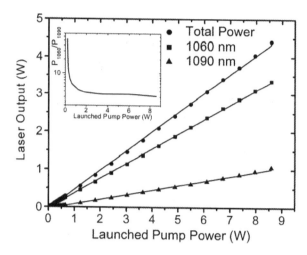

Fig. 12.5 Laser power at 1060 nm and 1090 nm as a function of pump power.[21] The inset shows the ratio of 1060 to 1090 power as a function of pump power. The 1060 nm wavelength reaches threshold at lower pump power due to higher gain.

~4 W is obtained for a launched power of 8 W. Higher total output power (~10 W) is obtained (for ~14 W of pump) using a 100 m long low Nd-doped fiber. Nd-doped fiber lasers also emit in other Nd transitions such 940 nm. Laser emission in these transitions is generally obtained using a wavelength selective reflector such as fiber Bragg grating.

12.2.3. *Yb-Doped Fiber Laser*

Yb-doped fiber lasers which emit near 1100 nm have been studied for a high power laser source which has many applications. As a result many Yb-doped fiber lasers are made in the cladding pumped geometry[22–27] Although the high power lasers are discussed in Sec. 12.5, for the purpose of completeness, an example of Yb-doped fiber laser is provided here. The fiber used is a double clad fiber with an inner cladding diameter of 240 μm and an outer cladding diameter of 355 μm. The Yb core is 10 μm in diameter with a NA of 0.06. The Yb doping is 1.4×10^{21} cm^{-3} (about 12 wt.% of Yb$_2$O$_3$).

This is about 10 times higher than typical values often used. The active core is off set from the inner cladding and the outer cladding is

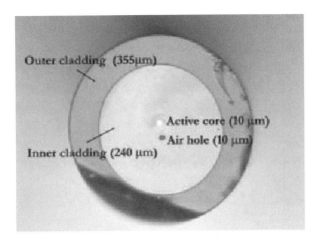

Fig. 12.6 Image of the Yb-doped fiber end. The core has a diameter of 10 μm, inner cladding has a diameter of 240 μm and the outer cladding has a diameter of 355 μm.[27]

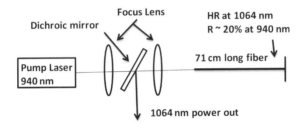

Fig. 12.7 Schematic of the experimental set up for Yb-doped fiber.[27]

made of phosphate glass. An air hole 10 μm diameter is added 30 μm from the core to increase pump absorption (Fig. 12.6). The schematic of the experimental set up and a microscopic image of the fiber end are shown in Fig. 12.7. The pump laser emits at 940 nm.

The fiber gain medium is 71 cm long and the laser has a high reflector (bulk) at one end and the cleaved fiber end (reflectivity ∼3–4%) serves as the second reflector. The 940 nm pump light is coupled at the cleaved end using a dichroic mirror. The Yb laser output power as a function of pump power is shown in Fig. 12.8. The laser emits near 1062 nm. The measured laser slope efficiency against launched power and absorbed power are 24% and 37% respectively.

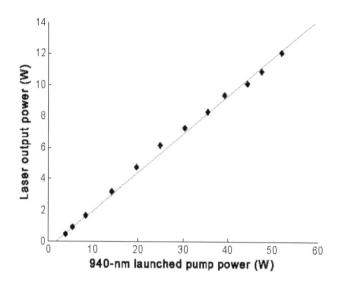

Fig. 12.8 Yb-laser output as a function of pump power.[27]

12.3. Multiwavelength Laser

For some applications such as WDM systems it is important to have a multiwavelength laser source. Multiwavelength fiber lasers have been widely studied for their potential applications in optical communications, wavelength-division-multiplexing (WDM) communication systems, optical fiber sensors and optical instrument testing.[28–38] The Er-doped fiber has been used as the gain medium for the lasers. However, since erbium-doped fiber (EDF) is a homogenous gain medium, the fiber lasers based on EDF often suffer from strong mode competition and unstable multi-wavelength lasing at room temperature. There have been a range of approaches used to solve this problem which includes cooling EDF to liquid-nitrogen temperature,[28] using inhomogeneous gain medium in the laser cavity (such as SOA) instead of EDF,[29–32] or utilizing four wave mixing effect[32–35] or inhomogeneous loss mechanism[36] by using highly-nonlinear fiber.

Schematic of a stable room-temperature multiwavelength laser is shown in Fig. 12.9. A simple setup based on hybrid gain medium and a double-ring spectrum reshaping structure is used to improve

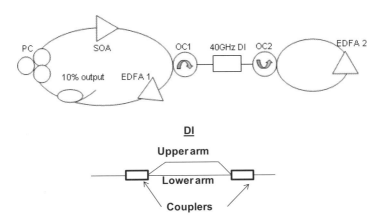

Fig. 12.9 Schematic of a multiwavelength laser.[38] Schematic of a delayed interferometer (DI) is also shown.

the mode suppression ratio and obtain low spectral linewidth of the output.

In Fig. 12.9 EDFA1 is used as the gain medium with the small gain of ∼30 dB and the saturation power of 23 dBm. The SOA is used in the cavity to suppress the mode competition. Optical circulator 1 (OC1) transfers the light from the left ring to the right ring. DI is a delay interferometer with 25 ps delay between the two arms. It has a comb like transmission spectrum. EDFA2 in the right ring compensates the optical loss due to DI. Optical circulator 2 (OC2) transfers the light back to DI. Polarization controller (PC) is used to optimize the polarization state in the cavity. An optical spectrum analyzer is used to measure the optical spectrum of the laser using the 10% output port of the optical coupler.

The DI which is fabricated using Si–SiO$_2$ waveguide technology has two arms with a 25 ps time delay between the upper arm and the lower arm. The light is split into two beams, and at the output of DI, two beams of optical signals with the phase difference (corresponding to 25 ps delay) recombine and interfere with each other. The optical intensity at the DI output is given by:

$$I_{\text{out}}(\lambda) = I_{\text{up}}(\lambda) + I_{\text{low}}(\lambda) + 2\sqrt{I_{\text{up}}(\lambda) \times I_{\text{low}}(\lambda)} \cos \Delta\theta, \qquad (12.1)$$

with $\Delta\theta = \frac{2\pi c \times \Delta t}{\lambda}$, where I_{up} and I_{low} are intensity of two beams traveling along the upper arm and the lower arm of the DI, respectively; Δt is the travel time delay between the upper beam and the lower arm in the DI; c is the speed of light in vacuum and λ is the wavelength of the optical signal. The DI acts as a comb filter which makes the wavelengths that match the peaks of the comb oscillate when it is in the optical cavity. The wavelength spacing between two adjacent transmission peaks is 0.32 nm for $\Delta t = 25$ ps. In the experiment, the current in SOA is 300 mA. The EDFA1 can supply the gain as high as 23 dBm. The power of the EDFAs can be adjusted by changing the pump power coupled into the EDF. The SOA has been used to suppress the mode competition in EDF. Figure 12.10 shows the measured transmission spectrum of DI used in the experiment. The extinction ratio is about 15 dB. The DI is relatively insensitive to power, temperature and polarization changes. When the pump power of EDFA2 is increased, there is no change in the shape of spectrum. For changes in input polarization the transmissions peaks move by <0.02 nm.

Figure 12.11 illustrates the stable multiwavelength lasing achieved by appropriately adjusting the polarization controller. Up to 60

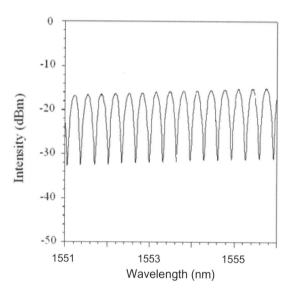

Fig. 12.10 Transmission spectrum of DI.[38]

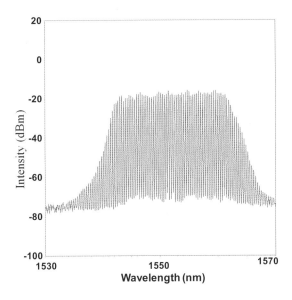

Fig. 12.11 Output optical spectrum of ring laser with double-ring structure.[38]

simultaneous lasing lines are obtained within the 3-dB bandwidth at room temperature with an identical wavelength spacing of 0.32 nm, which coincides with the transmission profile of the DI filter. The SNR is measured at ~50 dB. The hybrid gain medium effectively reduces the noise and supports stable multiwavelength lasing operation, and the double-ring structure reshapes the transmission spectrum and generates lasing lines with narrow linewdith. The measured linewidth is about 0.019 nm.

The well packaged DI is important in eliminating the influence of thermal and power fluctuation in the ring.[29] The double-ring structure generates lasing lines with narrow linewidth and stable output power. The group of wavelengths can be shifted to shorter wavelengths (for the same power) by increasing the loss in the ring and increasing the SOA current to compensate for increased loss. The shift is due to gain peak shift to short wavelength in the SOA. The wavelength can be tuned from ~1526 to ~1562 nm. During the tuning (with higher loss), the number of lasing wavelengths and the SNR are decreased.

For multiwavelength operation it is important to have inhomogeneous spectral width of the gain i.e., it is important to suppress the homogeneous broadening of the EDFA gain. Refs. 39–45 describe other schemes for multiwavelength operation. One of these schemes using a SOA as a phase modulator in a ring cavity is now described.[39] SOA suppresses the homogeneous broadening. The SOA current is modulated at low frequencies ($\sim$10 to 100 kHz). The modulation of the SOA current introduces a time varying frequency shift which suppresses the homogeneous broadening. For a phase modulation (provided by the SOA) $\varphi_m(t)$ at a modulation frequency ω_m, the cavity length will be shifted by $\varphi_m(t)/k$ at the frequency ω_m, where k is the propagation constant in the fiber. When the rate of the cavity length shift is comparable with the relaxation time of the laser, none of oscillation modes will be temporarily dominant over others and a simultaneous multiwavelength lasing is possible. The phase change is approximately given by:

$$\phi_m(t) = (2\pi L/\lambda)(dn/dN)(dN/dI)I(t), \qquad (12.2)$$

where L is the length of SOA, λ is the wavelength, dn/dN is the rate of change of index with carrier density, and dN/dI is the rate of change of carrier density with current and $I(t)$ is the modulation current. Using typical values $dn/dN = -2 \times 10^{-20}$ cm^3, $L = 500\,\mu$m, and $dN/dI = 8 \times 10^{16}$ cm^{-3}mA^{-1},[39] the phase change at 1550 nm is approximately given by:

$$\phi_m(t) = 3.2\,I_m \cos(\omega_m t), \qquad (12.3)$$

where I_m is the amplitude of the modulation current in mA. The experimental set up is shown in Fig. 12.12. It consists of a EDFA pumped by a 980 nm laser and a SOA which can be modulated at low frequencies. The circulator and the chirped fiber Bragg grating (CFBG) acts a band pass filter. The second ring cavity has a high birefringent (HiBi) fiber which ensures single polarization in that ring cavity. The cavity has a comb like transmission spectrum (determined by the length of the loop and the index) which is responsible for multiwavelength operation similar to the DI in Fig. 12.9. The wavelength separation of the multiwavelength laser can be varied by varying the length of the loop.

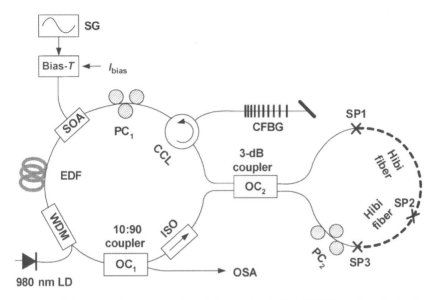

Fig. 12.12 Schematic of a multiwavelength laser using EDFA.[39] PC1, PC2: polarization controller, EDF: Er-doped fiber, WDM: wavelength division multiplexer for pump coupling, OC1: optical output coupler, ISO: isolator, CCL: circulator, CFBG: chirped fiber Bragg grating, OC2: optical coupler, Hibi fiber: highly birefringent fiber.

The SOA has a transparency current of 110 mA and a 3-dB bandwidth of 75 nm around 1550 nm. By applying a 30 kHz sinewave signal with a modulation current of few mA to the SOA, the homogeneous broadening is effectively suppressed. A multiwavelength spectrum of the fiber laser is shown in Fig. 12.13 when the comb filter transmission peaks are 0.19 nm apart.

Stable multiwavelength laser emission has also been demonstrated using a nonlinear medium in the fiber laser cavity.[46–48] Graphene deposited at the end of the fiber acts as a nonlinear medium and stabilizes the laser by mixing the modes of the comb like spectrum through four wave mixing (FWM). The nonlinear coefficient of grapheme is sufficiently high (10^8 times higher than silica) that 20 μm thick graphene layers at fiber ends is sufficient to cause enough FWM to stabilize the laser.

An experiment where graphene acts a nonlinear medium is shown in Fig. 12.14. The 3 m long EDF is pumped by a 974 nm laser diode.

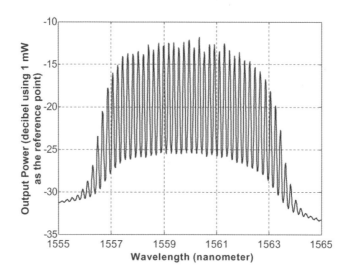

Fig. 12.13 Spectrum of the multiwavelength fiber laser.[39]

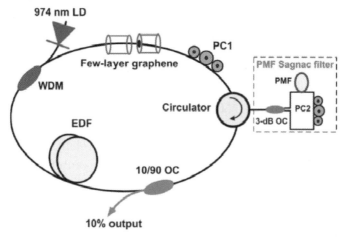

Fig. 12.14 Schematic of a grapheme assisted multiwavelength fiber laser set up.[46] PC1, PC2: polarization controller, OC: output coupler 10% output, 90% through, PMF: polarization maintaining fiber.

A circulator provides a connection to the second cavity. It consists of a polarizing maintaining fiber (PMF) and has a comb like output spectrum. The wavelength separation in the laser output is determined by this comb like separation. Results of multiwavelength

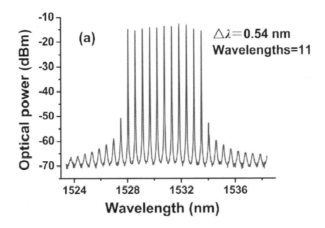

Fig. 12.15 Multiwavelength laser operation using graphene in the optical cavity.[48]

operation is shown in Fig. 12.15. In the absence of graphene, the intensities of the wavelengths are not equal and they fluctuate.[46]

12.4. Tunable Fiber Lasers

Many fiber laser designs utilize a FBG for optical feedback. The FBG generally provides feedback at a specific wavelength, i.e., it reflects light at a specific wavelength, often called the Bragg wavelength. The Bragg wavelength of FBG varies with the changes in the physical properties of the grating or its environment (e.g., strain, temperature). This is the basis of strain sensors using FBGs.[49-53] The Bragg wavelength (the wavelength of the reflected signal, λ_B) is given by[49]:

$$\lambda_B = 2n\Lambda, \tag{12.4}$$

where Λ is the grating pitch and n is the effective index of the core. The shift in Bragg wavelength (λ_B) due to a change in strain or temperature can be expressed by[53]:

$$\Delta\lambda_B = 2n\Lambda[\{1 - (n^2/2)(P_{12} - \nu(P_{11} + P_{12}))\}e + \{\alpha + (dn/dT)/n\}\Delta T], \tag{12.5}$$

where P_{ij} are the Pockel's (piezo) coefficients of the stress-optic tensor, ν is Poisson's ratio, e is the applied strain, and α is the coefficient of thermal expansion (CTE) of the fiber material (e.g., silica), and ΔT is the temperature change. The quantity $(n^2/2)(P_{12} -$

$\nu(P_{11} + P_{12}))$ has a numerical value of ~ 0.22. The strain response of a FBG at constant temperature has been measured. It is found to be[53]:

$$(1/\lambda_B)(\delta\lambda_B/\delta\varepsilon) = 0.78 \times 10^{-6}\mu\varepsilon^{-1}, \tag{12.6}$$

This response gives a "rule-of-thumb" measure of the grating shift with strain of 1 nm per 1000 $\mu\varepsilon$ at 1.3 μm wavelength. In silica fibers, the thermal response is the dominant effect, which accounts for 95% of the observed shift. The normalized thermal response at constant strain is[53]:

$$(1/\lambda_B)(\delta\lambda_B/\delta T) = 6.7 \times 10^{-6}\,\mathrm{C}^{-1}, \tag{12.7}$$

A wavelength resolution of ~ 1 pm (0.001 nm) is required (at $\sim 1.3\,\mu$m) to resolve a temperature change of ~ 0.1 C, or a strain change of 1 μ strain. So, either the temperature or the strain can be varied to make a tunable FBG.

The schematic of an EDF laser with a broadband mirror at one end and a tunable FBG is shown in Fig. 12.16. The Broadband mirror has essentially the same reflectivity at all wavelengths. The Bragg wavelength of the FBG is varied by changing the strain keeping the temperature constant.[54] The pump laser wavelength is 1480 nm. The Er ion concentration and core diameter of the single mode EDF are 800 ppm and 5 μm respectively. To produce a strain tunable FBG, it is embedded in a strip of composite material which is then stretched

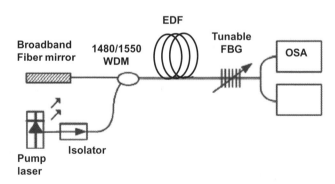

Fig. 12.16 Schematic of a tunable fiber laser with tunable FBG.[54] EDF: erbium-doped fiber, OSA: optical spectrum analyzer, WDM: wavelength division multiplexer for pump coupling, TFBG: tunable fiber Bragg grating.

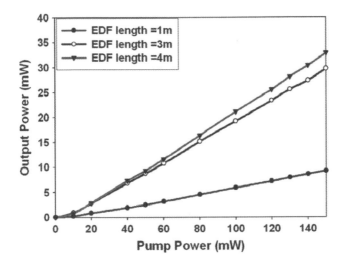

Fig. 12.17 Laser output power as a function of pump power for no strain for three EDFA lengths.[54]

or compressed using a precision stage with high resolution micrometers. A tuning rage of 16 nm is obtained. The reflectivity of FBG is ~40 to 50% and it varies with the amount of strain applied.[54-56]

The fiber laser light output as a function of 1480 nm pump power for three EDFA lengths of 1, 2 and 3 m is shown in Fig. 12.17. The output power for 1 m length is low compared to that for longer lengths showing the pump laser is not totally absorbed.

The spectrum of the tunable laser as the FBG is tuned is shown in Fig. 12.18. Power variation of less than 2 dB is observed for a tuning range of 16 nm. A larger tuning range (covering the entire C-band) from ~1532 to 1562 nm has been observed using the same EDFA but two tunable FBGs.[54]

Tunable fiber lasers have been demonstrated using two long period cascaded FBGs (LPFBG).[57] The schematic of the laser design is shown in Fig. 12.19[57] It uses an Er-doped single mode fiber gain medium (EDFA) with 400 ppm Er concentration. The EDFA length is 12 m and is pumped by a 980 nm laser. The two FBGs form two sets of comb filters and the laser operates at wavelengths where these filters match up. The transmission spectrum (and peak transmission wavelength) of the cascaded LPFGs varies with the state of

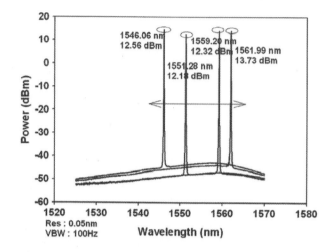

Fig. 12.18 Tunability of an Er-doped fiber laser using strain tunable fiber Bragg grating.[54]

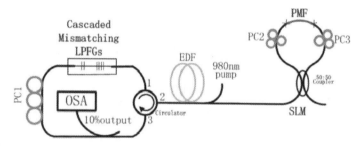

Fig. 12.19 Schematic of a tunable fiber laser.[57] LPFG: Long period fiber Bragg grating, OSA: optical spectrum analyzer, EDF: Erbium-doped fiber, PMF: polarization maintaining fiber, PC1, PC2, PC3: polarization controllers, SLM: single mode loop mirror.

polarization (SOP) of the incident light. The SOPs controlled by PC1, produces wavelength dependent cavity losses so that the lasing oscillations can be switched by changing the SOP. A Sagnac loop mirror (SLM) using a high birefringent fiber (HiBi-SLM) is used as a wavelength independent mirror for all polarizations. By varying the polarization controllers PC2 and PC3 properly, individually switchable and widely tunable operations in the laser have been realized.[57]

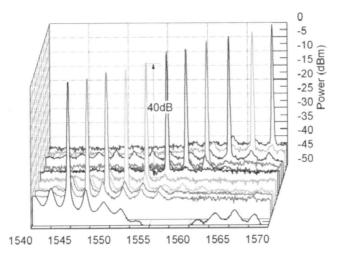

1540 1545 1550 1555 1560 1565 1570

Fig. 12.20 Successively tuned single wavelength spectrum of the tunable fiber laser of Fig. 12.19.[57]

The output spectrum of the laser is tuned by varying the polarization controllers. Successively tuned output spectrum showing single wavelength operation is shown in Fig. 12.20.

The results illustrate tunability of single mode Er-doped fiber lasers. Tunable fiber lasers at other wavelengths have been reported.[58]

12.5. High Power Fiber Lasers

High power fiber lasers are important for a wide range of commercial and medical applications. In many cases, they are being considered as replacement for CO_2 lasers for metal cutting systems. The lasers have a large mode area (LMA) fiber, both for pump coupling and for increasing the emitting area so that high power can be obtained without catastrophic degradation due to high intensity. In some instances, the pump is coupled into a large cladding area, and the fiber generally has a single mode (small area) doped core where the laser light is generated.[59–66] Thus often a single mode high power output can be obtained from these lasers. There is a second cladding in these fibers for pump confinement similar to that for double clad amplifiers. Nearly all fiber lasers are pumped by high power diode lasers which makes them compact compared to other types (such as gas lasers) of high power lasers. Various index designs of the fiber core and cladding have been studied for fiber lasers for optimizing pump utilization and pump/laser mode confinement.

12.5.1. *Yb-Doped Fiber Laser*

In recent years, for high power applications Yb-doped fibers have been studied the most. This is due to the lack of concentration quenching and exited state absorption in Yb which allows high concentrations in the doped region unlike the Er-doped fibers. Also, semiconductor high power pump lasers for Yb-doped fibers are reliable and available. Although fiber lasers with high power can be made by increasing the size of the doped region, this reduces the beam quality i.e., brightness defined as the power per unit solid angle.

High power, high brightness Yb-doped fiber sources at around 1.1 μm are of interest for various applications such as micromachining, welding and material processing. For high brightness, a single transverse mode lasing is preferred. However, stimulated Raman scattering (SRS) limits the output power in single mode operation. In order to reduce SRS, a large core size and short length has been used, but the core size leads to multimode operation which can be reduced using fiber taper and/or bending. An experimental result using bending losses to reduce/eliminate SRS and higher order modes is described in Ref. 65. Results of this Ref. are described in Sec. 7.3.

A fiber design called W fiber (Fig. 12.21) has been investigated for single mode high power operation. In this fiber, the fundamental (LP01) mode cutoff is located between the signal wavelength and the first order Stokes (Raman) wavelength. Thus the fiber filters out the Stokes signal effectively without causing any additional loss at the signal wavelength. A laser design using a W type fiber is shown in Fig. 12.22.[66] The pump light at 975 nm (from laser diode) is coupled into the fiber using a lens and dichroic mirror which has high transmission at 975 nm and nearly 100% reflectivity in the laser wavelength range of 1030–1150 nm. The output mirror of the laser

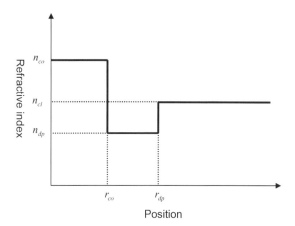

Fig. 12.21 Index profile of a W-type fiber.[69] The origin refers to the center of the circular cross section of the fiber.

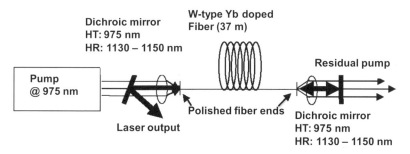

Fig. 12.22 Schematic of Yb-doped fiber laser set up.[66] HT: high transmission, HR: high reflection.

cavity is simply the 4% Fresnel reflection from the cleaved fiber end. The fiber has a inner cladding diameter of 370 μm and is coated with a polymer cladding. The size of the inner cladding is determined by efficient coupling from diode laser stack. The numerical aperture of inner cladding, NA = 0.5. The fiber has a core diameter of 7 μm, with a depressed ring in the inner cladding of thickness 7 μm (Fig. 12.21).

The core and the depressed cladding index differences are 0.003 and 0.002, respectively, both with respect to the silica inner cladding. The fundamental LP01 mode cut-off in the fiber is calculated to be ~1100 nm. Thus a significant loss at the 1st order Raman Stokes

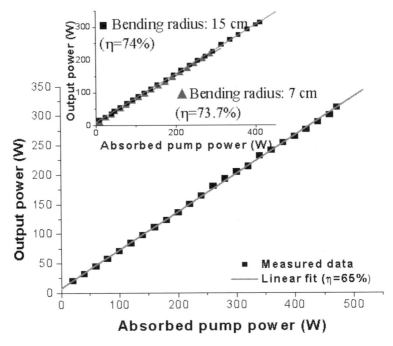

Fig. 12.23 Laser output as a function of pump power for 37 m long fiber. (Inset) same data gor 23 m long fiber for two bend radii. The laser wavelength for 7 cm bend radii is 1058 nm and that for 15 cm bend radii is 1080 nm.[66]

band at around 1120 nm can be expected. The small signal absorption at the pump wavelength is ∼0.3 dB/m.[66] The CW laser output as a function of pump power is shown in Fig. 12.23. More than 300 W of output power is obtained with a slope efficiency of 65%. This exceeds the estimated SRS threshold power of 140 W and this is possible due to the W-type index profile. Higher slope efficiency is obtained with a shorter fiber (23 m) due to more complete power absorption. The data for short fiber is shown in the inset.

As discussed previously, a large core fiber is needed for high power output because a large pump absorption without an excessively long fiber. A double clad Yb-doped fiber has been fabricated and used to demonstrate 1 kW CW operation of a Yb-doped fiber laser.[67] The fiber had 43 μm Yb-doped core with an effective mode field area of 1100 μm^2. The inner cladding is D-shaped (by milling) for large overlap between cladding and core modes. The long and short axis of

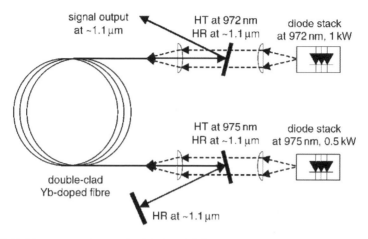

Fig. 12.24 Experimental set up for Yb-doped DCF laser HR: High reflectivity; HT: High transmission.[67]

the D- shape are 650 and 600 μm respectively. The Yb concentration in the core is 4500 ppm by weight. The fiber is coated with a low refractive index polymer outer cladding which provides a NA of 0.48 for pump coupling.

The experimental set up is shown in Fig. 12.24. Two diode laser stacks emitting in the 970 to 975 nm range are used for end pumping the fiber. The fiber length is 8 m. The pump beams are coupled into the fiber using collimators and lenses. The coupling efficiency is estimated to be 85%. The high reflectivity mirror is coupled to the fiber using a lens and the Fresnel reflectivity ($\sim$4%) of the cleaved end provides the second mirror. The laser output is obtained from this low reflectivity end. The laser output as a function of launched pump power is shown in Fig. 12.25. The slope efficiency is 80%. The emission wavelength is $\sim$1090 nm.

12.5.2. *Nd-Doped Fiber Laser*

Nd-doped slab and rod laser for high power operation have been extensively studied. In this section, a few experimental results on Watt level operation of Nd-doped fiber lasers are discussed.[68–72] Nd can be used as a dopant in different types of glass (including silica) for the purpose of light amplification and laser action.

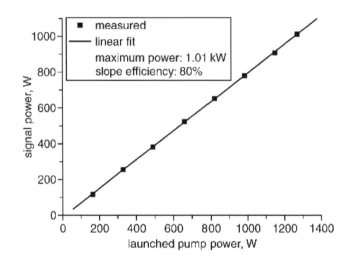

Fig. 12.25 Laser output as a function of pump power.[67]

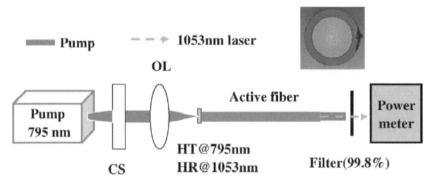

Fig. 12.26 Schematic of Nd-doped fiber laser experiment.[68] HT: high transmission, HR: high reflectivity. A photograph of the fiber cross section is also shown.

A short Nd-doped fiber has been used to produce Watt-level powers[68] The fiber has a double clad structure. The fiber preform is made of alkaline earth phosphate glasses (K_2O–BaO–Al_2O_3–P_2O_5). The double clad fiber has $360\,\mu$m diameter outer cladding, a $285\,\mu$m diameter inner cladding and a $14\,\mu$m diameter Nd-doped core. The doping density of Nd is $3.5 \times 10^{20}\,cm^{-3}$. The schematic of the fiber laser experimental set up is shown in Fig. 12.26. The fiber laser has 26 cm long double clad fiber placed in an optical cavity pumped by

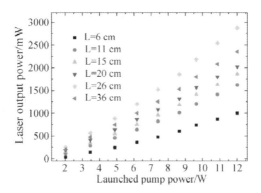

Fig. 12.27 The laser output power near 1060 nm as a function of pump power for different fiber lengths.[68]

semiconductor diode laser emitting near 795 nm. A broadband mirror is used as a reflector for one end of the cavity and the second mirror consists of Fresnel reflection ($\sim$4%) from the cleaved end of the gain fiber. The broadband reflector is butt coupled to the gain fiber. The laser outputs for different fiber lengths are measured. The data is shown in Fig. 12.27. As the length increases the output power becomes higher, due to higher pump absorption. Beyond a certain length (26 cm), the power decreases somewhat possibly due to unpumped regions.

Nd-doped glass also exhibits gain near 940 nm which is close the absorption line of water vapor. A tunable laser in this wavelength range is important for some applications. The optical gain near 940 nm is smaller than that near 1060 nm. Hence it is desirable to have a frequency selective feedback using a grating (for example) or wavelength selective propagation loss (such as a W fiber) to get Nd-doped fiber laser emission in the 920 to 940 nm range. The method used in Ref. 69 utilizes a W-type index profile for the core region of the fiber. The W-profile is used to suppress guidance and hence stimulated emission at 1060 nm. The LP01 mode cut off of the Nd-doped fiber is at 1000 nm. It is also important to have high pump absorption to achieve gain and population inversion near 930 nm. The truncated fiber geometry shown in Fig. 12.28, is used to increase the overlap of the cladding modes with the Nd-doped core modes. For 12 dB pump

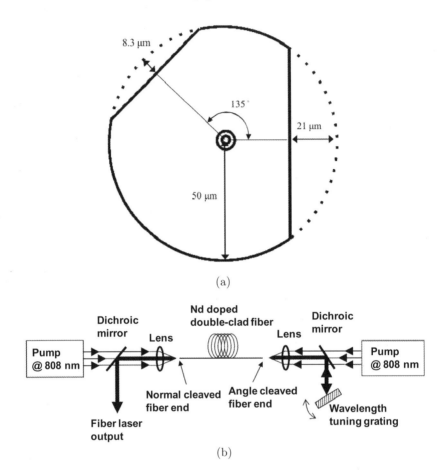

Fig. 12.28 (a) Fiber geometry (b) Experimental set up for tunable laser emission near 930 nm.[69]

absorption a fiber length of 30 m is needed. The core diameter is 10 μm and the Nd concentration in the core is 1.6×10^{19} cm^{-3}.

The experimental set up for tunable laser emission near 930 nm is shown in Fig. 12.28. The Nd-doped fiber ($\sim$14 to 25 m long) is pumped by 808 nm laser diodes from both sides. Dichroic mirrors are used at both ends for high pump transmissions and generated laser light separation at both ends as shown in Fig. 12.30. The laser cavity is formed by Fresnel reflection (4%) at one end and by a tunable grating at the other end. The maximum laser output power as

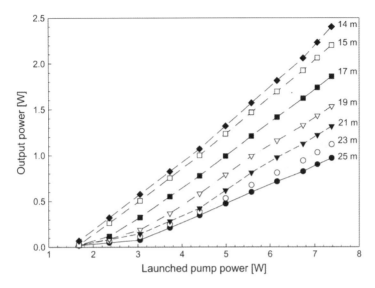

Fig. 12.29 The laser output as a function of pump power for different fiber lengths at wavelengths between 926 and 931 nm is shown.[69]

a function of pump power for different fiber lengths is measured. The result is shown in Fig. 12.29. This maximum occurred in the wavelength range of 926 to 931 nm.

The emission wavelength of the laser can be varied by tuning the grating. Tunable laser spectrum for a 14 m long fiber is shown in Fig. 12.30. As expected, at either end of the tuning range the power decreases due to a finite spectral width of the gain spectrum.

12.5.3. *Er–Yb Co-Doped Fiber Laser*

Er–Yb co-doped fiber is the material of choice for high power fiber lasers emitting near 1550 nm. The fiber lasers typically have double clad fiber (DCF) design. The core is doped with Er–Yb. The pump laser light propagating in the inner cladding excites the Yb ions to a higher energy level. The excited Yb ions transfer the energy to Er which then relaxes to the upper laser level (Sec. 7.4). Er transition from the upper laser level to lower level produces the 1550 nm laser light[70–77] The energy transfer process from Yb to Er is very efficient. Yb does not suffer from excited state absorption and concentration

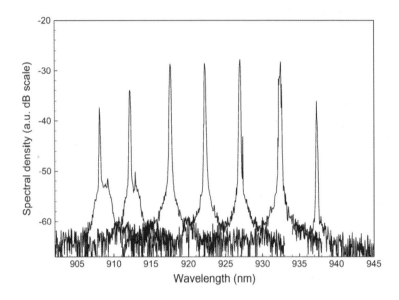

Fig. 12.30 Nd fiber laser spectrum as the grating is tuned.[69]

quenching, as a result high Yb doping can be incorporated in the Er–Yb-doped fiber.

Generally the EYDFL (Er–Yb-doped fiber laser) has a double clad structure with large inner cladding diameter ($\sim$100 to 400 μm depending on the desired output power). This allows efficient coupling of pump light from diode bars. The Er–Yb-doped core could be single mode (i.e., $\sim$4 to 5 μm in diameter) for single mode output or it may have a larger diameter ($\sim$20 to 30 μm) for higher power output. Result of an experiment is now described.

The EYDFL has a D-shaped inner cladding with 400 μm/360 μm size along the long and short axis. The D-shape allows better coupling between core and cladding modes. The D-shape is formed by milling the fiber. The fiber has a 30 μm diameter Er–Yb co-doped phosphosilicate glass core with a numerical aperture (NA) of 0.20. The fiber is coated with a low index polymer to provide a NA of 0.46 for the pump light. The schematic of the experimental set up is shown in Fig. 12.31.

The pump source is a multiple laser diode stack emitting near 975 nm which is the absorption peak of Yb. The pump is coupled into

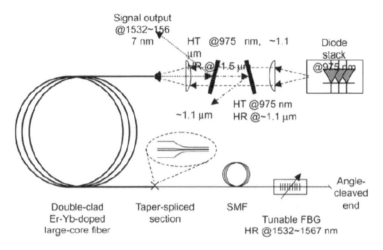

Fig. 12.31 Schematic of a tunable high power fiber laser set up.[78] HT: high transmission, Hr: hgh reflection, SMF: single mode fiber, FBG: fiber Bragg grating.

the fiber using a dichroic mirror which provides high transmission for pump and high reflectivity for laser light. The large core EYDF is spliced to a single mode fiber (SMF) after tapering. The SMF is spliced to single mode FBG, the output of which is angle cleaved to eliminate Fresnel reflection back into the laser cavity. The reflecting wavelength of the FBG is continuously tuned from ~1530 to 1570 nm using strain on the FBG. The reflectivity of the FBG is ~99% and the spectral bandwidth is <1 nm. Although the Er–Yb gain medium supports multiple modes (due to its large size), the laser emission is primarily in a single mode due to the feedback from single mode FBG. The EYDF length is 3.5 m.

The signal power output as a function of wavelength for different pump powers is shown in Fig. 12.32. Nearly uniform power at all wavelengths suggest the FBG reflectivity is nearly the same at all wavelengths. Figure 12.33 shows the laser output at 1545 nm as a function of pump power. The slope efficiency is 32%.

Higher output powers have been reported in the Er–Yb co-doped fiber laser systems utilizing a large mode area fiber.[79] The core is made of phosphosilicate glass co-doped with Er and Yb ions. The Er–Yb co-doped core has a diameter of 30 μm and a NA of 0.21. The calculated effective area of the fundamental mode is 390 μm^2 at

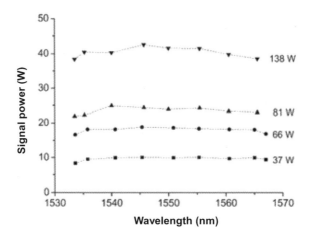

Fig. 12.32 Laser output power as a function of wavelength for different pump powers. The pump powers are shown on the right.

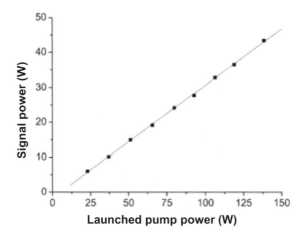

Fig. 12.33 Laser output power at 1545 nm as a function of pump power. The slope efficiency is 32%.[78]

1567 nm. The inner cladding has a D-shape design to improve the overlap of cladding and core modes. The long axis of the D-shape is ~600 μm. The outer cladding is a low index polymer. The light absorption coefficient in the core takes place due to Er and Yb ions and is ~0.11 dB/m at 1535 nm. The pump absorption in the core also due to Yb ions is ~3.8 dB/m at 976 nm.

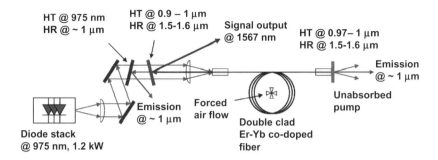

Fig. 12.34 Schematic of a high power Er–Yb co-doped fiber experimental set up.[79]

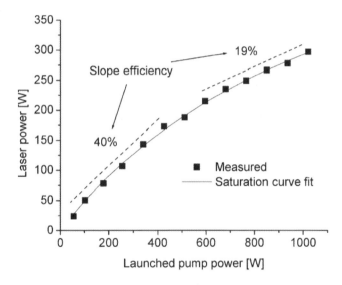

Fig. 12.35 Laser output power at 1567 nm as a function of launched pump power.[79]

The EYDF is 8 m long and is pumped at both ends using diode bars. (Fig. 12.34) The light from the diode bars are coupled into the fiber using collimating optics and lenses. The pump coupling efficiency is estimated to be 85%. About 99% of the pump light is absorbed in the fiber. Dichroic mirrors are used for high pump and Yb emission transmission and high reflection for the laser light near 1560 nm. The laser power output as a function of launched pump power is shown in Fig. 12.35. At high pump powers, Yb remains excited to the higher energy level which results in a build-up of amplified spontaneous emission followed by lasing at Yb emission wavelength of $\sim$1100 nm. The co-lasing causes a saturation of the 1560 nm output power as stated in Fig. 12.35. The threshold for Yb lasing is estimated to be $\sim$210 W of launched power.

Rare earth-doped fiber lasers are important for a range of applications. Low power lasers are important for communication and sensor systems. High power lasers are important for industrial applications such as metal cutting and shaping. A wide range of wavelengths in the near infrared range can be obtained from these lasers.

References

1. D. Hanna, Chapter B4.1. In *Handbook of Laser Technology and Applications*, C. Webb and J. Jones (Eds). Institute of Physics. 2004.
2. A. Tunnermann and H. Zellmar Chapter B4.2. In *Handbook of Laser Technology and Applications*, C. Webb and J. Jones (Eds). Institute of Physics. 2004.
3. G.A. Ball and W.W. Morey, *IEEE Photon. Technol. Lett.* **3** (1991) 1077.
4. Y. Alain, J.F. Bayon, P. Bernage, T. Georges, M. Monerie and P. Niay. In *Topical Meet. on Optical Amplifiers and Their Applications*, Tech. Dig., Washington, DC, Optical Society of America. **14**, (1993) 57.
5. J.T. Kringlebotn, J.L. Archambault, L. Reekie, J.E. Townsend, G.G. Vienne and D.N. Payne, *Electron. Lett.* **30** (1994) 972.
6. S.V. Chernikov, J.R. Taylor and R. Kashyap, *Opt. Lett.* **18** (1993) 2023.
7. G.A. Ball, G. Meltz and W.W. Morey, *Opt. Lett.* **18** (1993) 1976.
8. V. Mizrahi, D.J. DiGiovanni, R.M. Atkins, S.G. Grubb, Y.K. Park and J.M. Delavaux, *J. Lightwave Tech.* **11** (1993) 2021.
9. J.L. Zyskind, V. Mizrahi, D.J. DiGiovanni and J.W. Sulhoff, *Electron. Lett.* **28** (1992) 1385.
10. J.L. Zyskind, J.W. Sulhoff, P.D. Magill, K.C. Reichmann and D.J. DiGiovanni, *Electron. Lett.* **29** (1993) 1105.
11. E. Snitzer, Proceedings of the 3rd international Conference on solid-state lasers, (1963) pp. 999.
12. J. Stone and C.A. Burrus, *Appl. Phys. Lett.* **23** (1973) 388.
13. R.J. Meers, L. Reekie, S.B. Poole and D.N. Payne , *Electron. Lett.* **21** (1985) 738.
14. L. Reekie, *J. Lightwave Tech.* LT-4 (1986) 956.
15. M. Shimizu, H. Suda and M. Horiguchi, *Electron. Lett.* **23** (1987) 769.
16. H. Zellmer, U. Willamowski, A. Tunnermann, H. Welling, S. Unger, V. Reichel, H. R. Muller, T. Kirchhof and P. Albers, *Opt. Lett.* **20** (1995) 578.
17. C.G. Bethea, *IEEE J. Quantum Electron.* QE-**9** (1973) 254.
18. M. Nakazawa and Y. Kimura, *Appl. Phys. Lett.* **51** (1987) 1768.

19. K. Otsuka, *IEEE J. Quantum Electron.* QE-**14** (1978) 1007.
20. K. Otsuka, R. Kawai, Y. Asakawa, P. Mandel and E.A. Viktorov, *Opt. Lett.* **23** (1988) 201.
21. S.D. Jackson and Y. Li, *IEEE, JQE.* **39** (2003) 1118.
22. Y. Jeong, J.K. Sahu, D.N. Payne and J. Nilsson, *Optics Express.* **12** (2004) 6088.
23. A. Liem, J. Limpert, H. Zellmer, A. Tünnermann, V. Reichel, K. Mörl, S. Jetschke, S. Unger, H.-R. Müller, J. Kirchhof, T. Sandrock and A. Harschak. In *Conference on Lasers and Electro-Optics*, May 2004, postdeadline paper CPDD2. (2004).
24. V.P. Gapontsev, D.V. Gapontsev, N.S. Platonov, O. Shkurikhin, V. Fomin, A. Mashkin, M. Abramov and S. Ferin. In *European Conference on Lasers and Electro-Optics*, July 2005, paper CJ1-1, (2005).
25. N.S. Platonov, D.V. Gapontsev, V.P. Gapontsev and V. Shumilin. In Proceedings, CLEO 2002, May 2002, postdeadline paper CPDC3, (2002).
26. J. Limpert, A. Liem, H. Zellmer and A. Tunnermann, *Electron. Lett.* **39** (2003) 645.
27. Y.W. Lee, S. Sinha, M.J.F. Digonnet, R.L. Byer. In *Proceedings. CLEO.* 2006, paper CTuI5, (2006).
28. R. Hayashi, S. Yamashita and T. Said, *IEEE Photon. Technol. Lett.* **15** (2003) 1692.
29. H. Dong, G. Zhu, Q. Wang, H. Sun, N.K. Dutta, J. Jaques and A.B. Piccirilli, *IEEE Photonic Tech. Lett.* **17** (2005) 303.
30. G. Sun, D.S. Moon, A. Lin, W. Han and Y. Chung, *Opt. Express.* **16** (2008) 3652.
31. D.S. Moon, B.H. Kim, A. Lin, G. Sun, W. Han, Y. Han and Y. Chung, *Opt. Express.* **15** (2007) 8371.
32. A. Zhang, H. Liu, M.S. Demokan and H.Y. Tam, *IEEE Photon. Technol. Lett.* **178** (2005) 2535.
33. S. Yamashita and Y. Inoue, *Jpn. J. Appl. Phys.* **44** (2005) L1080.
34. X. Liu, X.Yang, F. Lu, J. Ng, X. Zhou and C. Lu, *Opt. Express* **13** (2005) 142.
35. T.V.A. Tran, K. Lee, S.B. Lee and Y. Han, *Opt. Express* **16** (2008) 1460.
36. S. Pan, C. Lou and Y. Gao, *Opt. Express.* **14** (2006) 1113.
37. D.N. Wang, F.W. Tong, X. Fang, W. Jin, P.K.A. Wai and J.M. Gong, *Opt. Commun.* **228** (2003) 295.
38. Z. Chen, S. Ma and N.K. Dutta, *Optics Express.* **17** (2009) 1234.
39. J. Yao, J. Yao, Z. Deng and J. Liu, *J. Lightwave Tech.* **23** (2005) 2484.
40. S. Yamashita and K. Hotate, *Electron. Lett.* **32** (1996) 1298.
41. N. Park and P.F. Wysocki, *IEEE Photon. Technol. Lett.* **8** (1996) 1459.
42. A. Bellemare, M. Karasek, M. Rochette, S. Larochelle and M. Tetu, *J. Lightwave Technol.* **18** (2000) 825.
43. K. Zhou, D. Zhou, F. Dong and N.Q. Ngo, *Opt. Lett.* **28** (2003) 893.
44. J. Yao, J.P. Yao and Z. Deng, *Opt. Express.* **12** (2004) 4529.
45. J. Yao, J.P. Yao, Z. Deng and J. Liu, *IEEE Photon. Technol. Lett.* **17** (2005) 756.

46. Z. Luo, M. Zhou, Z. Cai, C. Ye, J. Weng, G. Huang and H. Xu, *IEEE Photonics Tech. Letts.* **23** (2011) 501.
47. X. Feng, H. Tam and P.K.A. Wai, *Opt. Express.* **14** (2006) 8205.
48. X. Liu and C. Lu, *IEEE Photon. Technol. Lett.* **17** (2005) 2541.
49. W.W. Morey, J.R. Dunphy and G. Meltz. In Proceedings., *SPIE Distributed and Multiplexed Fiber Optic Sensors*, Boston, MA, 1991 September (1991) pp. 216.
50. S.M. Melle, K. Liu and R.M. Measures, *IEEE Photon. Technol. Lett.* **4** (1992) 516.
51. M.A. Davis and A.D. Kersey, *Electron. Lett.* **30** (1994) 75.
52. M.A. Davis, D.G. Bellemore and A.D. Kersey. In *Proceedings., SPIE 1995 North American Conf. Smart Structures Materials*, San Diego, CA, (1995) pp. 227.
53. A.D. Kersey, M.A. Davis, H.J. Patrick, M. LeBlanc, K.P. Koo, C.G. Askins, M.A. Putnam and E.J. Friebele, *J. of Lightwave Tech.* **15** (1997) 1442.
54. S.K. Liaw and G.S. Jhong, *IEEE JQE.* QE-**44** (2008) 520.
55. S.-K. Liaw, K.-L. Hung, Y.-T. Lin, C.-C. Chiang and C.-S. Shin, *Opt. Laser Technol.* **39** (2007) 1214.
56. R. Kashyap, Fiber Bragg Gratings. 1st Edition. New York: Academic Press. 1999.
57. X. Liu, L. Zhan, S. Luo, Y. Wang and Q. Shen, *IEEE J. Lightwave. Tech.* **29** (2011) 3319.
58. Y.G. Han, G. Kim, J.H. Lee, S.H. Kim and S.B. Lee, *IEEE Photon. Technol. Lett.* **17** (2005) 989.
59. Y. Jeong, J.K. Sahu, D.N. Payne and J. Nilsson, *Opt. Express.* **12** (2004) 6088.
60. V.P. Gapontsev, N.S. Platonov, O. Shkurihin and I. Zaitsev. In *Proceedings, CLEO.* 2003, postdeadline paper CPDB9, (2003).
61. N.S. Platonov, D.V. Gapontsev, V.P. Gapontsev and V. Shumilin. In *Proceedings. CLEO.* 2002, postdeadline paper CPDC3, (2002).
62. J.A. Alvarez-Chavez, A.B. Grudinin, J. Nilsson, P.W. Turner and W.A. Clarkson, CLEO/QELS 1999 paper CWE7, (1999).
63. J. Limpert, A. Liem, H. Zellmer and A. Tunnermann, *Electron. Lett.* **39** (2003) 645.
64. P. Dragic, *Opt. Commun.* **250** (2005) 403.
65. C.-H. Liu, B. Ehlers, F. Doerfel, S. Heinemann, A. Carter, K. Tankala, J. Farroni and A. Galvanauskas, *Electronics Lett.* **40** (2004) 23.
66. J. Kim, C. Codemard, Y. Jeong, J. Nilsson and J.K. Sahu, Proceedings, CLEO2006, paper CTuQ2, 2006.
67. Y. Jeong, J.K. Sahu, D.N. Payne and J. Nilsson, *Electronics Letts.* **40** (2004) 8.
68. G. Zhang, M. Wang, C. Yu, Q. Zhou, J. Qiu, L. Hu and D. Chen, *IEEE Photonics Tech. Letts.* **23** (2011) 350,.
69. D.B.S. Soh, S. Yoo, J. Nilsson, J.K. Sahu, K. Oh, S. Baek, Y. Jeong, C. Codemard A and P. Dupriez, *IEEE JQE.* QE-**40** (2004) 1275.

70. J. Dawson, R. Beach, A. Drobshoff, Z. Liao, D. Pennington, S. Payne, L. Taylor, W. Hackenberg and D. Bonaccini, *Adv. Solid-State Photon.* **83** (2003) 118.

71. J. Nilsson, W.A. Clarkson and A.B. Grudinin, *Opt. Fiber Technol.* **10** (2004) 5.

72. M.A. Noginov, G.B. Loutts, B.D. Lucas, D. Fider, P.T. Higgins, A. Truong, N. Noginova, N.P. Barnes and S. Kuck, *IEEE J.Quantum Electron.* **37** (2001) 469.

73. J.K. Sahu, Y. Jeong, D.J. Richardson and J. Nilsson, *Opt. Commun.* **227** (2003) 159.

74. J. Nilsson, W.A. Clarkson and A.B. Grudinin, *Opt. Fiber Technol.* **10** (2004) 5.

75. M. Laroche, W.A. Clarkson, J.K. Sahu, J. Nilsson and Y. Jeong. In Proceedings, Conference on Lasers and Electro-Optics 2003, paper CWO5, (2003).

76. G.G. Vienne, J.E. Caplen, L. Dong, J.D. Minelly, J. Nilsson and D.N. Payne, *J. Lightwave Technol.* **16** (1998) 1990.

77. J. Nilsson, S.U. Alam, J.A. Alvarez-Chavez, P.W. Turner, W.A. Clarksonm and A.B. Grudinin, *IEEE J. Quantum Electron.* **39** (2003) 987.

78. Y. Jeong, C. Alegria, J.K. Sahu, L. Fu, M. Ibsen, C. Codemard, M.R. Mokhtar and J. Nilsson, *IEEE Photonic Tech. Lett.* **16** (2004) 756.

79. Y. Jeong, S. Yoo, C.A. Codemard, J. Nilsson, J.K. Sahu, D.N. Payne, R. Horley, P.W. Turner, L. Hickey, A. Harker, M. Lovelady and A. Piper, *IEEE J. Select. Topic of Quantum Electronics*, **13** (2007) 573.

Chapter 13

Fiber Raman Lasers
and Amplifiers

13.1. Introduction

Fiber Raman lasers are based on the nonlinear process of stimulated Raman scattering.[1-10] When a sufficiently intense light beam is incident on a material, light at a new of wavelength is generated by a process called Raman scattering. Typically the energy of the photons $(h\nu_p)$ at the incident wavelength is larger than the energy of Raman process generated photon $(h\nu_s)$ by an amount equal to the separation between two energy levels (δE) in the material, i.e., $h\nu_p - h\nu_s = \delta E$. The photons at the lower energy are generated by both spontaneous and stimulated emission.

The stimulated Raman scattering produces Raman gain and hence fiber Raman lasers. The energy levels in the material include both electronic, vibration and rotational energy. For typical fiber Raman lasers the excitations are vibration energy in the SiO_2 glass matrix i.e., vibration energy in the Si–O bond. The energy depends both on the bond strength and the mass of the atoms. Thus the vibration spectrum is different in different glasses. The strength of Raman scattering also varies with different glasses. The schematic of a Raman process is shown in Fig. 13.1. The frequency shift and relative strength of Raman scattering cross section for different glasses is shown in Table 13.1.

Since Raman fiber lasers, are based on stimulated Raman scattering (which produces gain at the energy of the Raman scattered light), the incident light (known as the pump) needs to be

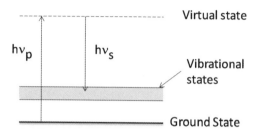

Fig. 13.1 Schematic of quantum mechanical transition in a Raman process. The figure shows that a molecule is excited to a virtual state when a pump photon is incident and it quickly decays to a different energy level emitting a photon at a lower energy.

Table 13.1 Frequency shift and Raman gain for various substances.[8]

Substance	Frequency shift (cm^{-1})	Gain (cm/GW)
Benzene	992	2.8
Nitrobenzene	1345	2.1
Silica	467	0.8
Hydrogen (P = 10 atm)	4155	1.5
Carbon disulphide	656	24

sufficiently intense. The Raman gain for the generated Raman signal is proportional to $P_p \sigma N$ where P_p is the intensity of the incident pump, σ is the stimulated Raman cross section, and N is the number of participating molecules per unit volume. The quantity $\sigma N = g_R$ is often called the Raman gain coefficient. The difference in energy between the pump and signal photons (Raman scattering produced or injected) is determined by the molecular vibration of the host material. This frequency difference is called the Stokes shift. The amorphous nature of silica makes the Raman gain curve quite broad in optical fiber. The simplest Raman fiber laser consists of a single mode fiber to which pump light is injected. The single mode fiber has fiber Bragg grating (FBG) attached at both ends (Fig. 13.2a). The FBG has the unique property that it reflects at a very narrow band of wavelengths (by proper choice of the periodicity of the grating) and can be easily spliced to a single mode fiber with low loss. The grating reflectivity can also be varied by varying the length of the FBG. At the input pump end, the FBG reflects the Raman signal light but

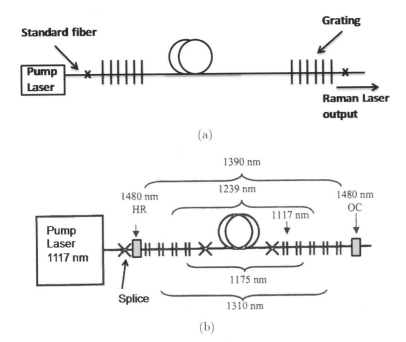

Fig. 13.2 (a): Typical schematic of a fiber Raman laser with fiber Bragg gratings (FBGs). (b): A cascaded Raman laser design.[14] The laser emits at 1480 nm using a 1117 nm pump laser. HR: high reflection, OC: output coupler.

lets the pump light through. At the output coupler, it allows some of the signal light to escape (reflectivity ∼90%).

FBGS have been used for providing feedback for both fiber lasers and fiber Raman lasers.[11–17] Using a series of gratings at appropriately chosen wavelength cascaded Raman lasers (Fig. 13.2b) has been demonstrated.[14, 15] In this design, four nested pair of gratings (with reflectivities close to 100%) at appropriate Stokes wavelength is used to build up the pump light for each Stokes scattering. The pump light is at 1117 nm. The first Stokes scattering produces stimulated emission at 1239 nm, which acts as pump for second Stokes scattering producing stimulated emission at 1390 nm and this acts a pump for the third Stokes scattering which produces stimulated emission at 1480 nm. The 1480 nm light could be used as a pump source for Er-doped fibers. Thus the cascaded Raman process utilizing FBGs produces stimulated emission at 1480 nm using 1117 nm pump light. This is discussed further in Sec. 13.4.

13.2. Fiber Bragg Gratings

From the previous section and also from subsequent sections in this chapter, it is important to note that FBGs are an important component of fiber Raman lasers. They are used for providing feedback to the gain region, and as both input and output couplers.

For a multilayerd planar dielectric medium with a small refractive index difference between the layers, reflections take place at every interface for a normally incident light. For a significant reflection from the dielectric stack, the reflections at each interface must add up in phase. Similar phenomenon must happen for an index grating close to a waveguide. For the schematic shown in Fig. 13.3 (an index grating near a dielectric layer is a periodic region of alternating high and low index), the small reflections of the optical field outside the waveguide from the "crests" of the grating must add up in phase to produce a significant reflectivity.

This constructive interference occurs if the period of the grating (Λ) obeys the following equation:

$$2n\Lambda = m\lambda \tag{13.1}$$

where n is the index of the material, ($n \sim 1.5$ for silica glass), λ is the wavelength in free space, and m is an integer. Equation (13.1) is

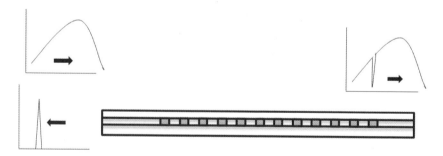

Fig. 13.3 Schematic of an index grating and its operation. The grating reflects a specific wavelength. The grating period is ∼500 nm for reflection near 1550 nm. The reflected light spectrum and transmitted light spectrum is sketched for an incident light signal with the spectrum shown.

called the Bragg condition. For $m = 1$, the grating is called a first order grating. For a first order grating, the Bragg wavelength λ_B for a grating with a period Λ is $\lambda_B = 2n\Lambda$. Thus for reflection at $\lambda \sim 1500\,\text{nm}$, the grating period is $\sim 500\,\text{nm}$ for first order gratings in silica ($n = 1.5$). Typically, first order gratings are used in FBG applications. In a laser cavity, the light travels both in the forward and backward direction. Thus for a FBG in a laser cavity, the FBG reflection couples the forward and backward traveling waves. The reflectivity of FBG has been derived using coupled mode equations. The result for reflectivity, R is[7]:

$$R = \frac{K^2 \sin h^2(|S|L)}{\delta\beta^2 \sin h^2(|S|L) + |S|^2 \cos h^2(|S|L)} \quad \text{for } K^2 > \delta\beta^2$$

$$= -\frac{K^2 \sin h^2(|S|L)}{\delta\beta^2 - K^2 \cos h^2(|S|L)} \quad \text{for } K^2 < \delta\beta^2,$$

with $S = \sqrt{[\delta\beta^2 - K^2]}$, \hfill (13.2)

In these equations, $\delta\beta = 2\pi n_e/\lambda - m\pi/\Lambda$, where n_e is the effective index of the waveguide. The quantity $\delta\beta$ is a measure of the mismatch between Bragg condition and the actual free space wavelength (λ). The quantity K is the coupling constant between the forward and backward traveling waves and L is the length of the grating region. For uniform sinusoidal modulation of the grating index

$$K = (\pi \delta n/\lambda_B)\eta, \hfill (13.3)$$

where η is the overlap of the electric field in the waveguide core with the grating and δn is the difference between the maximum and minimum index in the grating region. If the grating is far from the core, K decreases. The maximum reflectivity occurs for $\delta\beta = 0$, i.e., when the Bragg condition is satisfied. The maximum reflectivity, R_{max} is given by:

$$R_{\text{max}} = \tan h^2(KL), \hfill (13.4)$$

For $KL > 3$, the reflectivity approaches 100%. For a significant reflectivity, few mm of grating length is needed. Another measure of a FBG

is its bandwidth. A measure of this quantity is the wavelength difference $(\Delta\lambda)$ between the two minimum on either side of the maximum
reflection peak. It is given by (for $\lambda \sim \lambda_B$),

$$\Delta\lambda = \frac{\lambda_B^2}{\pi n_e L}[(kL)^2 + \pi^2]^{1/2}, \qquad (13.5)$$

Thus the reflection peak wavelength, bandwidth and the maximum
reflectivity can be varied by varying the grating pitch and the grating
length respectively.

There are several techniques for writing gratings. The principles
among them are the dual beam holographic technique and the phase
mask technique. In the holographic technique, the light from a UV
laser is split up into two beams using a beam splitter. The beams
are focused back using lenses on a fiber with the cladding removed.
Cylindrical lenses are used to elongate the beams along the fiber
length. The interfering light on the fiber produces an intensity pattern. Figure 13.4 shows the schematic of the holographic method.

The interference pattern writes a grating on the fiber. This is due
to changes in absorption in fiber when exposed to UV light. An ideal
silica fiber would have SiO_2 bonds. When dopants, such as Ge, are
introduced to change the index to form the fiber waveguide, defects
are introduced which can take the form of Si–Si, Si–Ge and Ge–Ge
bonds. In the presence of UV light (~ 244 nm) these bonds break
increasing the absorption. An index change is then caused through

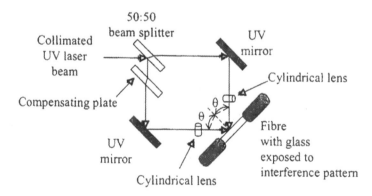

Fig. 13.4 Schematic of grating writing using a dual beam holographic method.[7]

the Kramers–Kronig relationship. Thus a periodic index change is produced by the periodic interference pattern of UV light. The grating period is given by:

$$\Lambda = \frac{n_{\text{eff}}\lambda_{\text{laser}}}{n_{\text{laser}}\sin\theta},\qquad(13.6)$$

where λ_{laser} is the wavelength of laser, n_{laser} is the index at laser wavelength in the fiber, n_{eff} is the index of fiber near Bragg wavelength and θ is the angle shown in Fig. 13.4. The quality of the grating can be improved by increasing the photosensitivity of the fiber using different dopants.

The dual beam holographic technique requires a highly coherent laser source, a stable grating writing system over a large area (few m), and low alignment tolerances. These disadvantages are overcome using a phase mask technique. In this technique a phase mask with the required grating period is generated using the standard integrated circuit fabrication technique. The UV light falls on the fiber through the phase mask. The majority of the transmission through the mask is in the $m = 0$ and $m = 1$ and $m = -1$ orders. The interference pattern between the first order beams induces a periodic change in index in the fiber placed behind the phase mask. The grating period in this approach is given by:

$$\Lambda = \Lambda_{PM}/2\qquad(13.7)$$

where Λ_{PM} is the periodicity of the grating in the phase mask. Thus any UV wavelength can be used and the grating period is independent of the UV wavelength used for FBG writing. The schematic of FBG writing using phase mask is shown in Fig. 13.5.

13.3. Raman Laser

A typical Raman laser involves a gain medium which produces stimulated Raman emission (i.e., Raman gain using a pump laser light) and fiber gratings which act as reflectors. The optical cavity is produced by gratings at each end of the fiber which produces gain at the Raman scattered wavelength. A schematic of a Raman laser fabricated using phospho-silicate fiber is shown in Fig. 13.6. The fiber has FBGs at

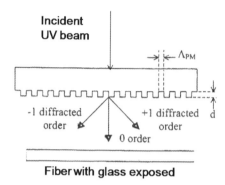

Fig. 13.5 Schematic of grating writing using a phase mask.[7]

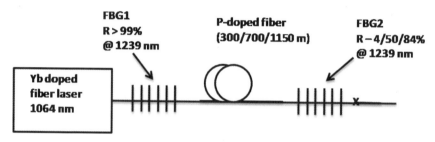

Fig. 13.6 Schematic of a fiber Raman laser.[18] The pump laser is a double clad Yb-doped fiber laser.

each end. The CW light from a Yb-doped fiber laser emitting at 1064 nm serves as the pump laser. The stimulated Raman scattered signal is at 1239 nm. The FBG reflectivity at 1239 nm is 99% for the pump coupler end. At the output end three different FBGs are used with reflectivity of 4%, 50% and 84% respectively. Three different fiber lengths (300, 700 and 1100 m) are also studied.

The variation of first Stokes power as a function of pump power for the 700 m long fiber with 4% output coupler is shown in Fig. 13.7. The laser threshold is 3.3 W and an efficiency of 47% (output power of 4 W) is obtained at 8.4 W of pump laser power.

Other fiber lengths and FBG reflectivity produced less output power.

Raman lasers with higher output power have been studied and demonstrated.[19–22] The experimental set up (Fig. 13.8) using

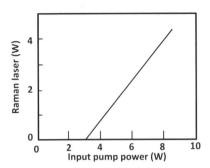

Fig. 13.7 Raman laser power (first Stokes) at 1239 nm as a function of pump power at 1064 nm. Fiber length is 700 m.[18]

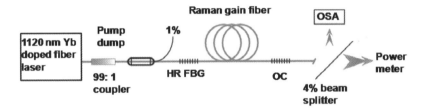

Fig. 13.8 Schematic of a high power Raman laser pumped by a Yb-doped DCFL emitting at 1120 nm.[22] HR FBG: high reflection fiber Bragg grating, OC: output coupler, OSA: optical spectrum analyzer.

Yb-doped double clad pump lasers is similar to that shown in Fig. 13.6. The Raman gain fiber is a 75 m long commercial grade fiber with 10 μm core diameter. The FBGs has a reflectivity of 99% (HR FBG) at the pump input end and has a reflectivity of 50% at the output coupler end. The 3 dB bandwidth of the HR FBG is 1.49 nm, and that of the output coupler is 0.52 nm. The high power from YDFL (at 1120 nm) is delivered by a regular fiber with core diameter of 10 μm. A 99%/1% coupler is spliced before the pump to monitor the stability of pump source.

The Raman laser output at 1173 nm as a function of injected pump power is shown in Fig. 13.9. The figure shows 119 W of Raman laser power has been obtained with 144 W of pump power. The conversion efficiency is 82%. Also shown is the unused pump power. The spectrum of the output light at the highest Raman laser output (∼119 W) is shown in Fig. 13.10. The Raman laser spectrum has a

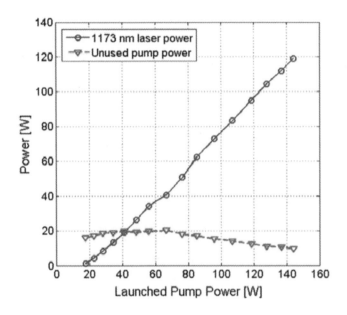

Fig. 13.9 Raman laser output as a function of pump power.[22]

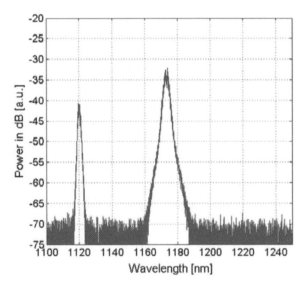

Fig. 13.10 Output spectrum from the fiber at the highest Raman laser power output.[22]

full width at half maximum of ∼2 nm. For shorter Raman gain fiber lengths, the output power is lower. One importance of high power output near 1230 nm is for its use as pump source for a Raman amplifier or laser emitting near 1300 nm. First stokes shift from a silica fiber produces Raman output near 1300 nm. Thus a Raman amplifier for 1300 nm spectral region, which is an important wavelength for optical communication, can be built using this process. Such an amplifier has been demonstrated.

Using essentially similar schemes as described earlier, tunable fiber Raman lasers have been demonstrated.[23–30] They involve tunable fiber Bragg gratings (TFBGs). The wavelength of peak reflectivity of the TFBGs can be tuned by compression by as much as 60 nm.[30] The experimental configuration of a tunable fiber Raman laser is shown in Fig. 13.11. The two TFBGs are the tunable input coupler (TIC) and the tunable output coupler (TOC). Either or both are tuned to vary the Raman laser wavelength. Two sets of pairs

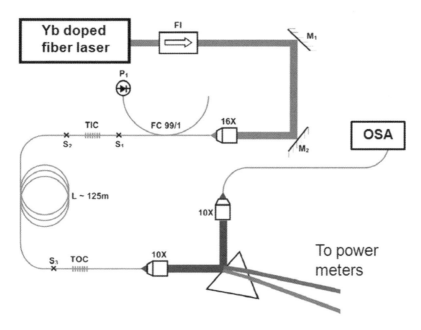

Fig. 13.11 Schematic of a tunable Raman fiber laser. It uses tunable fiber Bragg gratings (TIC and TOC).[30] OSA: optical spectrum analyzer. S: splices.

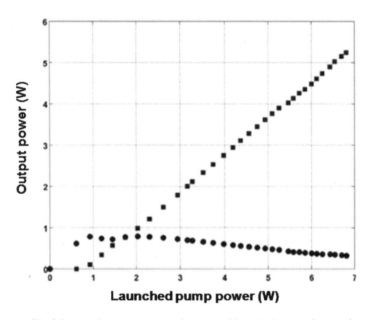

Fig. 13.12 (Top) Raman laser output as a function of launched power (squares), residual pump power (circles). (Bottom) Laser spectrum at three different powers, 0.87, 2.3 and 6.7 W.[30]

of TFBGs are used for the demonstrated tuning range of 1075 to 1135 nm. The reflectivity of TIC is in the 90 to 99% range as it is tuned and that of the TOC is in the 60% to 54% range as it is tuned. The Raman fiber is a 125 m long fiber with a core diameter of 4.1 μm. Yb-doped fiber laser emitting at 1064 nm is used as a pump. The Raman laser output power as a function of launched pump power is shown in Fig. 13.12. The Raman laser emission is at 1109 nm. The residual pump power is also shown. The Stokes spectrum is centered around 1109 nm. It has one peak for 0.9 W Stokes power. As the power increases, the spectrum broadens and can have two peaks.

The Stokes output power as a function of wavelength (as the FBGs are tuned) for 2 launched powers (3 W and 6 W) are shown in Fig. 13.13. The higher output powers are obtained for 6 W of launched power.

Raman laser has been fabricated using short fiber lengths.[31,32] In Ref. 32, a 17 cm long fiber is used to produce a Raman laser using

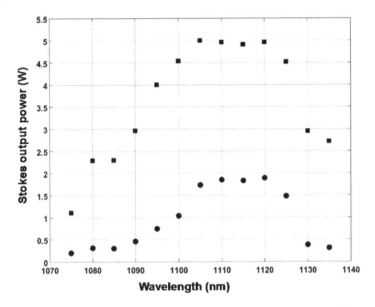

Fig. 13.13 Stokes output power as a function of wavelength for 3W (circles) and 6W (squares) of launched pump power.[30]

a pump beam from a Yb-doped laser and FBGs. The Raman laser emission is at 1151 nm using 1100 nm pump laser. The spectral width is ~60 pm. The longitudinal modes of the cavity have been observed using the beat spectrum of the oscillating longitudinal modes of the laser.

13.4. Cascaded Raman Laser

Cascaded Raman fiber lasers involve the multiple stokes scattering in the same fiber.[33–36] The first Stokes signal is confined using FBGs within the fiber cavity and acts as a pump for the generation of second Stokes scattered signal. The second Stokes signal acts as a pump for a third Stokes scattered signal. The schematic of the mechanism is shown in Fig. 13.2. Cascaded Raman fiber lasers are considered as sources for distributed pumping of transmission lines, and remote pumping of Er-doped fibers in fiber communication systems.[2–4]

High power cascaded Raman fiber laser using Yb-doped double clad fiber laser as a pump source has been demonstrated. The pump

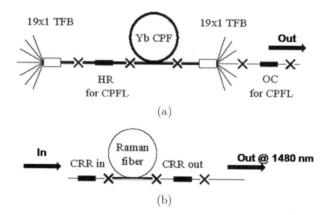

Fig. 13.14 Schematic of a cascaded Raman fiber laser. The Yb-doped pump laser is also shown.[36] CPFL: cladding pumped Yb fiber laser. HR: high reflector, OC: output coupler, Yb–CPF: Yb-doped cladding pumped fiber, TFB: tapered fiber bundle, CRR: cascaded Raman resonator. The output of laser (a) is input to the Raman gain medium (b).

laser emits at 1117 nm and is pumped by laser diodes both in the co-propagating and counter propagating configuration. The diode lasers emit at 915 nm and the laser output is coupled to the Yb-doped fiber using tapered fiber bundles (TFBs). The maximum output power of the Yb-doped fiber laser is 103 W. The schematic of the Raman fiber laser along with the Yb-doped pump laser is shown in Fig. 13.14.

The cascaded Raman resonator (CRR) consists of two sets of fiber Bragg gratings and a 65 to 125 m long silica fiber. The input grating set includes 5 high reflectors written at 1175, 1239, 1310, 1391 and 1480 nm. The output FBG set includes one output coupler at 1480 nm and 5 high reflectors operating at 1117, 1175, 1239, 1310 and 1391 nm. These reflectors correspond to first, second, third, fourth and fifth Stokes scattered signal. The output power at 1480 nm as a function of Yb laser pump power is shown in Fig. 13.15 for three different Raman fiber lengths.

13.5. Raman Amplifier

Silica fiber based Raman amplifiers have been extensively studied for use as a broadband amplifier in wavelength division multiplexed

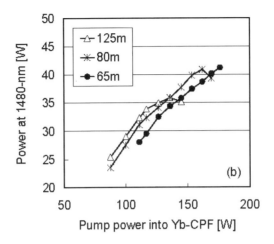

Fig. 13.15 Power in the 1480 nm band as a function of Yb-doped laser pump power.[36]

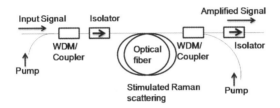

Fig. 13.16 Schematic of a typical Raman amplifier.[46]

(WDM) fiber communication systems.[37–48] As described in Sec. 10.3 Raman gain spectrum is about 8 THz wide. Thus if a single pump laser is used the Raman gain would be downshifted by about 8 THz. The schematic of a typical Raman amplifier is shown in Fig. 13.16. It has two pumps at about the same wavelength for stimulated Raman scattering.[46]

The Raman gain spectrum of optical fiber exhibits a broad continuum shape due to amorphous nature of glass (Sec. 10.3). The magnitude of the Raman gain is determined by nonlinearity and the profile is determined by the fractions of GeO_2 and SiO_2.[43] The Raman gain for three different fiber types is shown in Fig. 13.17. They are SMF: regular single mode fiber, DSF: dispersion shifted fiber, and DCF: dispersion compensating fiber. The concentration

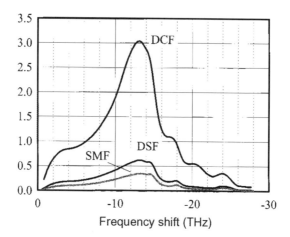

Fig. 13.17 Relative Raman gain in different fiber types. They are single mode fiber (SMF), dispersion shifted fiber (DSF) and dispersion compensating fiber (DCF). The differences is due to different germanium oxide concentration.[46]

of germanium oxide becomes larger in the order of SMF, DSF, and DCF. It is useful to compare Raman amplifier with erbium-doped fiber amplifier (EDFA). The polarization state of light is maintained during stimulated Raman scattering (SRS), while the gain is almost unpolarized for EDFA. Another difference is the stimulated emission process in Raman amplification occurs through virtual energy states. The luminescence lifetime of Raman is $\sim 10^{-15}$ s while that of EDFA it is $\sim 10^{-3}$ s.

Using multiple pump lasers at different wavelength, it is possible to increase the width of the gain spectrum significantly. By choosing multiple pump wavelengths separated by approximately the Raman gain spectrum width and by combining them into a single fiber, a wide gain Raman spectrum has been demonstrated. Figure 13.18 shows the measured Raman gain profile of an experiment using a 25 km long DSF as the Raman fiber. The pump lasers are used in a counter propagating configuration. Twelve pump lasers are used with a frequency spacing of ~ 1 THz. The pump frequencies span from 212 to 199 THz. They are combined using a silica based planar waveguide combiner. The average Raman gain is almost 10.5 dB

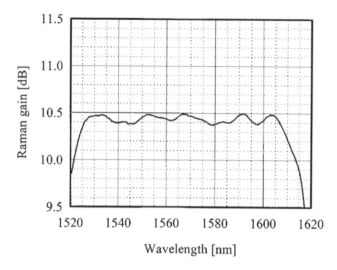

Fig. 13.18 Flat Raman gain spectrum using 12 pump lasers, ∼1 THz apart, and a 25 km long dispersion shifted fiber.[46] A frequency of 200 THz corresponds to a wavelength of 1500 nm.

and the gain flatness is about 0.1 dB over the wavelength range of 1527–1607 nm. This corresponds to the entire C-band and L-band of EDFA. Since the wavelengths near the middle have overlapping gains from adjacent pump wavelengths and the end regions get gain mostly from the end pumps, for obtaining the flat gain spectrum it is important to optimize both the pump wavelengths and pump powers appropriately. The maximum available Raman gain in this scheme is determined by the maximum output power of the longest and shortest wavelength pumps. It is also feasible to tailor the Raman gain spectrum to any desired shape using appropriately chosen pump laser wavelength and power.

Raman amplifiers have been used in optical transmission experiments.[38–42] Puc and coworkers[39] have demonstrated a cascaded Raman amplifier system using 11 Raman amplifiers. They transmitted error free 20 WDM channels (200 GHz apart) modulated at 10 Gb/s over 867 km of standard single mode fiber. The transmitter wavelengths span from 1493 to 1521 nm. The typical spacing between the Raman amplifiers are ∼80 to 90 km and dispersion compensation

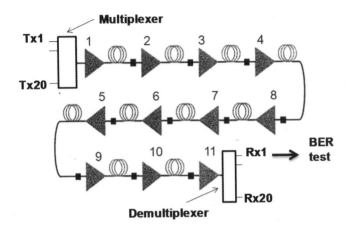

Fig. 13.19 Schematic of a transmission experiment using Raman amplifiers. There are 10 spans of single mode fibers with a total length of 867 km. The average span loss including connectors is 21 dB.[45] The output power is +14 dBm for all Raman amplifiers i.e., +1 dBm per channel output. T × 1, T × 2 ... T × 20 are 20 transmitter modules each operating at a different wavelength. At the receiver the signal is demultiplexed prior to photodiode followed by BER test.

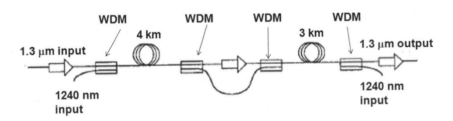

Fig. 13.20 Schematic of Raman amplifier at 1300 nm.[51]

is used after every amplification stage. The schematic of the experiment is shown in Fig. 13.19.

The Raman gain is downshifted from the pump wavelength by about 13 THz. Thus it is possible to get Raman amplification at any wavelength in the transparency region of the optical fiber using a suitable pump wavelength. Many communication systems operate near 1300 nm where EDFAs do not operate. However, it was recognized early on in the development of Raman amplifiers that a Raman amplifier near 1300 nm is feasible.[49-51] A design of a 1300 nm Raman amplifier is shown in Fig. 13.20.[51] The figure shows a two

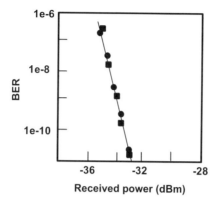

Fig. 13.21 The BER results for 2.5 Gb/s transmission with (circles) and without (squares) Raman amplification. The amplification is 29 dB in the experiment.

stage Raman amplifier with a counter propagating pump at 1240 nm. The pump light is generated by a cascaded Raman laser (emitting at 1240 nm) which is pumped by a cladding pumped Nd fiber laser. The Nd laser operates at 1060 nm. The two-stage configuration reduces the noise for Raman amplification.[52] The 1.3 μm Raman amplifier has a small signal gain of 29 dB. The output power could be as high as 16 dBm.

The absence of noise is verified using a transmission experiment at 2.5 Gb/s modulated data at 1300 nm. The result of the BER test is shown in Fig. 13.21. The result shows no BER penalty with 29 dB of Raman gain.

Raman amplifiers are one of the first widely commercialized nonlinear optical devices in telecommunications. They are important for nearly every ultra-long distance fiber-optic transmission systems. Raman amplifiers are primarily used to increase the capacity of fiber-optic networks, opening up new wavelength windows for wavelength-division multiplexing such as the 1300, 1400, and 1500–1600 nm. Ability to provide gain at any wavelength is one of the key advantages of Raman amplifiers over rare earth-doped amplifiers. Suitably designed Raman amplifiers improve the noise figure and reduce the nonlinear penalty of fiber systems, allowing for longer amplifier spans, higher bit rates, closer channel spacing and operation near the zero-dispersion wavelength.

References

1. G.P. Agrawal, Nonlinear Fiber Optics. 4th Edition. New York: Academic Press. 2007.
2. R.G. Smith, *Appl. Opt.* **11** (1972) 2489.
3. R.H. Stolen, Chapter 10 In *Optical Fiber Telecommunications*, S.E. Miller and A.G. Chynoweth (Eds) New York: Academic, 1979.
4. R.H. Stolen and J.E. Bjorkholm, *IEEE J. Quantum Electron.* QE-**18** (1982) 1062.
5. N. Bloembergen, The stimulated Raman effect. *Am. J. Phys.* **35** (1967) 989.
6. W. Kaiser and M. Maier, In *Laser Handbook*, F.T. Arecchi and E.O. Schulz-Dubois (Eds) Amsterdam: North-Holland. pp. 1077.
7. C. Headley, Chapter B4.3 In *Handbook of Laser Technology and Applications*, C. Webb and J. Jones (Eds) Institute of Physics. 2004.
8. A.J. Stentz and R.W. Boyd, Chapter 5 In *Handbook of Photonics*, M.C. Gupta (Ed) CRC press. 1997.
9. Y.R. Shen, *Principles of Nonlinear Optics*, New York: John Wiley. 1984.
10. A.R. Chraplyvy, *IEEE J. Lightwave Tech.* **8** (1990) 1548.
11. K.O. Hill, Y. Fujii and D.C. Johnson, *Appl. Phys. Lett.* **30** (1976) 647.
12. C. Lin, L.G. Cohen, R.H. Stolen, G.W. Tasker and W.G. French, *Opt. Comm.* **20** (1977) 426.
13. D. Innis, *Proceedings CLEO*, paper CPD-31. (1997).
14. S. Grubb, *Proceedings. Optical amplifiers and their applications*, paper PD3-1, (1994).
15. S. Grubb, *Proceedings. Optical amplifiers and their applications*, paper SA-4, 197. (1995).
16. V.M. Karpov, E.M. Dianov, A.S. Kurkov, V.M. Paramonov, V.N. Protopopov, M.P. Bachynski and W.R.L. Clements, *Proceedings. OFC*, paper WM3, (1999) 202.
17. E.M. Dianov and A.M. Prokhorov, *IEEE J. Select. Top. Quantum Electron.* **6** (2000) 1022.
18. M. Prabhu, N.S. Kim, C. I.i, J. Song, K. Ucda and C. Allen, *Proceedings. CLEO*, 2000, paper CThV2, (2000).
19. Y. Feng, L.R. Taylor and D.B. Calia, *Opt. Exp.* **17** (2009) 23678.
20. C.A. Codemard, J. Ji, J.K. Sahu and J. Nilsson, In *Proceedings. SPIE*, San Francisco, CA, USA. (2010).
21. J. AuYeung and A. Yariv, *J. Opt. Soc. Amer.* **69** (1979) 803.
22. H. Zhang, H. Xiao, P. Zhou, X. Wang and X. Xu, *IEEE Photonics Journal.* **5**, (2003) 1501706.
23. R. Vallée, E. Bélanger, B. Déry, M. Bernier and D. Faucher, *J. Lightw. Technol.* **24** (2006) 5039.
24. R.K. Jain, C. Lin, R.H. Stolen, W. Pleibel and P. Kaiser, *Appl. Phys. Lett.* **30** (1977) 162.
25. C.S. Goh, M.R. Mokhtar, S.A. Butler, S.Y. Set, K. Kikuchi and M. Ibsen, *IEEE Photon. Technol. Lett.* **15** (2003) 557.

26. E. Bélanger, B. Déry, M. Bernier, J.P. Bérubé and R. Vallée, *Appl. Opt.* **46** (2007) 3089.
26. E. Bélanger, S. Gagnon, M. Bernier, J.P. Bérubé, D. Côté and R. Vallée, *Appl. Opt.* **47** (2008) 652.
27. S. Cierullies, E. Lim and E. Brinkmeyer, In *Proceedings. OFC*, 2005, paper OME11, (2005).
28. S.A.E. Lewis, V. Chernikov and J.R. Taylor, *Opt. Commun.* **182** (2000) 403.
29. P.C. Reeves-Hall and J.R. Taylor, *Electron. Lett.* **37** (2001) 491.
30. E. Bélanger, M. Bernier, D. Faucher, D. Côté and R. Vallée, *IEEE Photonics Journal, J. Lightwave Tech.* **26** (2008) 1696.
31. Y. Zhao and S.D. Jackson, *Opt. Commun.* **253** (2005) 172.
32. A. Siekiera, R. Engelbrecht, A. Nothofer and B. Schmauss, *IEEE Photonic Tech. Letts.* **24** (2012) 107.
33. S.K. Sim, H.C. Lim, L.W. Lee, L.C. Chia, R.F. Wu, I. Cristiani, M. Rini and V. Degiorgio, *Electron. Lett.* **40** (2004) 738.
34. D. Georgiev, V.P. Gapontsev, A.G. Dronov, M.Y. Vyatkin, A.B. Rulkov, S.V. Popov and J.R. Taylor, *Optics Express,* **13** (2005) 6772.
35. Z. Xiong, N. Moore, Z.G. Li and G.C. Lim, *J. Lightwave Tech.* **21** (2003) 2377.
36. Y. Emori, K. Tanaka, C. Headley and A. Fujisaki, *Proceedings, CLEO* 2007, paper CFI2, (2007).
37. R.H. Stolen and E.P. Ippen, *Appl. Phys. Lett.* **22** (1973) 276.
38. A. Mathur, M. Ziari and V. Dominic, In *Optical Fiber Communication Conf. OSA Tech. Dig.* Washington, DC. (2000).
39. A.B. Puc, M.W. Chbat, J.D. Henrie, N.A. Weaver, H. Kim, A. Kaminski, A. Rahman and H.A. Fevrier, In *Optical Fiber Communication Conf. OSA Tech.Dig.* Washington, DC. (2001).
40. V. Dominic, E. Mao, J. Zhang, B. Fidric, S. Sanders and D. Mehuys, In *Optical Amplifiers and Their Applications OSA Tech. Dig.* Washington, DC. (2001).
41. A.J. Stentz, T. Nielsen, S.G. Grubb, T.A. Strasser and J.R. Pedrazzani, In *Optical Fiber Communication Conf. OSA Tech. Dig.* Washington, DC. (1996).
42. C.R.S. Fludger and V. Henderek. In *Optical Fiber Communication Conf. OSA Tech. Dig.* Washington, DC. (2001).
43. F. Galeener, J. Millelsen, R. Geils and W. Mosby, *Appl. Phys. Lett.* **32** (1978) 34.
44. M. Nissov, C.R. Davidson, K. Rottwitt, R. Menges, P.C. Corbett, D. Innis and N.S. Bergano, In *European Conference Optical Commun.* (1997) pp 9.
45. M.N. Islam, *IEEE J. Sel. Top. of Quantum Electron.* **8** (2002) 248.
46. S. Namiki and Y. Emori, *IEEE J. Sel. Top. of Quantum Electron.* **7** (2001) 3.
47. C.R.S. Fludger, V. Handerek and R.J. Mears, In *Optical Fiber Communication Conference. Technical Dig.* 2002, Paper TuJ3, pp. 60–62.
48. T. Naito, T. Tanaka, K. Torii, N. Shimojoh, H. Nakamoto and M. Suyama, In *Optical Fiber Communication Conference. Technical Dig.,* 2002, Paper TuR1, pp. 116–117.

49. S.G. Grubb *et al.*, In *Optical Amplifiers and Their Applications*. 1994, PD1.
50. Y. Aoki, *J. Lightwave Technol.* **6** (1988) 1225.
51. A.J. Stentz, S.G. Crubb, C.E. Headley, J.R. Simpson, T. Strasser and N. Park, In *Optical Fiber Communication Conference. Technical Dig.* 1996, Paper TuD3, pp. 16–17.
52. J.L. Gimlett and N.K. Cheung, *J. Lightwave Technol.* **7** (1989) 888.

Chapter 14

Mode Locked Pulse Generation

14.1. Introduction

Mode locked pulses have been reported using rare earth-doped lasers using both active and passive mode locking schemes. For active mode locking the laser cavity generally has a modulator which modulates the loss or phase in the optical cavity.[1–8] When the modulation frequency equals the inverse of cavity round trip time, mode locked pulses at the modulation frequency is generated. Also, if the modulation frequency equals an integer multiple (n) of the inverse of the cavity round trip time (f_c), the mode locked pulses are generated at frequency of $f_m(= nf_c)$. This phenomenon is called harmonic mode locking. If the modulation frequency equals $(n + 1/p)f_c$, i.e., $f_m = (n + 1/p)f_c$ where p is an integer, mode locked pulses are also generated at a frequency of pf_m, i.e., at a multiple of the modulation frequency. This phenomenon is called rational harmonic mode locking and it is useful for generating optical pulses at a high data rate. For passive mode locking, a saturable absorber is generally used in the optical cavity. The saturation characteristics, particularly the time constant and the saturation power, of the saturation mechanism determine the mode locking characteristics. In some cases, both active and passive mode locking are used in conjunction to produce stable mode locked pulses.

The generation of ultrashort pulses with high repetition rate with wavelength near 1550 nm is important for high bit rate optical communication. Actively mode-locked Er-doped fiber laser are a potential source of such pulses, however, the pulse repetition rate is usually limited by the bandwidth of the active mode-locker used in the cavity unless a rational harmonic mode locking scheme is used. Typically a fiber laser in a ring cavity is used for active mode locking. The ring cavity has an optical loss modulator, typically a LiNbO₃ modulator. As mentioned earlier, when the modulation frequency is an integer multiple of the inverse of the cavity round trip time, a series of pulses at the modulation frequency is generated. This process is called harmonic mode locking and is described in the next section. Other mode clocking schemes such as rational harmonic mode locking and saturable absorber based mode locking are also discussed in this chapter.

14.2. Harmonic Mode Locking

The experimental set-up for a harmonic mode locking scheme is shown in Fig. 14.1. The fiber laser has a 23-meter long Er-doped fiber (EDF), a WDM coupler, a 10% output coupler, two polarization-independent isolators, a LiNbO₃ electro-optical modulator with a bandwidth of 11 GHz, and a wavelength-tunable optical filter with a 3 dB bandwidth of 1.0 nm. A synthesizer is used to generate the RF signal which is amplified to 30 dBm to drive the modulator. All

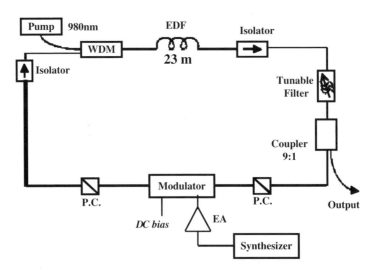

Fig. 14.1 Schematic of the fiber laser.[5] EDF: erbium-doped fiber, PC: polarization controller.

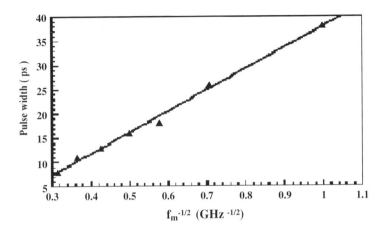

Fig. 14.2 Pulse width versus inverse square root of the modulation frequency for harmonic mode-locking case. The corresponding frequency changes from 1 GHz to 10 GHz.[5]

components are connected by a regular single mode fiber. The fundamental cavity frequency f_c ($= c/nL$) is 2.58 MHz. The gain in EDF is created using a single mode laser emitting at 980 nm as a pump.

The active harmonic mode-locking in this fiber laser is obtained when the modulation signal at frequency $f_m = nf_c$ in the 1 to 10 GHz range is applied. The shortest and most stable optical pulses are obtained by careful tuning of the modulation frequency f_m, and polarization of the circulating light through the polarization controller. The pulse width of mode-locked pulse trains is measured by a sampling oscilloscope or by an autocorrelator.

Figure 14.2 shows that for harmonic mode-locking case $f_m = nf_c$, pulse width is proportional to $f_m^{-1/2}$. Figure 14.3 shows harmonic mode-locking is possible for wavelengths from 1525 to 1565 nm for both $f_m \approx 1$ GHz and $f_m \approx 10$ GHz in this fiber laser. This is due to the broad gain spectrum of EDF. The measured pulse width as a function of wavelength is shown in Fig. 14.3 for two different modulation frequencies.

For the active mode-locking theory of fiber laser, the analysis of Refs. 4, 9 are used. Assuming that the ring cavity has a length L, then the fundamental cavity frequency is $f_c = c/(Ln_{\text{eff}})$, where c is the velocity of light in vacuum and n_{eff} is the effective refractive

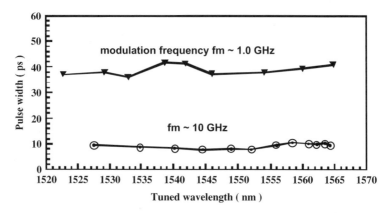

Fig. 14.3 Pulse width as a function of wavelength for harmonic mode locking at 1 GHz and 10 GHz respectively for various laser wavelengths.[5]

index of the cavity. A modulation signal with frequency f_m is applied to the modulator to modulate the loss in the cavity. For harmonic mode-locking, $f_m = nf_c$, or $\omega_m = n\omega_c$, where n is an integer and $\omega_c = 2\pi f_c$. As stated previously for a typical ring fiber laser $f_c \sim 1$ to 3 MHz and $f_m \sim 1$ to 10 GHz. Thus $n \sim 500$ to 5000. However, the gain spectrum of the fiber laser is >1000 GHz, i.e., $\sim 10^6$ cavity modes are present within the gain spectrum. This phenomenon allows harmonic mode locking, i.e., although the modulator couples every ~ 1000th mode, the gain spectrum is broad enough that coupling of $\sim 10^5$ to 10^6 cavity modes can occur.

The envelope of mode locked pulse $a(t)$ consists of its Fourier components a_q at frequency ω_q. There are various sources of losses in the fiber lasers, they are lumped into one single parameter l here, so that after one round trip, the qth mode amplitude (a_q) is multiplied by $1 - l$ as it circulates once through the fiber laser. Similarly it is assumed that due to gain the qth mode amplitude (a_q) is multiplied by $G(q) = 1 + g(q)$ as it circulates once through the fiber laser where $g(q)$ is the gain for the qth Fourier component at frequency ω_q. Assuming a Lorentzian spectral profile for the gain, and $\omega_q = \omega_0 + q\omega_c$ where ω_0 is the center frequency:

$$G(q) = 1 + \frac{g}{1 + \frac{(q\omega_c)^2}{\Omega_g^2}} = 1 + g\left[1 - \frac{(q\omega_c)^2}{\Omega_g^2}\right], \qquad (14.1)$$

where Ω_g is the gain bandwidth and g is the gain at the center frequency. The modulator is assumed to pass the light at periodically timed sequences so that the Fourier component $a_q \exp(i(\omega_0 + q\omega_c)t)$ becomes after one pass (using $\omega_m = n\omega_c$):

$$a_q \exp(i(\omega_0 + q\omega_c)t)M(1 - \cos(\omega_m t))$$

$$= -\left(\frac{M}{2}\right) a_q \exp(i\omega_0 t)[e^{i(q-n)\omega_c t}$$

$$- 2e^{iqn\omega_c t} + e^{i(q+n)\omega_c t}], \tag{14.2}$$

In Eq. (14.2), the modulation factor is given by $M(1 - \cos(\omega_m t))$ at each pass of the components, where M is modulation depth. So each Fourier component acquires sidebands that are injected into the nth adjacent modes.

Considering these three elements, a recursion equation is obtained for the Fourier component $a_q^{(k+1)}(\omega)$ traveling around the cavity the (k+1)th time in terms of its value $a_q^{(k)}$ upon the kth time:

$$a_q^{(k+1)} = a_q^{(k)} + g\left[1 - \frac{(q\omega_c)^2}{\Omega_g^2}\right] a_q^{(k)} - la_q^{(k)}$$

$$+ \frac{M}{2}\left(a_{q+n}^{(k)} - 2a_q^{(k)} + a_{q-n}^{(k)}\right), \tag{14.3}$$

The (14.3) is the basis of discussing harmonic mode-locking. If q' is defined $q' = q/n$, then Eq. (14.3) becomes:

$$a_{q'}^{(k+1)} = a_{q'}^{(k)} + g\left[1 - \frac{(nq'\omega_c)^2}{\Omega_g^2}\right] a_{q'}^{(k)} - la_{q'}^{(k)}$$

$$+ \frac{M}{2}\left(a_{q'+1}^{(k)} - 2a_{q'}^{(k)} + a_{q'-1}^{(k)}\right), \tag{14.4}$$

Equation (14.4) shows that there are n pulses traveling around the cavity. In steady state, $a_{q'}^{(k+1)} = a_{q'}^{(k)}$, the superscript (k) can be dropped, and (14.3) and (14.4) reduces to a second order difference equation. Moreover, when the number of oscillating modes is large, it is useful to replace the second order difference by a second order derivative, so Eq. (14.4) is written as:

$$\left[g\left(1 - \frac{\omega^2}{\Omega_g^2}\right) - l + \frac{M\omega_m^2}{2}\frac{d^2}{d\omega^2} \right] a(\omega) = 0, \qquad (14.5)$$

where a_q has been replaced by the function $a(\omega)$ of the continuous frequency variable $\omega = q\omega_c$. The solution of Eq. (14.5) is the Hermite–Gaussian function and is given by:

$$a(\omega) = H_\nu(\omega\tau)\exp\left(\frac{-\omega^2\tau^2}{2}\right), \qquad (14.6)$$

where:

$$\tau = \left(\frac{2g}{M}\right)^{1/4}\left(\frac{1}{\omega_m\Omega_g}\right)^{1/2} \quad \text{and} \quad g - l = M\omega_m^2\tau^2\left(\nu + \frac{1}{2}\right),$$

$$(14.7)$$

In general, the 0th order ($\nu = 0$) solution dominates. The following expressions for $a(\omega)$ and $a(t)$ follows:

$$a(\omega) = A\exp\left(\frac{-\omega^2\tau^2}{2}\right),$$

$$a(t) = \frac{\sqrt{2\pi}}{\tau}A\exp\left(\frac{-t^2}{2\tau^2}\right). \qquad (14.8)$$

So for harmonic mode-locking case $f_m = nf_c$, the solution is a Gaussian pulse, where the pulse width is proportional to τ, and hence to $f_m^{-1/2}$. This is in agreement with the measurement shown in Fig. 14.2. Furthermore, from Eq. (14.7), lower pulse width is obtained by increasing the modulation frequency and modulation power while reducing the pump power for the cavity of the fiber laser.

So far, harmonic mode locking has been described. For low repetition rate pulses with short pulse width, mode locking at the cavity frequency (inverse of cavity round trip time) has been reported. Figure 14.4 shows the experimental set up. The Er-doped fiber ring laser has a 20 m long Er-doped fiber pumped by a 980 nm laser. The ring cavity has a dispersion shifted fiber (DSF) and a 200 m long single mode fiber (SMF) so that the cavity frequency is less than 1 MHz.

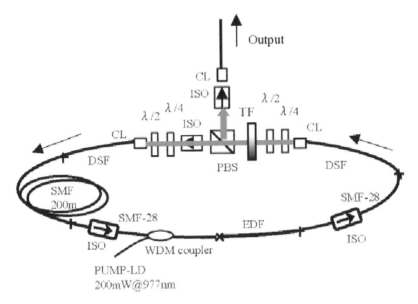

Fig. 14.4 Experimental set up for low frequency mode locked pulses at cavity round trip frequency. ISO: isolator, CL: collimating lens, TF: tunable filter, DSF: dispersion shifted fiber, EDF: Er-doped fiber, WDM: wavelength division multiplexer for pump coupling, $\lambda/2$ — half wave plate, $\lambda/4$ — quarter wave plate.[10]

By adjusting the tunable filter to 1534 nm (bandwidth of 4.3 nm), four wave-plates, and the pump power, stable mode locked pulses at a repetition rate of 920 kHz is achieved at a pump power of 200 mW. The average laser output power is 4 mW. The autocorrelation trace of the pulse is shown in Fig. 14.5. The Gaussian fit shows a pulse width of 815 fs. The time bandwidth product is ~0.44.

14.3. Rational Harmonic Mode Locking

A technique called rational harmonic mode-locking has attracted considerable interest, where an optical pulse train with a repetition rate of $(np + 1)f_c$ can be produced when the modulation frequency is set at $(n + 1/p)f_c$, where f_c is the longitudinal mode spacing or fundamental cavity frequency of the fiber laser ring, and n, p are integers. Several researchers have demonstrated their experimental results in actively rational harmonic mode-locked fiber laser: Ahmed

Fiber Amplifiers and Fiber Lasers

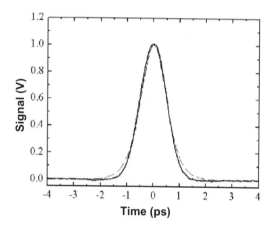

Fig. 14.5 Autocorrelation trace of mode locked pulse. The repetition rate is 920 kHz. The solid line is measured data and the dashed curve is a fit.[10]

and Onodera[1] demonstrated the generation of 14 and 21 GHz repetition rate optical pulses when the RF drive frequency of the modulator was $\sim$7 GHz. Jeon et $al.$[2] observed a 15th rational harmonic mode-locking when the modulation frequency f_m was $\sim$1.5 GHz. Li et $al.$[3] showed a 19th rational harmonic active and passive mode-locking in a figure-of-eight fiber laser when f_m was $\sim$100 MHz. Das et $al.$[4] developed a theory of the rational mode-locking, they also demonstrated 20th rational harmonic mode-locking for the modulation frequency $f_m \approx 1.5$ MHz and 10th rational harmonic mode-locking for $f_m \approx 15$ MHz. It is important to generate several GHz repetition rate pulses for optical communication studies.

Rational harmonic mode locking has been demonstrated using the laser schematic shown in Fig. 14.1. The phenomena of rational harmonic mode-locking is observed when the modulation frequency $f_m = (n + 1/p)f_c$, where n and p are integers. Figure 14.6 shows the rational harmonic mode-locking when $f_m \approx 1$ GHz, corresponding to the harmonic order $n = 388$. 22nd order of rational harmonic mode-locking was achieved in Fig. 14.6.

The theoretical analysis of the rational harmonic mode-locking follows the analysis of harmonic mode-locking. For the rational harmonic mode-locking case, the modulation frequency is $\omega_m = (n + 1/p)\omega_c$. So the modulation factor is given by $M\{1 - \cos[(n + 1/p)t]\}$

and the recursion Eq. (14.3) becomes:

$$a_q^{(k+1)} = a_q^{(k)} + g \left[1 - \frac{(q\omega_c)^2}{\Omega_g^2} \right] a_q^{(k)} - la_q^{(k)}$$

$$+ \frac{M}{2} \left(a_{q+n+\frac{1}{p}}^{(k)} - 2a_q^{(k)} + a_{q-n-\frac{1}{p}}^{(k)} \right), \qquad (14.9)$$

For this case as $(n+1/p)$ is not an integer, the modes in the cavity do not couple. But if a cavity of equivalent length pL is considered, then the modes can couple. This means that the pulse has to propagate p times through the cavity before it can get through gain. Following the steps in the Sec. 14.2, the equations can be rewritten as:

$$a_q^{(k+1)} = a_q^{(k)} + g \left[1 - \frac{(\frac{q}{p}\omega_c)^2}{\Omega_g^2} \right] a_q^{(k)} - la_q^{(k)}$$

$$+ \frac{M}{2} \left(a_{qp+np+1}^{(k)} - 2a_q^{(k)} + a_{qp-np-1}^{(k)} \right), \qquad (14.10)$$

where $\omega_c = 2\pi f_c$. The quantity q' is redefined as:

$$q' = \frac{q}{np+1},$$

Then Eq. (14.10) is written as:

$$a_{q'}^{(k+1)} = a_{q'}^{(k)} + g \left[1 - \frac{\left[\left(n + \frac{1}{p} \right) q'\omega_c \right]^2}{\Omega_g^2} \right] a_{q'}^{(k)} - la_{q'}^{(k)}$$

$$+ \frac{M}{2} \left(a_{q'+1}^{(k)} - 2a_{q'}^{(k)} + a_{q'-1}^{(k)} \right), \qquad (14.11)$$

Equation (14.11) is similar to Eq. (14.4). Following the same process as in Sec. 14.2, it is possible to conclude that the solution for rational harmonic mode-locking is also a Gaussian pulse given by Eq. (14.8) and the pulse width τ is expressed as:

$$\tau = \left(\frac{2g}{M} \right)^{1/4} \left(\frac{1}{(n+\frac{1}{p})\omega_m\Omega_g} \right)^{1/2}, \qquad (14.12)$$

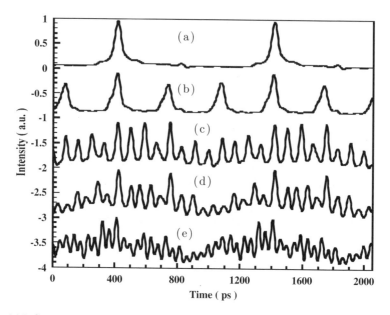

Fig. 14.6 Generation of pulse train using rational harmonic mode-locking around $f_m =$ 1 GHz (observed on sampling oscilloscope). The observed pulse width is limited by the bandwidth of the oscilloscope. (a) $f_m = 1001.7933$ MHz $= 388\ f_c$. Repetition rate of pulse train $= 1$ GHz (b) $f_m = (388 + 1/3)f_c$. Repetition rate of pulse train $= 3$ GHz (c) $f_m = (388+1/12)f_c$. Repetition rate of pulse train $= 12$ GHz (d) $f_m = (388+1/15)f_c$. Repetition rate of pulse train $= 15$ GHz (e) $f_m = (388+1/22)f_c$. Repetition rate of pulse train $= 22$ GHz.[5]

Comparing Eqs. (14.11) and (14.4), it is possible to conclude that the repetition rate of the optical pulses traveling around the ring cavity with an effective cavity length pL is $(n + 1/p)\omega_c$, so the actual repetition rate of the optical pulses traveling around the ring cavity with a real cavity length L is $(np + 1)\omega_c$, which is p times of the modulation frequency.

The pulse width parameter τ is proportional to $(n + 1/p)^{-1/2}$. Since n is much larger than 1 for the modulation frequencies used here, it is possible to conclude that the pulse width for rational harmonic mode-locking is almost same as that for harmonic mode-locking. Rational harmonic pulse trains have been produced with a modulation frequency (f_m) of 10 GHz using the laser shown in Fig. 14.1. Oscilloscope traces of the result (for $p = 2, 3, 4$) are shown in Fig. 14.7.

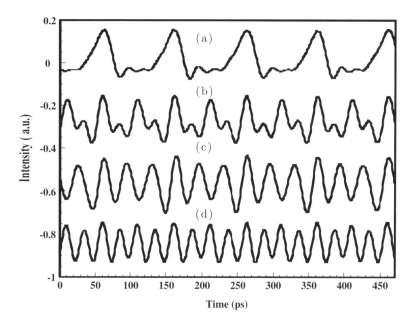

Fig. 14.7 Rational harmonic mode-locking pulse trains using $f_m \approx 10\,\mathrm{GHz}$ (observed on sampling oscilloscope) (a) $f_m = 9992.5129\,\mathrm{MHz} = 3872 f_c$. Repetition rate of pulse train $= 10\,\mathrm{GHz}$ (b) $f_m = (3872 + 1/2)f_c$. Repetition rate of pulse train $= 20\,\mathrm{GHz}$ (c) $f_m = (3872 + 1/3)f_c$. Repetition rate of pulse train $= 30\,\mathrm{GHz}$ (d) $f_m = (3872 + 1/4)f_c$. Repetition rate of pulse train $= 40\,\mathrm{GHz}$.[5]

Radio frequency (RF) spectrum is an important measure of frequency components in the pulse train. The RF spectrum is measured using a high speed photodiode. Figure 14.8 shows the RF spectra of rational harmonic mode-locking using $f_m = 1\,\mathrm{GHz}$, there exist some harmonics of the modulation frequency f_m, but the peak component always appears at the frequency $p f_m$, which is the repetition rate of the pulse train due to the rational harmonic mode-locking. RF spectrum for p values of 3, 12, 15 and 22 are shown in Fig. 14.8. These p values correspond to modelocking at 3, 12, 15 and 22\,GHz respectively using a modulation frequency of 1\,GHz.

14.3.1. *Time Domain Analysis*

A theoretical analysis of harmonic and rational harmonic mode locking has been carried out in the time domain.[11] This is now discussed.

Fiber Amplifiers and Fiber Lasers

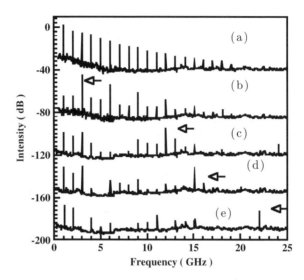

Fig. 14.8 RF Spectra of Rational Harmonic Mode-locking for $f_m \approx 1.0\,\text{GHz}$ (a) $f_m = 1001.7933\,\text{MHz} = 388\,f_c$. Repetition rate of pulse train = 1 GHz (b) $f_m = (388 + 1/3)f_c$. Repetition rate of pulse train = 3 GHz (c) $f_m = (388 + 1/12)f_c$. Repetition rate of pulse train = 12 GHz (d) $f_m = (388 + 1/15)f_c$. Repetition rate of pulse train = 15 GHz (e) $f_m = (388 + 1/22)f_c$. Repetition rate of pulse train = 22 GHz.[5]

The shape of the propagating pulse in the ring laser is assumed to be expressed by $f(t) = (1 + at + bt^2)\exp(-\Gamma t^2)$ where a, b, Γ are coefficients that describe the pulse. The polynomial term represent an envelope function, the pulse shape and pulse width is primarily determined by the exponential term. If it is assumed that before the first round trip, the pulse shape is Gaussian, i.e., $f(t) = \exp(-\Gamma_0 t^2)$, which implies that the initial value of a, b, Γ are $a = 0, b = 0$ and $\Gamma = \Gamma_0$, then, for the p order rational harmonic mode locking, the final values of a, b, Γ are required to be the same as their initial values after p round trips. The analysis is carried out in two steps. The first step is to establish a recursion relationship between the new values and the old values of a, b, Γ after one round trip. The second step is to obtain a numerical solution by using the fact the pulse returns to its original shape after p round trips.

Consider the modulated erbium-doped fiber laser (EDFL) as a ring composed of two components, one is the gain medium combined with the optical band pass filter, and the other is the modulator. The gain curve of the gain medium is modeled as (the center frequency of the gain curve (ω_0) is suppressed in the following)[9]:

$$g(\omega) = \exp\left[\alpha_m p_m \left(1 - \frac{4}{\Delta\omega_a^2}\omega^2\right)\right]$$

$$= \exp(\alpha_m p_m)\exp\left(-\frac{4\alpha_m p_m}{\Delta\omega_a^2}\omega^2\right)$$

$$= g_0 \exp(-\gamma\omega^2), \tag{14.13}$$

where:

$$g_0 = \exp(\alpha_m p_m), \tag{14.14}$$

$$\gamma = \frac{4\alpha_m p_m}{\Delta\omega_a^2}, \tag{14.15}$$

In the Eqs. (14.13)–(14.15), $\alpha_m \cdot p_m$ is the round trip gain coefficient,[9] and $\Delta\omega_a$ is the linewidth of the laser medium combined with the optical band pass filter inside the cavity. The pulse $f(t)$ whose shape is expressed by Eq. (14.16) travels through the gain medium:

$$f(t) = (1 + at + bt^2)\exp(-\Gamma t^2), \tag{14.16}$$

The transmitted pulse $f_1(t)$ is obtained by Fourier transform of $f(t)$, multiplying it by $g(\omega)$, and then inverse Fourier transform back to time domain. The pulse shape $f_1(t)$ is given by[11]:

$$f_1(t) = k(1 + a_1 t + b_1 t^2)\exp(-\Gamma_1 t^2), \tag{14.17}$$

here:

$$k = \frac{g_0}{\sqrt{1 + 4\Gamma\gamma}}\left(1 + \frac{2b\gamma}{1 + 4\Gamma\gamma}\right), \tag{14.18}$$

$$a_1 = \frac{a}{1 + 4\Gamma\gamma}\left(1 + \frac{2b\gamma}{1 + 4\Gamma\gamma}\right)^{-1}, \tag{14.19}$$

$$b_1 = \frac{b}{(1 + 4\Gamma\gamma)^2}\left(1 + \frac{2b\gamma}{1 + 4\Gamma\gamma}\right)^{-1}, \tag{14.20}$$

$$\Gamma_1 = \frac{\Gamma}{1 + 4\Gamma\gamma}, \tag{14.21}$$

where $g_0 \gamma$ are defined by Eqs. (14.14) and (14.15).

It follows from Eq. (14.12), that γ is inversely proportional to the square of the gain spectral width of the medium and the optical band pass filter, and is generally $\sim(200\,\mathrm{GHz})^{-2}$. The quantity b is proportional to the square of the modulation frequency, and is generally $\sim(10\,\mathrm{GHz})^2$, thus $b\gamma \ll 1$. Therefore, the quantities k, a_1, b_1, Γ_1 can be simplified as follows:

$$k = \frac{g_0}{\sqrt{1 + 4\Gamma\gamma}}, \tag{14.22}$$

$$a_1 = \frac{a}{1 + 4\Gamma\gamma}, \tag{14.23}$$

$$b_1 = \frac{b}{(1 + 4\Gamma\gamma)^2}, \tag{14.24}$$

$$\Gamma_1 = \frac{\Gamma}{1 + 4\Gamma\gamma}, \tag{14.25}$$

Thus after the pulse $f(t) = (1 + at + bt^2)\exp(-\Gamma t^2)$ exits the gain medium, its mathematical form is unchanged. When the pulse arrives at the modulator, the transfer function of the modulator may be written as $T(\omega_m t + \varphi_i)$, where $T(t)$ is periodic over 2π, ω_m is the modulation frequency, φ_i is the phase of the modulation when the pulse comes into the modulator for the ith time. Generally, the pulse width is much smaller than the modulation period, thus, it is possible to expand the transfer function $T_i(t) = T(\omega_m t + \varphi_i)$ as a Taylor series in time t around a time t_o (with a modulator phase φ_i) when the pulse enter the modulator:

$$T_i(t) = T(\omega_m t + \varphi_i) = J_i \cdot (1 + u_i t + v_i t^2), \tag{14.26}$$

where:

$$J_i = T(t)|_{t=\phi_i}, \tag{14.27}$$

$$u_i = \frac{T'|_{t=\phi_i}}{T|_{t=\phi_i}} \cdot \omega_m, \tag{14.28}$$

$$v_i = \frac{1}{2}\frac{T''|_{t=\phi_i}}{T|_{t=\phi_i}} \cdot \omega_m^2, \tag{14.29}$$

where T' and T'' denote the first order and second order derivative of $T(t)$. For p order rational harmonic mode locking, there exists p equally spaced optical pulses in one modulation period (2π). Therefore:

$$\varphi_i = \varphi_0 + \frac{2\pi}{p} i, \qquad (14.30)$$

It is easy to see that after a pulse passes through the modulator, the output pulse shape is just the product of the input pulse shape and the transfer function of the modulator at phase ϕ_i. Now assume that for every round trip, the pulse passes through the modulator first and then the gain medium. Before it starts its ith round trip, the pulse shape has the form $f_i(t) = A_i(1 + a_i t + b_i t^2)\exp(-\Gamma_i t^2)$, after this pulse exits the modulator, it becomes:

$$\begin{aligned} f_i'(t) &= A_i(1 + a_i t + b_i t^2)\exp(-\Gamma_i t^2) \cdot J_i \cdot (1 + u_i t + v_i t^2) \\ &\approx A_i J_i \cdot [1 + (u_i + a_i)t + (a_i u_i + v_i + b_i)t^2]\exp(-\Gamma_i t^2), \ldots \end{aligned}$$
$$(14.31)$$

where the higher order terms t^3 and t^4 have been neglected. After this pulse $f_i'(t)$ passes through the gain medium, its shape changes to:

$$f_{i+1}(t) = A_{i+1}(1 + a_{i+1} t + b_{i+1} t^2)\exp(-\Gamma_{i+1} t^2), \qquad (14.32)$$

where $A_{i+1}, a_{i+1}, b_{i+1}$ and Γ_{i+1} can be determined using Eqs. (14.22)–(14.25):

$$A_{i+1} = \frac{g_0}{\sqrt{1 + 4\Gamma_i \gamma}} A_i J_i, \qquad (14.33)$$

$$a_{i+1} = \frac{u_i + a_i}{1 + 4\Gamma_i \gamma}, \qquad (14.34)$$

$$b_{i+1} = \frac{a_i u_i + v_i + b_i}{(1 + 4\Gamma_i \gamma)^2}, \qquad (14.35)$$

$$\Gamma_{i+1} = \frac{\Gamma_i}{1 + 4\Gamma_i \gamma}, \qquad (14.36)$$

Thus, through Eqs. (14.30)–(14.33), the recursion relationship for the shape parameters after the pulse finishes one round trip is established. If it is assumed the initial pulse takes the form $f_0(t) = \exp(-\Gamma_0 t^2)$, and after p round trips, the pulse returns to its original shape for p order rational harmonic mode locking, it implies that $f_p(t) = A_p(1 + a_p t + b_p t^2) \exp(-\Gamma_p t^2) = f_0(t) = \exp(-\Gamma_0 t^2)$. Therefore, it follows:

$$A_p = 1, \tag{14.37}$$

$$a_p = 0, \tag{14.38}$$

$$\Gamma_p - b_p = \Gamma_0, \tag{14.39}$$

Equation (14.36) makes the usual approximation that the envelope function is small compared to the exponential function. In order to calculate the pulse width, the initial phase of modulation φ_0 must be known, and this can be done by solving Eq. (14.35). After obtaining φ_0, the pulse width can be calculated from Eq. (14.36). If it is assumed that the gain spectral width is much larger than the pulse spectral width, then the product of Γ_i and γ is small. Under this assumption, the following expression for $\Gamma_i a_i$ and b_i is obtained:

$$\Gamma_i = \Gamma_0(1 - 4i \cdot \Gamma_0 \gamma), \tag{14.40}$$

$$a_i = \sum_{j=0}^{i-1} u_j, \tag{14.41}$$

$$b_i = \sum_{j=0}^{i-1} a_j u_j + v_j, \tag{14.42}$$

where u_j and v_j are defined by Eqs. (14.28) and (14.29).

Therefore, Eq. (14.41) for the initial phase calculation becomes:

$$a_p = \sum_{j=0}^{p-1} u_j = \omega_m \sum_{j=0}^{p-1} \frac{T'|_{t=\phi_j}}{T|_{t=\phi_j}} = 0, \tag{14.43}$$

And the equation for pulse width calculation (14.36) becomes:

$$\Gamma_p - b_p = \Gamma_0(1 - 4p \cdot \Gamma_0 \gamma) - \sum_{j=0}^{p-1} (a_j u_j + v_j) = \Gamma_0, \tag{14.44}$$

Therefore, it follows:

$$\Gamma_0 = \sqrt{\frac{-\sum_{j=0}^{p-1} a_j u_j + v_j}{4p\gamma}}, \tag{14.45}$$

The pulse width τ_p can now be determined as:

$$\tau_p = 2 \cdot \sqrt{\frac{\ln 2}{\Gamma_0}}$$

$$= 4\sqrt{\ln 2} \cdot \frac{(p \cdot \alpha_m p_m)^{1/4}}{\sqrt{\omega_m \cdot \Delta\omega_a}}$$

$$\times \left[-\sum_{i=0}^{p-1} \sum_{j=0}^{i-1} \left(\frac{T''|_{t=\varphi_i}}{2T|_{t=\varphi_i}} + \frac{T'|_{t=\varphi_i}}{T|_{t=\varphi_i}} \cdot \frac{T'|_{t=\varphi_j}}{T|_{t=\varphi_j}} \right) \right]^{-1/4}, \quad (14.46)$$

where p is the order of rational harmonic mode locking. After Γ_0 is determined from Eq. (14.42), the parameters for the pulse after i round trips can be calculated from the recursion Eqs. (14.30)–(14.33). Thus, the shape of the pulse train generated by a ring fiber laser can be simulated theoretically. This is important in determining the optimum bias level and modulation depth for generating equalized amplitude short pulses.

Calculation using this model shows that it is possible to get equal amplitude pulse train for $p < 5$. The equalization of the pulse train occurs only when the transmission coefficient of the modulator is the same every time the pulse arrives at the modulator. This can be illustrated by Figs. 14.9 and 14.10 which show the simulated pulse trains (dashed line) together with the modulator's transfer function (solid line) for 2nd order and 4th order rational harmonic mode locking.

The experimental setup for verification of theory is similar to Fig. 14.1. A single pump EDFA is the gain medium and source of the ring laser cavity. A 90:10 splitter is placed at the output, so 10% of the total power is extracted out from the ring cavity. The center wavelength of the output was controlled by a optical filter with a 3 dB bandwidth of 1 nm. A LiNbO₃ electro-optic modulator with a bandwidth of 20 GHz is inserted in the cavity, which is modulated at 10 GHz by an electrical signal for mode-locking.

The optical transfer function of the modulator can be expressed by:

$$T(\omega_m t) = 1 + \cos\left(\pi \frac{V_b + V_m \sin(\omega_m t)}{V_\pi} \right), \quad (14.47)$$

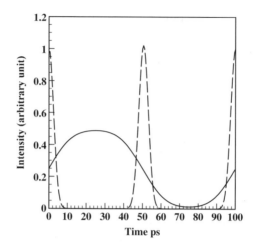

Fig. 14.9 Simulated pulse train (dashed curve) for second order ($p = 2$) rational harmonic mode locking. The RF frequency is 10 GHz (period = 100 ps). The modulator is biased at $V_b = 0.5\ V_\pi$ And the modulation peak is $V_{mod} = 0.4\ V_\pi$. The solid curve shows the transfer function of the modulator.[11]

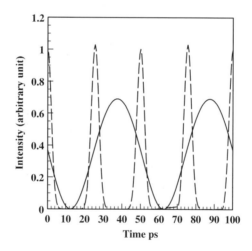

Fig. 14.10 Simulated pulse train (dashed curve) for fourth order (p = 4) rational harmonic mode locking. The RF frequency is 10 GHz (period = 100 ps). The modulator is biased at $V_b = V_\pi$. And the modulation peak is $V_{mod} = 0.4\,V_\pi$. The solid curve shows the transfer function of the modulator.[11]

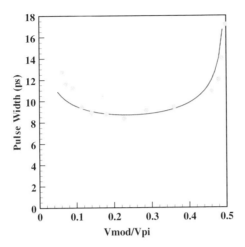

Fig. 14.11 Pulse width for the case of harmonic mode locking ($p = 1$). The modulator is biased at $V_b = 0.5\ V_\pi$. The X-axis represents the modulation amplitude in a unit of V_π. The dots show the measured pulse width, and the solid curve shows the theoretical results.[11]

where V_b is the modulator bias, V_m is the modulation amplitude, and V_π is the voltage needed to achieve π phase shift. By using the mechanism described earlier, the pulse width as a function of V_m as well as V_b has been calculated and then by measuring the pulse width using an autocorrelator, a comparison between the theory and the experiment has been made. Figures 14.11 and 14.12 show the measured pulse width (dots) and the calculated pulse width (solid curve).

The pulse widths calculated using this theory (as a function of the rational harmonic order and the optical transfer function of the modulator determined by bias and modulation voltage) agrees with the measured data. The theoretical work is based on a time domain analysis, which predicts that the pulse width decreases somewhat as the rational harmonic order goes up.

14.4. Stability of Mode Locked Operation

The stability of mode locked operation is important for many applications.[12–18] To commercialize the actively mode locked fiber laser, one important thing to consider is the stabilization of the pulse train. Due

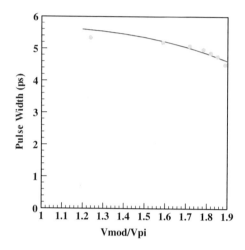

Fig. 14.12 Pulse width for the case of fourth order rational harmonic mode locking ($p = 4$) at 40 GHz. The modulator is biased at $V_b = V_\pi$. The X-axis represents the modulation amplitude in a unit of V_π. The dots show the measured pulse width, and the solid curve shows the theoretical results.[11]

to the cavity length drift caused by various environmental fluctuations (temperature and stress), without special treatment of the fiber laser, the mode locked state cannot be sustained for very long. To overcome this problem, Shan *et al.*[12] have demonstrated a technique to stabilize the laser by dynamically adjusting the cavity length. Nakazawa *et al.*[13] have also stabilized the fiber laser with the help of a phase locked loop based on the regenerative type feedback. In their experiments, a portion of the output is extracted and converted to an electrical signal. This signal is transmitted through a narrow-band high Q band-pass filter, amplified and then fed back to the RF port of the modulator and the loop is closed. The laser produced pulse train at the center frequency of the band-pass filter. The output of the laser is at the same frequency as the RF driving frequency and therefore belongs to the harmonic mode locking category.

Stable mode locked operation has been demonstrated by cavity length control using a feedback loop. In the experiment, a piezo-electric controller (PZT) is used inside the optical cavity of a fiber ring laser. The ring laser has EDFA, and a LiNbO$_3$ modulator for harmonic mode locking. The mode locking occurs even if there is a

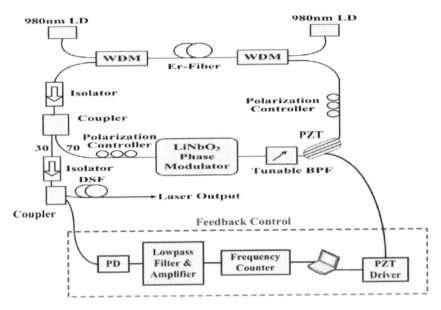

Fig. 14.13 Schematic of a harmonic mode locked laser with feedback control.[15] Various components in the cavity are noted.

slight deviation between the multiples of cavity frequency and the frequency of the external modulator.

In the experiment (Fig. 14.13), the cavity harmonic frequency is 10.005974 GHz and the modulator frequency is 10.5999 GHz. So the difference between the two is 25 kHz. This difference frequency (~25 kHz) can be observed in the RF spectrum of the mode locked pulse train. The difference frequency results in a slow periodic modulation in the temporal position of the pulses. To stabilize the fiber laser, the feedback loop in the dashed region in Fig. 14.13 is used. The deviation frequency is detected by the photodiode and the frequency counter and the computer sends a signal to the PZT driver to lock the deviation frequency. This is sometimes termed asynchronous mode locking.

14.4.1. *Stable Mode Locked Operation Using PLL*

In order to extend the regenerative type fiber laser to the rational harmonic region, a modified technique using a phase locked loop

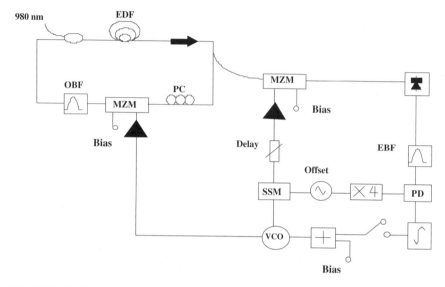

Fig. 14.14 Configuration of the modified regenerative type ring fiber laser employing the base-line extraction feedback technique. The frequency of the offset is Δf as described in the text. EDF: erbium-doped fiber. OBF: optical band-pass filter. MZM: Mach-Zehnder modulator. PC: polarization controller. SSM: single side-band modulator. VCO: voltage controlled oscillator. EBF: electrical band-pass filter centered at $4 \Delta f$. PD: phase detector. An integrator and an adder are also used in the circuits. The MZM inside the fiber laser cavity was driven at 10 GHz (VCO output) which is the fourth of the pulse train frequency at 40 Gb/s.[20]

(PLL) is used.[19, 20] When the laser pulse repetition rate is a multiple of the modulator's driving signal, the frequency of the optical pulse train is divided by the number of the rational harmonics (base-line extraction), and then the divided signal is fed back to the modulator, this modified regenerative mode locking technique has been used to stabilize the pulse train. In Fig. 14.14, the schematics of the modified regenerative type fiber laser is shown.

A base-line extraction circuit is designed to extract the 10 GHz electrical signal from the input 40 Gb/s optical pulse train. This base-line extraction circuit is based on the mixed optical-electrical phase locked loop. The principle can be briefly explained as follows. An offset signal Δf together with the output of the voltage controlled oscillator (VCO) f_{VCO} ($\sim$10 GHz) produces the sum frequency $\Delta f + f_{\text{VCO}}$ through the single side-band modulator (SSM).

This sum frequency is then sent to drive the Mach–Zehnder modulator which also takes the optical input at the rate of f_{train} ($\sim 40\,\text{GHz}$). Due to the high nonlinearity of the Mach–Zehnder modulator, a beat frequency at $4(\Delta f + f_{\text{VCO}}) - f_{\text{train}} = 4\Delta f + (4f_{\text{VCO}} - f_{\text{train}})$ is generated and is detected via the photo-diode. The beat signal is then sent to the band-pass filter centered at $4\Delta f$. The phase detector takes the filtered beat signal and a reference signal oscillating at $4\Delta f$ and produces the error signal proportional to $4f_{\text{VCO}} - f_{\text{train}}$. Therefore, when the loop is closed, the error is forced to be zero, and we get $4f_{\text{VCO}} - f_{\text{train}} = 0$ which means the frequency of the optical pulse train is divided by 4. The operation of the modified regenerative fiber laser follows the following steps. First, the output of the integrator after the phase detector is disconnected from one of the input port of the adder so that the loop is open. Then the DC bias voltage is carefully adjusted at the other input port of the adder which therefore changes the oscillating frequency of the VCO. At some VCO frequency which satisfies the requirement of 4th order rational harmonic mode locking, a temporally stable 40 Gb/s pulse train is obtained. At that point, the time delay inside the base-line extraction circuit is adjusted so that the output of the phase detector is minimum. Then the loop is closed by reconnecting the output of the integrator to one of the input port of the adder. In Fig. 14.15, the auto-correlator trace of the stabilized 40 Gb/s pulse train is shown. The pulse width is measured to be 2 ps (FWHM). A stable operation for more than 8 h has been observed.[20]

For high repetition rate pulse generation, a loop mirror consisting of several meters of polarization maintaining fiber (PMF) can be used as a repetition rate doubler. The polarization maintaining loop mirror has been previously used as the notch filter by Olsson, etc.[21] to filter out the original CW signal. The periodic notch effect in frequency space is caused by the phase difference between the fast and slow axis. The separation between two nearby notches is given by $2\pi c/(\Delta n L)$ where L is the length of the PMF, c is the velocity of the light, and Δn is the index difference between the fast and slow axis.

In Fig. 14.16, the schematics and the principal of the repetition rate doubling is shown. As shown in Fig. 14.17, if the notch separation

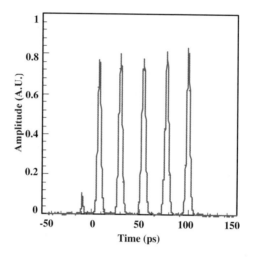

Fig. 14.15 Auto-correlation trace and trace of the 40Gb/s optical pulse train from the stabilized laser.[20]

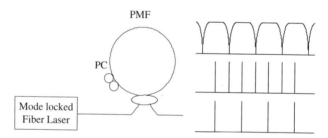

Fig. 14.16 The left part is the schematic of the repetition rate doubler. The output of the mode locked fiber laser is a pulse train at 40 Gb/s. After passing through the loop mirror, the repetition rate is doubled to 80 Gb/s. The upper trace of the right part shows the transmission of the loop mirror as a function of the wavelength. The middle trace of the right part shows the optical spectrum of the input low repetition rate pulse train. The bottom trace of the right part shows the optical spectrum of the output high repetition rate pulse train. PC: polarization controller. PMF: polarization maintained fiber.[20]

is set to be the double of the mode spacing of the low rate pulse train, some of the modes will be filtered out and thus produce a pulse train at the doubled repetition rate after passing through the loop mirror.

If the fiber length inside the loop mirror is ∼9 m, the notch separation becomes 80 GHz, and therefore, for an input signal at 40 Gb/s, an output at 80 Gb/s is expected. Figure 14.17 shows the

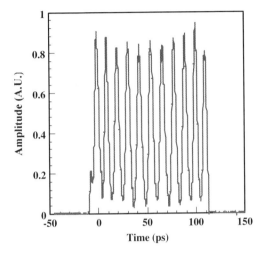

Fig. 14.17 Auto-correlation trace of the 80 Gb/s optical pulse train from the stabilized laser followed by a repetition rate doubler.[20]

auto-correlator trace of the output 80 Gb/s pulse train for the input 40 Gb/s pulse train shown in Fig. 14.15.

14.4.2. *Dual Wavelength Mode Locking*

The phase locked loop (PLL) has been used to produce a stable dual-wavelength laser which may be important for some applications.[22–28] The schematic of the experimental setup is shown in Fig. 14.18. The gain of the fiber laser is provided by an erbium-doped fiber amplifier (EDFA). The maximum output of the EDFA is 25 dBm. A LiNbO$_3$ Mach–Zehnder intensity modulator driven by the ouput of a voltage controlled oscillator (VCO) @10 GHz is utilized for active mode locking. The VCO is part of a phase locked loop circuit used to generate stable pulses at a precise repetition rate. The fiber laser is mode locked at 20 GHz. Tunable delay lines are used for adjusting the cavity length to recombine the seperated pulses for mode locked operation. A 70 m long dispersion compensating fiber (DCF) is used in the cavity. The dispersion parameter of the DCF is -89.6 ps/nm/km. The DCF produces a temporal separation between the pulses at two wavelengths which reduces gain competition in EDFA.

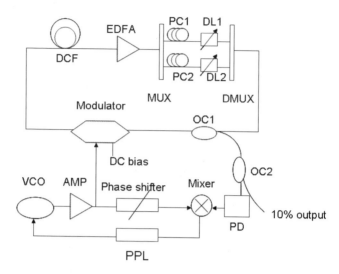

Fig. 14.18 The experimental setup for the dual wavelength fiber ring laser. EDFA: erbium-doped fiber amplifier, PC: polarization controller, DL: optical delay line, DCF: dispersion compensating fiber, MUX/DMUX: multiplier/demultiplier, OC: 90/10 optical coupler, VCO: voltage controlled oscillator, AMP: 10 GHz RF amplifier, PD: photodetector, PC1, PC2: polarization controllers, PLL: phase locked loop controller.[28]

The harmonic mode-locking happens at two different wavelengths when the modulation frequency f_m satisfies:

$$f_{m1} = N \cdot \frac{c}{n_{\text{eff}} L_1}, \quad f_{m2} = M \cdot \frac{c}{n_{\text{eff}} L_2}, \qquad (14.48)$$

where N, M represent the harmonic number, which are integers, for two different wavelengths, c is the speed of light in vacuum, n_{eff} is the effective refractive index of the ring cavity. Assuming two wavelengths have the same n_{eff}, L_1 and L_2 are the total length of the ring cavity in different wavelength channels. For simultaneous mode-locking:

$$f_{m1} = f_{m2}, \qquad (14.49)$$

or $\Delta L = (M - N) \cdot \frac{L_1}{N}$ where $\Delta L = L_2 - L_1$. From Eq. (14.48), the quantity $\frac{L_1}{N} = 50\,ps$ (the pulses are 50 ps apart), hence: $\Delta L = (M - N) \cdot 50\,ps$.

In high speed optical transmission systems, the stablility of the pulse trains is of major importance. Generally, for the EDF based mode-locked multiple wavelength lasers, two main factors contribute to pulse instability: (i) the competition between different channels, (ii) cavity length drift induced by the enviromental temperature fluctuation.

The two pulse trains produced here at different wavelengths are separated by 25 ps after DCF, so they acquire gain at different times in the EDFA. After arrival at the MUX at different times, the two pulses combine (by adjusting the delay lines) at the output of DMUX. However, although the DCF separates the pulses at two different wavelengths, the cavity lengths may drift due to the thermal fluctuations. For this reason, a phase locked loop (PLL) circuit is used in the cavity to maintain the mode locking condtions. The phase locked loop circuit includes a 10 GHz photo-detector, a narrow band RF amplifier (9–10 GHz), a phase shifter, a 10 GHz mixer, a phase locked loop controller and a voltage-controlled oscillator (VCO). The VCO has a center frequency at 9.953 GHz, the tuning range is 7 MHz. The tuning voltage is from 0 to 12 V. The mixer detects the phase diference between the photodiode output and the VCO. The output of the mixer is sent to the PLL controller, which includes an integration circuit, a switch and an analog adder circuit. When the switch is closed, the PLL controler will produce an output of $v_{\text{bias}} - \int v_{\text{mixer}} dt$. Thus the circuit continuously adjusts the modulation frequency to the mode locking freqency and the long-term stabiliztion of harmonic mode locking is realized.

By carefully tuning the delay line 1, the harmonic mode locking in one channel is obtained, and then by adjusting the delay line 2, the cavity length is varied to combine the pulses and to achieve mode locking in the other channel. Then the PLL is closed to stabilize the pulses. The laser can be operated for a various sets of mode locked pulse wavelengths by using different channels of MUX/DMUX as working channels. Figure 14.19 shows the mode locked dual wavelength laser operating at 1546 and 1550 nm. Since the modulator is polarization sensitive, by adjusting the polarization controller (PC) in either channel, it is possible to realize one wavelength or two wavelength operation. PLL is important for stable pulse output. Figure 14.20 (a) and (b) show RF spectra of the harmonic

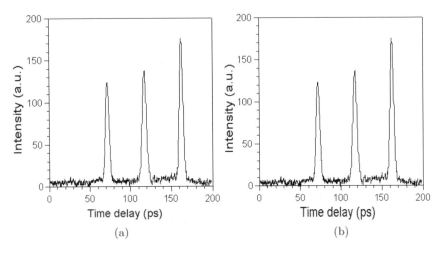

Fig. 14.19 (a) Autocorrelation trace for 1546 nm wavelength and (b) for 1550 nm wavelength.[28]

mode-locked pulses measured by a spectrum analyzer with the switch of PLL open at 1546 and 1550 nm respectively.

Without the PLL present, many sidebands are observed, and the separation between these sidebands is equal to the fundamental cavity frequency or the mode spacing of the fiber laser at 1.83 MHz, thus they are considered to be the supermodes of the fiber laser. Figure 14.20 (c) and (d) show the RF spectrum of the pulses after 1.5 h with the switch of PLL closed at 1546 and 1550 nm respectively. The supermode noise is suppressed. The RF spectrum is shown in Fig. 14.21. The timing jitter of the pulse is calculated using the following equation[28]:

$$Jitter(RMS) = \frac{1}{2\pi f_c}\sqrt{\frac{P_n \cdot \Delta f_{BW}}{P_{clk} \cdot Rs}}, \qquad (14.50)$$

where f_c is the center clock frequency, P_{clk} is the carrier frequency power, P_n is the 3 dB noise power of the shoulder, and Δf_{BW} is the noise shoulder bandwidth, R_s is the resolution of the spectrum analyzer. In this experiment, $P_{clk} = -20\,\text{dBm} = 0.01\,\text{mW}$, $P_n = -78\,\text{dBm} = 15.85\,\text{pW}$, $f_c = 19.9180046\,\text{GHz}$, $R_s = 1\,\text{kHz}$, $\Delta f_{BW} = 150\,\text{kHz}$, so the estimated RMS jitter of the clock is 123 fs. The measured RMS jitter from optical oscilloscope is 80 fs.

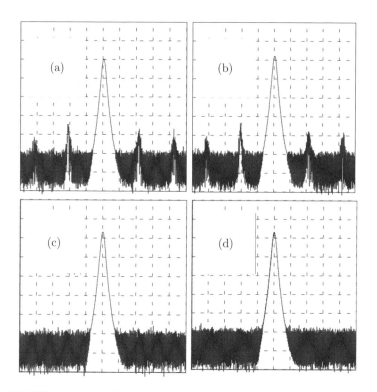

Fig. 14.20 RF spectrum of pulses with and without PLL in the cavity at 1546 and 1550 nm. Peak center: 19.918006 GHz, RES BW: 200 KHz, Supermode spacing ∼1.83 MHz (a, c): 1546 nm ; (b,d): 1550 nm.[28]

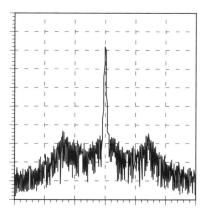

Fig. 14.21 RF spectrum of pulses with PLL in the cavity at 1546 nm. Peak center: 19.9180046 GHz, RES BW 1 kHz, Span: 300 kHz.[28]

14.5. Pulse Compression

Short pulses are important for some applications in biology and tomography. The pulses generated using a fiber laser can be compressed by propagation through various fiber types and loop mirror.[29-42] During the past two decades, a variety of pulse compression schemes have been proposed and demonstrated. The schemes include (i) adiabatic soliton compression techniques,[30-32] (ii) multiple-step compression based on self phase modulation in highly nonlinear fibers or semiconductor optical amplifiers (SOA),[33,34] (iii) parametric gain in a fiber-optic parametric amplifier,[29,35] (iv) a comb-like profiled fiber (CPF) to emulate dispersion decreasing fiber,[36,37] (v) saturable optical absorbers such as nonlinear optical loop mirror (NOLM) or nonlinear amplifying loop mirror (NALM).[38-42] The NOLM scheme can be adapted to various possible configurations of fiber types and fiber and laser designs.

14.5.1. *Pulse Compression Using NOLM*

The following describes a optical pulse train compression scheme using a photonic crystal fiber nonlinear optical loop mirror (NOLM). Pulse width of ~570 fs is realized at 40 GHz repetition rate. A ring structure consisting of a photonic crystal fiber (PCF) based nonlinear loop mirror (NOLM) and an EDFA is used for optical pulse compression. The structure of the loop mirror is schematically shown in Fig. 14.22. Light entering the system from port 1 of the coupler is split into two ports 3 and 4 by the ratio of α and $1 - \alpha$. If the coupling ratio is close to 50%, a $\pi/2$ phase lag is applied to the light each time it is coupled across the wave guide in the coupler,

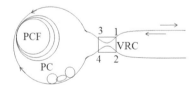

Fig. 14.22 Schematic of PCF-based NOLM, VRC: variable ratio coupler (split ratio α). PCF: photonic crystal fiber, PC: polarization controller.[42]

in this way, the two counter propagating lights will arrive at port 2 with similar amplitude but π phase difference, resulting in their destructive interference and very low transmittance from port 2.

Calculations reported in Ref. 41 show that for α close to 50% and with proper polarization orientation the NOLM reflectivity can reach higher than 95%. The fiber used in the loop mirror is 25 m of highly nonlinear, dispersion-flattened photonic crystal fiber. This type of fiber has high nonlinearity and low second order and third order dispersions, it also has good polarization maintaining characteristics, which is crucial for this scheme. The simulation results (obtained by solving the nonlinear Schrodinger equation[43] for pulse propagation using split-step Fourier method) show that using two cascaded NOLM can significantly improve result of pulse compression compared with that using a single NOLM. The impact of pulse energy on the output pulse width is shown in Fig. 14.23 (a). When input pulse width is 1.8 ps, good compression results start at input pulse energy ~1.5 pJ, for which the width of reflected pulse from the first NOLM is 910 fs, after the second NOLM, pulse width reduces to 540 fs. The dependence of output pulse width on input pulse width is shown in Fig. 14.23 (b) with input pulse energy fixed at 1.5 pJ. In both cases [Figs. 14.23 (a) and (b)], 2-NOLM scheme has advantage

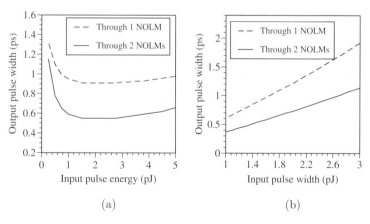

(a)   (b)

Fig. 14.23 Simulated output pulse width through single or 2 cascaded NOLM (a) As a function of input pulse energy (with input pulse width 1.8 ps) and (b) As a function of input pulse width (with input pulse energy 1.5 pJ).[42]

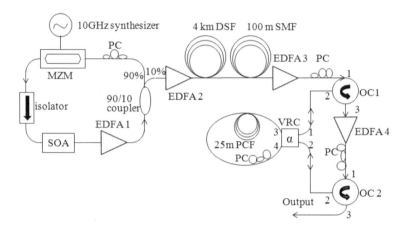

Fig. 14.24 Experiment setup: MZM: Mach–Zehnder modulator, OC: optical circulator, PC: polarization controller, SOA: semiconductor optical amplifier, VRC: variable ratio coupler with coupling ratio α. DSF: dispersion shifted fiber, PCF: photonic crystal fiber, SMF: single mode fiber, EDFA: erbium-doped optical amplifier.[42]

over using the 1-NOLM scheme. It increases the amount of pulse width compression by >30%.

The schematic of the experimental setup is shown in Fig. 14.24. A rational harmonic mode locked ring laser incorporating a Mach–Zehnder type modulator driven by a 10 GHz RF synthesizer is used to generate stable 40 and 20 GHz RZ optical pulse trains.

In the cavity a semiconductor optical amplifier (SOA) is used to serve as a fast saturable absorber in order to suppress self-pulsing behavior.[16] Without the SOA, similar pulse is observed with less stability. The pulse autocorrelation trace of the generated pulse trains from the ring laser show pulse widths of 4.4 ps and 4.1 ps for 20 GHz (2nd order rational harmonic) and 40 GHz (4th order rational harmonic) pulses respectively. These pulses are compressed after traversing the NOLM pulse compressor. The first external compression step is important as pulses shorter than 2 ps are in general, needed for the NOLM to get good compression result. An EDFA is used to amplify the pulse. train to an average power of ~17 dBm followed by a 4 km long dispersion shifted fiber (DSF), where the pulse spectrum is significantly broadened as a result of self-phase modulation. The DSF is followed by a segment of 100 m long single mode fiber in order to

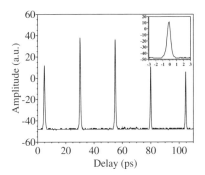

Fig. 14.25 Autocorrelation trace of 40 GHz pulse train after the DSF–SMF and PCF–NOLM compressor. DSF length is ~4 km, SMF length is ~100 m pulse width ~570 fs. The inset shows the autocorrelation trace of a single pulse.[42]

compensate the chirp induced by the DSF. The output pulse width for 20 and 40 GHz pulses from the two types of fibers is measured to be around 1.8 ps. The pulse train is then guided through a circulator into port 1 of the variable ratio coupler. The coupling ratio and the polarization orientation in the loop mirror are carefully adjusted to make sure almost all the injected light emerge from port 1. The reflected light then goes into port 2 and out of port 3 of OC1 to enter another EDFA which amplify the pulse train so that its average pulse energy is similar to that before it enters OC1. Through a second circulator (OC2), the light goes into the NOLM for a second time from port 2 of the variable coupler. The reflected light then exits from port 3 of OC2 as output. The autocorrelation traces of the output pulse train for 40 GHz pulses is shown in Fig. 14.25. The results show good agreement with theoretical simulation, using input pulse width ~1.8 ps and input pulse energy ~1 pJ. The cascaded NOLM pulse compression process shown produces pulse train operating at 20 GHz with full width at half maximum (FWHM) of ~610 fs and at 40 GHz with FWHM of ~570 fs.

14.6. Passive Mode Locking Schemes

Although it is easier to generate stable mode locked pulses at specific repetition rate using active mode locking where the repetition rate is determined by frequency of intracavity electrically driven optical modulators (as described in previous sections) , mode locked pulses have been generated using other methods. These methods, generally known as passive mode locking schemes, use saturable absorbers, or comb filters along with highly nonlinear fibers.

Generation of high repetition rate pulses using several types intracavity optical filtering has been demonstrated. These include a Fabry–Perot filter,[44] a sampled fiber Bragg grating,[45] a programmable optical processor,[46] and a micro-ring resonator.[47,48] A mode locking experiment using a silicon microring resonator (SMRR) based comb filter along with a highly nonlinear fiber (HNLF) is now described. The schematic of the experimental set up is shown in Fig. 14.26.[48] The EDFA has a wide gain spectrum. The SMRR acts a comb filter with a filter spacing of ~2 nm. The dispersive four wave mixing in the HNLF locks the modes of the comb filter and causes passive mode locking of the laser.

The SMRR only allows the optical harmonic modes with 2 nm spacing to build up in the cavity by the filtering effect. The phases

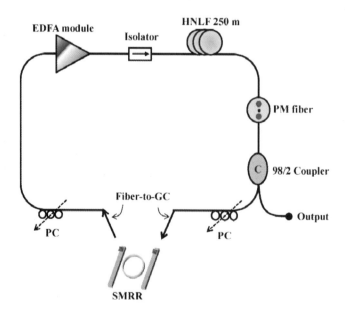

Fig. 14.26 Schematic of the experimental set up.[48]

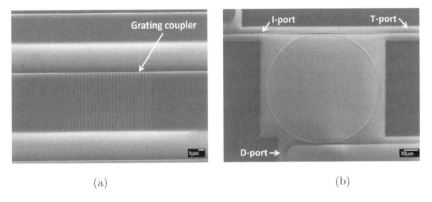

(a)   (b)

Fig. 14.27 SEM photograph of (a) grating coupler with 14 μm in length, 9 μm in width, and 580 nm in period; (b) silicon micro-ring resonator with two silicon nano-wires, the input port (I-port) and the drop port (D-port).[48]

of these modes are locked by the FWM effect induced by the HNLF. The polarization independent isolator forces the optical pulses to propagate in a single direction. A short (1 cm) section of PMF (polarization maintaining fiber) is inserted in the cavity, as shown in Fig. 14.26. Silicon-on-insulator (SOI) based SMRR with polarization dependent grating coupler (GC) is used for coupling to single mode fiber. The scanning electron photomicrograph of the SMRR is shown in Fig. 14.27.

The 250 m long HNLF is used for enhancing the FWM effects. The group velocity dispersion of HNLF is ~0:86 ps/nm/km and the nonlinear coefficient is ~$10.7 \text{W}^{-1}\text{km}^{-1}$. To couple the light between the single mode fiber (SMF) and the SMRR effectively, the grating coupling (GC) technique is used. The GCs are 14 μm long and 9 μm wide with 580 nm period and 70 nm in depth. The introduced birefringence by the PMF with the polarization dependence of the GCs of the SMRR can act as a Lyot filter to help stabilize the laser through the combined effects of optical filtering and nonlinear spectral broadening. The EDFA output power can be measured without completing the ring cavity. When the output power is ~18 dBm, 10 comb filter modes are observed and when it is ~21 dBm, 12 comb filter modes at 2 nm spacing is observed. These modes lock due to

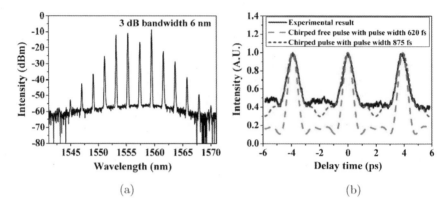

(a)   (b)

Fig. 14.28 (Top) Optical spectrum of the laser output (bandwidth ∼6 nm, 12 lasing modes above −65 dBm power level); (Bottom) autocorrelation trace of the 250 GHz pulse train (pulse width ∼875 fs).[48]

FWM in HNLF. The laser modes and the autocorrelation trace for 12 modes are shown in Fig. 14.28.

Several types of saturable absorbers have been used for mode locking of fiber lasers. Over the last few years carbon nano-tubes (CNT) has been used as saturable absorbers.[49-56] The CNT can be deposited at the end of a single mode fiber. For film fabrication, 1.0± 0.2 nm diameter CNTs made by the high pressure carbon monoxide (HiPCO) method are suspended in a UV-curable, commercial optical polymeric adhesive based on urethane. This adhesive is chosen for its transparency and good adherence to silica. It has a refractive index of 1.56 and a transparency of 90% at 1.55 μm. For a homogeneous CNT/polymer dispersion, the samples are mixed in an ultrasonic bath for 90 minutes. The weight concentrations CNT are in the 20 to 50 mg/ml range. A droplet of CNT/polymer suspension is collected with a micro-tip and transferred to the surface of the ferrule of an FC/APC fiber connector. The micro-tip has a 1 μm diameter tip and is fabricated by tapering a 1 mm diameter glass capillary. Sometimes the CNT droplet is positioned using a micro-positioner. Figure 14.29 shows the microscope image of the side view and front view of a CNT droplet at the end of a fiber connector (FC/APC type).

The connector with the CNT droplet is included in a standard ring fiber laser cavity. It has an Er-doped fiber, a polarization controller,

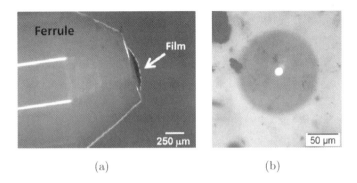

(a)   (b)

Fig. 14.29 Side view (a) and front view (b) of a droplet containing carbon nanotubes at the end of a FC/APC fiber connector.[56]

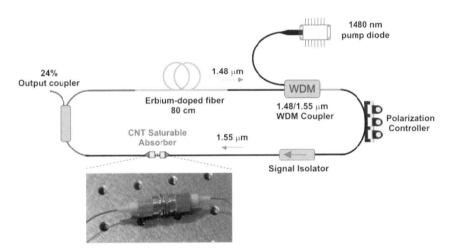

Fig. 14.30 Schematic of a fiber laser set up with a photograph of the fiber connector containing CNT.[56]

an isolator, and a WDM for pump laser light coupling. The EDF is pumped by a pump laser emitting near 1480 nm to produce gain (Fig. 14.30).

The pump laser power is 47 mW and the rest of the fiber laser has 8 m long standard telecommunication fiber. The EDF length is 0.8 m. The shortest pulse width is obtained for a 20 μm thick CNT sample with a concentration of 40 mg/ml. The autocorrelation trace showing ∼370 fs pulse width is shown in Fig. 14.31.

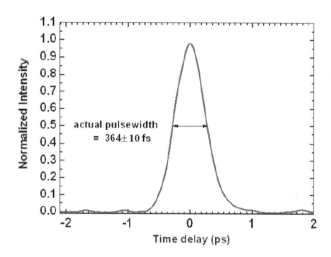

Fig. 14.31 Autocorrelation trace of output pulses using carbon nano tube (CNT) saturable absorber.[56]

Among other saturable absorbers (SA) that has been studied is graphene.[57-63] In the experiment described here, a few layers of graphene deposited on a fused silica substrate is used as the saturable absorber. The performance of the SA is determined using a power-dependent transmission measurement. A mode locked laser operating at 1556 nm at a repetition rate of 169 MHz with 150 fs pulse width (1560 nm) and 3 mW average output power is used as a source for transmission experiment. The signal is transmitted through a variable optical attenuator and then to the SA. The results of the transmission as a function of average power is shown in Fig. 14.32. The transmission data can be expressed by the equation:

$$\alpha(I) = \alpha/(1 + I/Is) + \alpha_{ns}, \qquad (14.51)$$

where $\alpha(I)$ is the power dependent absorption coefficient, I is the intensity, I_s is the saturation intensity and α_{ns} is the unsaturable absorption. Based on the results of Fig. 14.32 a large modulation in transmission (55%) can be obtained with only 8% unsaturable absorption losses.

The mode locked laser set up using graphene as a saturable absorber is shown in Fig. 14.33. The Er fiber is 30 cm long and is

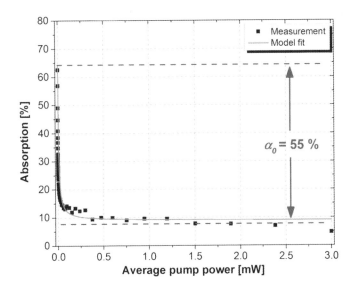

Fig. 14.32 Optical transmission as a function of power of a film of grapheme.[63]

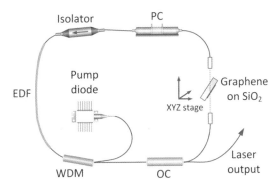

Fig. 14.33 Schematic of the grapheme mode locked laser set up.[63]

pumped by a 980 nm pump laser. Two collimators on XYZ translation stages are used for transmitting the light through the grapheme film. The total optical loss between the collimators is 0.9 dB. The total length of the fiber laser loop is 3.1 m.

The threshold for laser action is 15 mW of pump power. At 60 mW of pump power mode locked operation is observed after adjusting the polarizer. The pulses are equally spaced by ∼17 ns which correspond to 58 MHz repetition rate. The repetition rate agrees well with the inverse of cavity round trip time. The autocorrelation trace of the pulses is measured and is found to be 315 fs. The pulses have 1.9 mW average power, 104 W of peak power, and pulse energy of 33 pJ. The time-bandwidth product of the pulses is 0.44.

14.7. Other Mode Locked Laser Systems

The methods described previously have been used for mode locking studies of mode locked lasers using dopants other than Er such as Yb, Nd and Tm. These laser systems emit at different wavelengths as described previously (Chapter 2). For high repetition rate mode locking it is important to have a modulator at the appropriate wavelength and all of the techniques (harmonic and rational harmonic mode locking and pulse stabilization) described earlier can be used to produce stable high repetition rate pulses. The availability of $LiNbO_3$ modulator for near 1500 nm wavelength allowed extensive study of Er-doped mode locked lasers which is important for optical fiber communication studies. For other laser systems short mode locked pulses are generally produced using saturable absorbers.

14.7.1. *Yb-Doped Mode Locked Laser*

Carbon nano tube (CNT) has been used for mode locking of Yb fiber lasers. As stated in Sec. 14.6, the CNTs are immersed in an aqueous solution of polyvinyl alcohol (PVA) and PVA films with CNTs are created.[64–66] The films are cut into small pieces (1 mm × 1 mm) and are sandwiched between two FC/PC fiber connectors. A schematic of the YDFL (Yb-doped fiber laser) in a ring cavity is shown in Fig. 14.34. The Yb-doped gain medium is pumped by a diode laser emitting near 976 nm. The ring laser has an isolator for unidirectional light propagation and a polarization controller for optimizing the polarization state needed for optimum performance of CNTs. The YDF fiber is 0.8 m long and the total cavity length is 9.56 m. A filter is used to ensure mode locking at a certain wavelength.

Mode locked pulses are observed at pump powers of ∼47 mW. The pulse repetition rate is 21.5 MHz which represents the inverse of

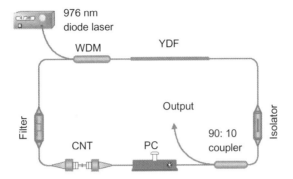

Fig. 14.34 Schematic of a Yb-doped fiber laser. The laser uses carbon nano tubes (CNTs) for mode locking.[66]

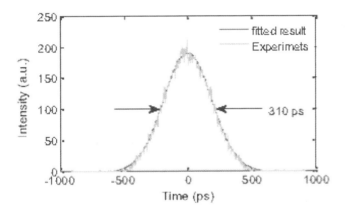

Fig. 14.35 Autocorrelation trace of mode locked pulses.[66]

the round trip time for the 9.56 m long cavity. The autocorrelation trace of the pulse is shown in Fig. 14.35 which shows a pulse width of 310 ps. At higher pump powers the mode locking changes to Q-switching.

Another type of saturable absorber is a semiconductor material whose bandgap is near the laser wavelength. It is configured in the form of a saturable absorber mirror (SESAM). It consists of a semiconductor waveguide material of appropriate band gap sandwiched between cladding layers (higher band gap layers) on both sides and is grown on a binary semiconductor substrate.

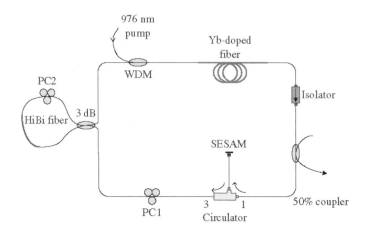

Fig. 14.36 Schematic of a mode locked tunable Yb fiber laser set up.

It can be attached to the end of a connector using transparent epoxy. This fiber attached SESAM can be included in a fiber laser cavity using a circulator. An Yb fiber laser set up using SESAM is shown in Fig. 14.36.[67] The Yb-doped fiber is 3 m long and is pumped by a diode laser emitting at 976 nm. The SESAM is mounted on a FC/PC connector and is connected to the fiber laser using a three-port polarization independent circulator.

In the saturated mode, the SESAM has a modulation depth of 25% and a saturation intensity of 21 μJ/cm,^{2} and a relaxation time constant of 5 ps. A fiber polarizer is used to control the polarization state in the cavity. A Sagnac loop mirror is added to the optical cavity. A highly birefringement (HiBi) fiber is used in the Sagnac loop mirror. The loop mirror has comb like transmission spectrum (as mentioned in Chapter 12). Using a short length of HiBi fiber (~6 cm) only one transmission maximum is allowed creating a filter. The peak wavelength of this filter can be tuned by varying PC2 and thus mode locked pulses at different wavelengths can be obtained. By adjusting PC2, stable mode locked pulses are observed at pump power of ~110 mW. The pulse period repetition rate is 8.4 MHz which corresponds to inverse round trip time of the 24 m long cavity. The pulse width measured using a scope is ~92 ps and is shown in Fig. 14.37.

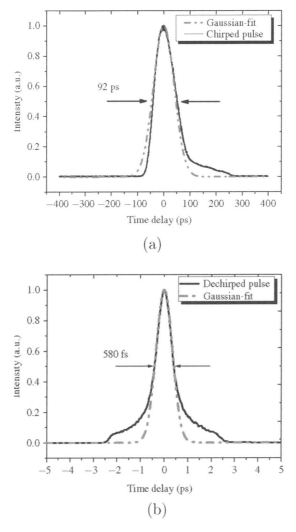

Fig. 14.37 (a) Oscilloscope trace of a pulse before pulse compression (b) Autocorrelation trace after pulse compression using gratings.[67]

The pulse is highly chirped (i.e., wavelength of light varies significantly at different temporal position in the pulse). The chirped pulse is compressed using a pair of gratings external to the laser cavity. The autocorrelation trace of the resulting pulse has a width of 580 fs (Fig. 14.37). The pulse wavelength can be tuned from 1030 to 1060 nm.

14.7.2. *Passive Mode Locking Theory*

In this section and in the previous section, several passive mode locking schemes and laser systems have been described. The theory of passive mode locking using saturable absorbers has been extensively studied by Haus and others.[68-71] The passive mode locking can be separated into three categories: (i) slow saturable absorber modelocking,[68,69] (ii) fast saturable absorber modelocking[70] and (iii) soliton modelocking.[71,72] The variation of gain, loss, and the light pulse as a function of time for the three categories are shown in Fig. 14.38. For soliton mode locking, the pulse shaping is done by soliton formation i.e., the balance of group velocity dispersion and self phase modulation produces a steady state for soliton pulse formation. In the first two cases a short gain window is formed which defines the pulse width of a stable short pulse. For Fig. 14.38 (a), when the gain is higher than the loss, the pulse forms (rises), and the gain gets depleted due to upper state population depletion by the pulse, it results in the laser going below threshold, i.e., (gain is less than loss) and the pulse intensity goes to zero. In Fig. 14.38 (a), a net-gain window is formed by the combined effect of saturation of the absorber and gain for which the absorber has to saturate and recover faster than the gain.

For rare earth-doped lasers, the upper state lifetimes are long ($\sim$1 to 10 ms). This is much longer than the pulse duration which

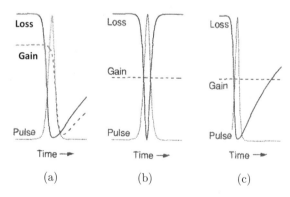

Fig. 14.38 A schematic plot of pulse amplitude, loss and gain as a function of time for three cases (a) Slow saturable absorber, (b) Fast saturable absorber and (c) Soliton modelocking.[72]

is typically less than 1 ns. As a result, there is no significant gain saturation [depletion as shown in Fig. 14.38 (b)]. For fast saturable absorbers (absorber saturation time much shorter than the gain saturation time) shown in Fig. 14.38 (b), the gain is saturated to an average level determined by intracavity intensity. The short gain window is formed by the fast recovering saturable absorber alone. The pulse formation by fast saturable absorber is now described using the formalism developed by Haus in Ref. 72.

Consider the case when a light pulse of amplitude $A(t)$, travel through a gain medium, a saturable loss medium and a constant loss medium. The cavity mirrors are included in the last term. In the frequency domain $A(t)$ is written as $A(\omega)$, where $A(\omega)$ is the Fourier transform $A(t)$. For a homogeneously broadened gain medium described by a Lorentzian lineshape:

$$g(\omega) = \frac{g}{1 + \left(\frac{\omega - \omega_0}{\Omega_g}\right)^2} \sim g\left(1 - \frac{\Delta\omega^2}{\Omega_g^2}\right), \qquad (14.52)$$

$$\text{for } (\omega - \omega_0)^2/\Omega_g^2 \ll 1,$$

where $\Delta\omega = \omega - \omega_0$, g is the saturated gain coefficient for a cavity round trip and Ω_g is the full width at half maximum (FWHM) of the gain bandwidth. Thus in the frequency domain (for $g \ll 1$):

$$A_{\text{out}}(\omega) = e^{g(\omega)} A_{\text{in}}(\omega) \sim [1 + g(\omega)] A_{\text{in}}(\omega), \qquad (14.53)$$

From the previous equations:

$$A_{\text{out}}(\omega) = \left[1 + g - \frac{g}{\Omega_g^2}\Delta\omega^2\right] A_{\text{in}}(\omega), \qquad (14.54)$$

It can shown, the previous equation in the time domain becomes:

$$A_{\text{out}}(t) = \left[1 + g + \frac{g}{\Omega_g^2}\frac{\partial^2}{\partial t^2}\right] A_{\text{in}}(t), \qquad (14.55)$$

Thus the change in $A(t)$, in going through the gain medium, $\Delta A(t)$ is given by:

$$\Delta A \sim \left[g + D_g \frac{\partial^2}{\partial t^2}\right] A \quad \text{with } D_g = \frac{g}{\Omega_g^2} \qquad (14.56)$$

The quantity D_g is the gain dispersion. For the case of an ideal fast absorber, the loss (q) recovers instantaneously and thus it has the same time dependence as the pulse envelope. The loss q as a function of time is written as (with I as the pulse intensity and I_{sa} as the saturation intensity of the absorber):

$$q(t) = \frac{q_0}{1 + I(t)/I_{sa}} \sim q_0 - \gamma I(t), \qquad (14.57)$$

with $\gamma = q_0/I_s$

Thus the output pulse A(t) from the loss modulator is given by:

$$A_{\text{out}}(t) = e^{-q(t)} A_{\text{in}}(t) \sim [1 - q(t)] A_{\text{in}}(t), \qquad (14.58)$$

The change in output $\Delta A(t)$ for a saturable absorber is:

$$\Delta A(t) \sim \gamma |A|^2 A, \qquad (14.59)$$

For an optical loss l, the change in A(t), per pass is:

$$\Delta A(t) = -lA \qquad (14.60)$$

Following Haus, for an ideal fast saturable absorber, the pulse is given by the requirement that:

$$\sum \Delta A(t) = 0$$

i.e.,:

$$\left[g\left(1 + \frac{1}{\Omega_g^2}\frac{\partial^2}{\partial t^2}\right) - l + \gamma |A|^2 \right] A(t) = 0, \qquad (14.61)$$

Equation (14.61) is obtained by substituting for $\Delta A(t)$ from previous equations for $\Delta A(t)$ for gain, saturable absorber and optical loss. The solution of this is:

$$I(t) = I_0 \sec h^2(t/\tau), \qquad (14.62)$$

with a FWHM pulse width of:

$$\tau_p = 1.76\tau = 1.76\frac{4D_g}{\gamma F_{pa}}, \qquad (14.63)$$

where I_0 is the peak intensity, and F_{pa} is the incident pulse energy (fluence) on the fast saturable absorber. An analytic solution is obtained, if it is assumed that the saturable absorber saturates linearly with pulse intensity over full modulation depth. In this case, $q_0 = \gamma I_0$ and for a soliton shaped pulse, the fluence:

$$F_{pa} = \int I(t)dt = 2I_0\tau, \tag{14.64}$$

The minimum pulse width for a fully saturated absorber is then given by:

$$\tau_{p,\min} = \frac{1.76}{\Omega_g}\sqrt{\frac{2g}{q_0}}, \tag{14.65}$$

Mode locked diode pumped solid state lasers are now commercially available. They provide compact, reliable, turn-key, ultra fast lasers. The pulse generation process is self starting and laser cavity adjustments are not critical. Such lasers are finding applications in material studies, tomography studies, optical communication and fiber Bragg grating based sensors.

References

1. Z. Ahmed and N. Onodera, *Electron. Lett.* **32** (1996) 455.
2. M.Y. Jeon, H.K. Lee, J.T. Ahn, D.S. Lim, H.Y. Kim, K.H. Kim and E-H Lee, *Electron. Lett.* **34** (1998) 182.
3. S. Li, C. Lou and K.T. Chan, *Electron. Lett.* **34** (1998) 375.
4. P. Das, W. Kaechele, J.P. Theimer and A.R. Pirich, *SPIE.* **3075** (1997) 21.
5. C. Wu and N.K. Dutta, *IEEE J. Quantum Electron.* **36** (2000) 145.
6. T. Pfeiffer and G. Veith, *Electron. Lett.* **29** (1993) 1849.
7. M. Nakazawa, E. Yoshida and Y. Kimury, *Electron. Lett.* **30** (1994) 1603.
8. E. Yoshida and M. Nakazawa, *Electron. Lett.* **32** (1996) 1370.
9. H.A. Haus, Short pulse generation. In *Compact sources of ultrashort pulses*, I.N. Duling (Ed) III, Cambridge, 1995.
10. M.S. Khan and N. Uehara, Sante. Corp. Report.
11. G. Zhu, H. Chen and N.K. Dutta, *J. Appl. Phys.* **90** (2001) 2143.
12. X. Shan, D. Cleland and A. Ellis, *Electron. Lett.* **28** (1992) 182.
13. M. Nakazawa and E. Yoshida, *IEEE Photon. Technol. Lett.* **12** (2000) 1613.
14. H. Takara, S. Kawanishi and M. Saruwatari, *Electron. Lett.* **31** (1995) 292.
15. W.W. Hsiang, C.Y. Lin, N.K. Sooi and Y. Lai, Proceedings. CLEO, paper OThC7 (2005).
16. H. Chen, G. Zhu, N.K. Dutta and K. Dreyer, *Applied optics.* **41** (2002) 3511.
17. G. Zhu, Q. Wang, H. Dong and N.K. Dutta, *J. Appl. Phys* **96** (2004) 1790.
18. H. Dong, G. Zhu and N.K. Dutta, *Optics Express.* **12** (2004) 4751.

19. M. Nakazawa, E. Yoshida and Y. Kimura, *Electron. Lett.* **30** (1994) 1603.
20. G. Zhu, H. Chen and N.K. Dutta, *IEEE JQE.* **40** (2004) 721.
21. B. Olsson, P. Ohlen, L. Rau and D. Blumenthal, *IEEE Photon. Tech. Lett.* **12** (2000) 846.
22. K.L. Lee and C. Shu, *IEEE Photon. Technol. Lett.* **12** (2000) 624.
23. H. Dong, G. Zhu, Q. Wang, H. Sun and N.K. Dutta, *Opt. Express.* **12** (2004) 4297.
24. D. Pudo and L.R. Chen, *Electron. Lett.* **39** (2003) 272.
25. S. Pan and C. Lou, *IEEE Photon. Technol. Lett.* **18** (2006) 604.
26. F. Shih, C. Chen and C. Lee, *Opt. Express.* **15** (2007) 13844.
27. W. Zhang, J. Sun, J. Wang and L. Liu, *IEEE Photon. Technol. Lett.* **19** (2007) 1418.
28. Z. Chen, S. Ma, N.K. Dutta, *Optics Express.* **17** (2009) 1234.
29. A.O.J. Wiberg, C.S. Bres, B.P.P. Kuo, J.X. Zhao, N. Alic and S. Radic, *IEEE J. Quant. Electron.* **45** (2009) 1325.
30. K.A. Ahmed, K.C. Chan and H.F. Liu, *IEEE J. Sel. Topics in Quant. Electron.* **1**(1995) 592.
31. M.N. Vinoj and V.C. Kuriakose, *J. of Opt. A: Pure and Appl. Optics.* **6** (1974) 63.
32. G.R. Lin, Y.C. Lin, K.C. Lin, W.Y. Lee and C.L. Wu, *Opt. Express.* **18** (2010) 9525.
33. K. Taira and K. Kikuchi, *IEEE Photon. Technol. Lett.* **15** (2003) 1288.
34. K. Taira and K. Kikuchi, *Electron. Lett.*, Vol. 40, 15 (2004).
35. T. Torounidis, M. Westlund, H. Sunnerud, B. E. Olsson and P. A. Andrekson, *IEEE Photon. Lett.* **17** (2005) 312.
36. Y. Ozeki, S. Takasaka, T. Inoue, K. Igarashi, J. Hiroishi, R. Sugizaki, M. Sakano and S. Namiki, *IEEE Photon. Technol. Lett.* **17** (2005) 1698.
37. Y. Ozeki, S. Takasaka, J. Hiroishi, R. Sugizaki, T. Yagi, M. Sakano and S. Namiki, *Electron. Lett.* **41** (2005) 1048.
38. C. De Dios and H. Lamela, *IEEE Photon. Technol. Lett.* **22** (2010) 377.
39. M.D. Pelusi, Y. Matsui and A. Suzuki, *IEEE J. of Quantum Electron.* **35** (1999) 867.
40. K. Smith, N.J. Doran and P.G.J. Wigley, *Opt. Lett.* **15** (1990) 1294.
41. D.B. Mortimore, *J. of Lightwave Technol.* **6**, 7, (1988) 1217.
42. S. Ma, W. Li, H. Hu and N.K. Dutta, *Optics Communication.* **285** (2012) 2832.
43. G.P. Agrawal, *Nonlinear fiber optics.* 4th Edition. Elsevier. 2007.
44. E. Yoshida and M. Nakazawa, *Opt. Lett.* **22** (1997) 1409.
45. S. Zhang, F. Lu, X. Dong, P. Shum, X. Yang, X. Zhou, Y. Gong and C. Lu, *Opt. Lett.* **30** (2005) 2852.
46. J. Schroder, T.D. Vo and B.J. Eggleton, *Opt. Lett.* **34** (2009) 3902.
47. S-S. Jyu, L-G. Yang, C-H. Yeh, C.W. Chow, H.K. Tsang and Y. Lai, *Proceedings. CLEO* 2013, paper CM1I3, (2013).
48. S.S. Jyu, L.G. Yang, C.Y. Wong, C.H. Yeh, C.W. Chow, H.K. Tsang and Y. Lai, *IEEE J. of Photonics* **5** (2013) 1502107.

49. J.W. Nicholson and D.J. DiGiovanni, *IEEE Photon. Technol. Lett.* **20** (2008) 2123.

50. J.W. Nicholson, R.S. Windeler and D.J. DiGiovanni, *Opt. Express.* **15** (2007) 9176.

51. Y.W. Song, S. Yamashita, C.S. Goh and S.Y. Set, *Opt. Lett.* **32** (2007) 148.

52. K. Kieu and M. Mansuripur, *Opt. Lett.* **32** (2007) 2242.

53. N. Nishizawa, *et al.*, *Opt. Express.* **16** (2008) 9429.

54. Z. Sun *et al.*, *Appl. Phys. Lett.* **93** (2008) 061114-1.

55. A.G. Rozhin, Y. Sakakibara, S. Namiki, M. Tokumoto, H. Kataura and Y. Achiba, *Appl. Phys. Lett.* **88** (2006) 051118-1.

56. R.M. Gerosa, D. Steinberg, H.G. Rosa, C. Barros, C.J.S. de Matos and E.A. T. de Souza, *IEEE Photonics Tech. Lett.* **25** (2013) 1007.

57. Q.L. Bao, H. Zhang, Y. Wang, Z.H. Ni, Z.X. Shen, K.P. Loh and D.Y. Tang, *Adv. Funct. Mater.* **19** (2009) 3077.

58. T. Hasan, Z. Sun, F. Wang, F. Bonaccorso, P.H. Tan, A.G. Rozhin and A.C. Ferrari, *Adv. Mater.* **21** (2009) 3874.

59. H. Zhang, D.Y. Tang, L.M. Zhao, Q.L. Bao and K.P. Loh, *Opt. Exp.* **17** (2009) 17630.

60. H. Zhang, D.Y. Tang, L.M. Zhao, Q.L. Bao, K.P. Loh, B. Lin and S.C. Tjin, *Laser Phys. Lett.* **7** (2010) 591.

61. H. Zhang, D. Tang, R.J. Knize, L. Zhao, Q. Bao and K.P. Loh, *Appl. Phys. Lett.* **96** (2010) 111112.

62. P.L. Huang, S. Lin, C. Yeh, H. Kuo, S. Huang, G. Lin, L. Li, C. Su and W. Cheng, *Opt. Exp.* **20** (2012) 2460.

63. G. Sobon, J. Sotor, I. Pasternak, K.Grodecki, P. Paletko, W. Strupinski, Z. Jankiewicz and K.M. Abramski, *IEEE J. Lightwave Tech.* **30** (2012) 2770.

64. S.M. Kobtsev, S.V. Kukarin and Y.S. Fedotov. *Laser Phys.* **21** (2011) 283.

65. X.H. Li, Y.G. Wang, Y.S. Wang, X.H. Hu, W. Zhao, X.L. Liu, J. Yu, C.X. Gao, W. Zhang, Z. Yang, C. Li and D. Y. Shen, *IEEE Photon. J.* **4** (2012) 234.

66. X. Li, Y. Wang, Y. Wang, Q. Wang, W. Zhao, Y. Zhang, X. Ya and Y. Zhang, *Proceedings IEEE Int. nanoelectronics Conf.* 139 (2013).

67. C. Ouyang, P. Shum, H. Wang, S. Fu, X. Cheng, J. H. Wong and X. Tia, *IEEE, JQE,* QE-**47** (2011) 198.

68. H.A. Haus, *IEEE JQE*, QE-**9** (1975) 736.

69. G.H.C. New *IEEE, JQE.* QE-**10** (1974) 115.

70. H.A. Haus, *J. Appl. Phys.* **46** (1975) 3049.

71. F.X. Kartner and U. Keller, *Opt. Lett.* **20** (1995) 16.

72. U. Keller, In *Advances in Lasers and Applications.* D.M. Finlayson and B.D. Sinclair Eds), Proceedings. of the Fifty Second Scottish Universities summer school in physics, St. Andrews. 1998.

Index

1480 nm pump laser, 37, 216
4f shell, 53
980 nm semiconductor laser, 33
980 nm laser, 209

absorption and emission cross
  sections, 115
absorption cross section, 57, 112
absorption rate, 144, 205
absorption spectrum, 40, 59, 106
absorption spectrum of Tm, 65
AC gain tilt, 250
acoustic wave, 271
actinides, 52
activation energy, 222
active harmonic mode-locking, 381
active mode locking, 379
add/drop, 133
Air–SF57–SiO$_2$ planar rib waveguide,
  311
AlGaAs, 198
AlGaAs/GaAs material, 222
AM CATV systems, 247
amplified spontaneous emission, 44,
  108
amplifier gain, 145
amplifier noise, 134
analysis of leakage currents, 218
antireflection, 212
antireflection coating, 225
atomic number Z, 52
atomic transitions, 51
autocorrelation, 415, 418, 421

BER, 141, 142, 150, 161, 238, 239,
  241, 254, 323, 375
Besssel functions, 27
binary substrates, 196
bit error rate, 235
bit-rate flexible link, 234
booster amplifiers, 237
Bragg condition, 361
Bragg wavelength, 335, 361
Brillouin gain, 272
Brillouin shifts, 272
broad area lasers, 208
buried heterostructure, 208
buried heterostructure design, 216
buried stripe design, 211

carbon nano-tubes, 414, 418
cascaded Raman fiber lasers, 369
cascaded Raman laser, 375
cascaded Raman process, 359
cascaded Raman resonator, 370
catastrophic mirror damage, 211, 227
CATV systems, 246
cavity length control, 398
cavity modes, 382
centrifugal potential energy, 52
chalcogenide planar waveguides, 310
chirped fiber Bragg grating, 332
clustering effect, 82
clustering of Er, 290
co-dopants, 75, 78
co-doping the Er-doped fiber, 178
coherence function, 314
coherence properties, 280

coherent transmission, 241
comb filter, 330
composite second order distortion,
    248
confinement factor, 203
core and cladding, 25
coulomb interaction, 56
Coulomb potential energy, 52
coupling constant, 187, 361
coupling pump light, 166
critical thickness, 199, 209
cross-phase-modulation, 275, 279
crystalline host, 70

D-shaped, 177, 342, 348, 350
D-shaped inner cladding, 46
data transmission experiment, 323
DCBH structure, 221
DCF, 253
DCF amplifier, 170
DCF laser, 174
DCF model, 187
DEDFA, 241
degree of coherence, 281
delay interferometer, 329
DFB laser, 241
dichroic mirror, 289, 325, 327, 346,
    351
Dieke diagram, 3
dielectric mirrors, 297
dielectric waveguide, 25, 201
direct gap, 196
dispersion compensating fiber, 235,
    371
dispersion shifted fiber (DSF), 253,
    262, 371, 410
distortion, 250
distributed EDFA, 240
double clad fiber, 166, 326, 344
double clad planar waveguide, 306
double clad structure, 289, 348
double clad Yb-doped fiber, 342
double heterostructure, 201
dual beam holographic technique,
    362, 363

dual wavelength mode locking, 403
dynamic networks, 129

EDFA, 6, 125
EDFA preamplifier, 235
effective absorption, 190
electric dipole transition, 71
electronic predistortion circuit, 251
electrons, 53
emission cross section, 64, 65, 67
emission rate, 144
emission spectrum, 60, 106
end pumping a DCF, 171
energy levels of a Nd, 40
epitaxial growth, 196
Er concentration, 31
Er^{3+} clusters, 182
Er–Yb co-doped cladding pumped
    amplifier, 177
Er–Yb co-doped DCF, 185
Er–Yb co-doped DCF amplifiers, 178
Er–Yb co-doped fiber laser, 347, 349
Er–Yb co-doped waveguide
    amplifiers, 299
Er–Yb double clad amplifiers, 179
Er–Yb gain medium, 349
Er–Yb-doped fiber amplifier, 250
Er-doped amplifier, 38, 69, 107
Er-doped amplifier noise, 144
Er-doped fiber amplifier, 4
Er-doped fiber characterization, 106
Er-doped films, 292
Er-doped glass fiber, 35
Er-doped PCF, 120
Er-doped silica fiber, 36
Er-doped silica glass, 56
Er-doped waveguides, 293
Erbium (Er)-doped fiber amplifiers, 2
error-free ultra long distance
    transmission, 252
excited state absorption, 67

fabrication of fiber lasers, 10
fabrications of rare earth-doped
    fibers, 9

far field emission, 221
fast saturable absorber, 422, 424
feedback circuit, 131
feedback loop, 399
Fermi factors, 205
fiber amplifier, 29
fiber Bragg grating, 321, 322, 338, 360
fiber raman lasers, 357
first order grating, 361
flame hydrolysis, 296
flame hydrolysis deposition (FHD), 291
flouride based fibers, 96
fluorescence spectrum, 37, 58
fluoride host, 96
fluorozirconate, 87
four wave mixing (FWM), 259
four-level laser, 22
Fourier component, 383
frequency response of the cross talk, 128
frequency shift keying, 241
FSK transmission, 243
Fuchtbauer–Landenberg relationship, 29, 113
FWM, 260
FWM crosstalk, 264, 266

gain, 32, 41
gain coefficient, 116
gain dynamics, 125
gain guided laser, 208
gain saturation, 21, 128
gain spectrum, 114, 293
gain tilt, 250
Gaussian approximation, 27
Gaussian pulse, 158, 387
graded index, 220
graded index fiber, 25
graphene, 333, 416
grating coupler, 173
grating coupling, 413
group velocity dispersion, 155

harmonic mode locking, 379, 380
HDTV signals, 246
Hermite–Gaussian function, 384
high power cladding pumped devices, 45
high power fiber lasers, 339
high power lasers, 352
high power optical amplifier and laser, 9
high reflection, 212
high-power planar waveguide lasers, 304
highly birefringement (HiBi) fiber, 420
highly nonlinear fiber, 412
homogeneous broadening, 332
hybrid gain medium, 328
hydrolysis, 88

$In_{1-x}Ga_xP_yAs_{1-y}$ material, 200
$In_xGa_{1-x}As$, 200
index grating, 360
index lowering dopants, 26
index raising dopants, 26
InGaAsP, 198
InGaAsP distributed feedback (DFB) laser, 234
inhomogeneous broadening, 108
ion exchange process, 300
ion exchanged waveguides, 301
ion migration process, 294

Judd and Ofelt, 72

L-band EDFA, 264
Ladenburg–Fuchtbauer relationship, 75
lanthanides, 52
large mode area (LMA) fiber, 339
laser, 1
laser chirp, 250
lattice mismatch, 199
leakage current, 218
$LiNbO_3$ electro-optical modulator, 380, 395

LiNbO$_3$ modulator, 234, 398
LiNbO$_3$ phase modulator, 253
line strength, 72
liquid phase epitaxy, 198, 302
long distance transmission, 234
loop transmission, 239
loop transmission experiment, 238
Lorentzian spectral profile, 382

Mach–Zehnder intensity modulator, 403
matrix modifiers, 74
Maxwell's equation, 26
Mayer's model, 53
MCVD, 88
metal organic chemical vapor deposition, 198
MOCVD, 198
mode field diameters, 120
mode gain, 204
mode locked fiber laser, 160
mode locked pulse, 379, 382
model of emission cross section, 69
molecular beam epitaxy, 198
multichannel WDM systems, 129
multimode 808 nm laser, 225
multimode 970 nm laser, 214
multiple stokes scattering, 369
multiquantum well, 34, 220
multiwavelength, 331
multiwavelength laser, 328, 332

NA, 46
Nd doped rare earth lasers, 39
Nd-doped double clad fiber, 325
Nd-doped fiber, 324
Nd-doped fiber laser, 2, 343
Nd-doped flourozirconate, 61
Nd-doped glass, 298
Nd-doped glass fiber, 39
Nd-doped laser, 62
Nd-doped single mode fiber laser, 324
Nd-doped waveguide amplifiers, 294
Nd-doped YAG, 289, 304
NF, 147, 149

noise analysis, 137
noise figure, 135, 294
noise measurements, 147
nonlinear coefficient, 153, 261, 333
nonlinear optical loop mirror, 408
nonlinear processes, 10
nonlinear Schrödinger equation, 156, 313, 409
nonradiative energy transfer, 180

ON/OFF keying, 141
optical circulator, 329
optical fiber amplifiers, 16
optical gain, 207, 302, 345
optical gain spectrum, 8
optical transfer function, 395
optically time division multiplexing (OTDM), 253
optimum fiber length, 118
OVD, 90

p-n junction, 201
parabolic pulse, 158, 159
passive mode locking, 379, 412
PCF amplifier, 120
PCVD, 89
phase locked, 398
phase locked loop, 399, 405
phase mask technique, 363
phase mismatch, 261
photonic crystal fiber, 119, 408
photonic crystal fiber fabrication, 99
planar waveguide amplifier, 287
plasma enhanced chemical vapor deposition (PECVD), 291
Pockel's (piezo) coefficients, 335
polarization, 152
polarization controllers, 338
polarization diversity receiver, 243
polarization diversity scheme, 243
polarization maintaining fiber, 413
polarization maintaining loop mirror, 401
population density, 19
population inversion, 23, 136

power transients, 131
preamplifier, 149
preform, 93
pulse compression, 408
pulse propagation, 9, 151, 152
pulse width, 381
pump absorption, 30, 350
pump laser, 33
pump photon, 20

Q factor, 147, 161
Q parameter, 143
quasi Fermi levels, 205

radiative lifetime, 73
radiative transition probability, 72
radiative transitions, 51
Raman amplification, 372
Raman amplifiers, 370
Raman gain, 358
Raman gain coefficient, 267, 268, 358
Raman gain spectrum, 371, 373
Raman laser, 359, 364, 368
raman process, 357
Raman responses, 277
Raman spectrum, 267
Raman threshold, 270
rare earth, 1
rare earth dopants, 51
rare earth doping, 94
rational harmonic mode locking, 379,
    385, 386
rational harmonic order, 397
rational harmonic pulse trains, 388
reactive ion etching (RIE), 291
receiver noise, 148
receiver sensitivity, 143
recirculating loop, 253
reflection peak, 362
ridge waveguide, 34, 296, 303
ridge waveguide design, 211
ring fiber laser, 382
ring laser, 395, 418
ruby, 18
ruby ($Cr:Al_2O_3$) laser, 20

Sagnac loop mirror, 338, 420
saturable absorber mirror, 419
saturated gain, 126
saturating signal power, 127
SBS threshold, 273
second-order nonlinearity, 152
self-phase modulation, 275
semiconductor lasers, 195, 196
semiconductor material, 196
semiconductor optical amplifier, 15
shot noise, 135, 141
side pumping, 171, 174
signal–spontaneous beat noise, 138,
    248
silica fiber drawing, 93
silicon microring resonator, 412
single mode, 322
single mode 808 nm laser, 223
single mode 980 nm laser, 209
single mode amplifier model, 111
single mode DCF, 166, 167
single mode fiber amplifier, 44
slope efficiency, 327
slow saturable absorber, 422
small signal gain, 107
soliton, 155, 280, 425
soliton modelocking, 422
soliton transmission, 156, 252
spectral gain, 107
spectrum of the laser, 339
spin orbit interaction, 56, 74
spontaneous emission, 30, 137, 201
spontaneous emission factor, 135
spontaneous–spontaneous beat noise,
    138
SRS threshold power, 342
stabilization of the pulse train, 397
stark components, 73
stark splitting, 71, 79
step index fiber, 25
step index perform, 98
stimulated brillouin scattering (SBS),
    271
stimulated emission, 5, 32, 113, 203

stimulated emission cross section, 75, 81
stimulated emission of Yb^{3+}, 76
stimulated emission rate, 205
Stimulated Raman scattering (SRS), 176, 266, 340, 357
Stokes scattering, 359
Stokes signal, 267, 340
strain sensors, 335
subscriber transmission, 245
supercontinuum generation, 274, 308
surviving channel, 130

tapered fiber bundle, 168
tapered waveguide, 312
tellurite fiber, 280
temperature dependence of gain, 111
TFB, 168
thermal expansion, 335
thermal noise, 135
Thomas–Fermi model, 52
three-level and four-level laser, 17
three-level laser, 18
three-level systems, 17
threshold gain, 24
threshold power, 43
threshold pump power, 121, 297
Thulium (Tm), 65
time domain analysis, 389
Tm-doped glass, 65
total cavity loss, 207
total noise, 147
transient gain response, 126
transition probability, 71
transparency current density, 207
transverse electric, 203
transverse magnetic, 203
Truewave fiber, 263
tunable FBG, 336
tunable fiber Bragg gratings, 367
tunable fiber lasers, 335
tunable fiber Raman laser, 367
tunable laser spectrum, 347

unsaturated gain, 21
up-conversion, 182, 290
up-conversion coefficient, 302

V-groove, 172
VAD, 90
vapor-phase epitaxy, 198
voltage controlled oscillator, 400

W fiber, 340
W-type index profile, 345
wavelength division multiplexed (WDM), 125, 233, 370
wavelength-division-multiplexing, 328
WDM system, 261
WDM transmission, 129
WDM transmission experiment, 237
weakly index guided laser, 208

Xenon, 54

Yb transition near 1060 nm, 185
Yb–YAG rods, 308
Yb-doped clad fiber laser, 46
Yb-doped DCF, 176
Yb-doped double clad fiber laser, 369
Yb-doped fiber, 340
Yb-doped fiber glasses, 77
Yb-doped fiber laser, 7, 326, 340, 342
Yb-doped glass amplifiers, 57
Yb-doped lasers, 78
Yb-doped planar waveguides, 303
Yb-doped waveguide amplifiers, 302
YDCF, 46
ytterbium-doped fiber amplifier, 157

ZBLAN (Zr, Ba, La, Al, Na) flourozirconate, 61
zero dispersion wavelengths, 275